Creating Healthy Habits

An Adventure Guide to Teaching Health and Wellness

MIDDLE SCHOOL

By Katie Kilty, Ed.D.

A Project Adventure, Inc. Publication   www.pa.org

ISBN: 0-934387-28-1

About the Author

Katie Kilty, Ed.D. is Associate Professor of Sport Management
at Endicott College and Adjunct Faculty in Physical Education,
Health and Coaching at Boston University. She holds a doctor-
al degree in Counseling and Developmental Studies with a specialty in Sport and Exercise Psychology from Boston University.
In addition to teaching, Katie is the principal of MindPower
Resources where she provides services in consulting and counseling for coaches, teams, and individual athletes at the elite, col-
legiate and developmental levels. Katie has devoted more than
15 years to developing, implementing and researching experiential curricula. Her work is focused in the areas of high performance teams, multiculturalism, health behavior change and facil-
itative leadership. She has consulted, facilitated and presented in
a variety of private, public and nonprofit environments
throughout the United States, Australia, Japan and Europe.

Acknowledgments

First and foremost I would like to acknowledge all of the people, young in age and young in spirit, who have participated in this adventure in wellness. It is your laughter, enthusiasm and collected wisdom that are the heart and soul of this book. I thank you for the opportunity to learn with you and from you during this process. Because of our experiences together I can say with utter confidence that "this curriculum really works"!

A book takes many forms until the final product is sitting in one's hands. This book has been through several iterations, each version incorporating integral feedback from the people who follow. Thank you to Dick Prouty for his perseverance in guiding this project. Thanks to Jane Panicucci and Nancy Stratton for structural suggestions. Thank you also to Alison Rheingold and Lisa Faulkingham Hunt for their considerable time and effort in providing detailed feedback enhancing the applicability and accessibility of each activity. I would also like to acknowledge the continuous support and creative suggestions from MB Buckner. Special thanks also to Sara Redman and Maura Dearing of Tewksbury Middle School and Dr. Eileen Sullivan of Boston University for their critical eye and timely suggestions in reviewing the curriculum from the perspective of professionals in the field of health education. Finally, I would like to thank Jean Walsh and Rufus Collinson for attending to the final editing phase of this book with integrity and care.

The process leading to this book began philosophically with my work in sport and exercise psychology. It was cultivated at the Boston University Wellness Center with Dr. Celine Kline and a staff of exuberant and adventurous students, and flourished while at Project Adventure with my work in Tuba City, AZ. I would especially like to thank Michelle Archuleta and Dr. Chris Hill from Tuba City, for investing in and expanding the adventure in wellness model. Michelle and I spent many hours discussing, modifying and clarifying curricula for teaching health and wellness through adventure in the community and classroom settings. We have come to the conclusion that laughter through play for everyone, no matter what age or culture is the best way to encourage people to develop healthy habits of heart, mind and action.

Thank you also to my family and friends for their encouragement and support amidst the chaos of all of our lives.

—Katie Kilty 2005

Contents

Preface

I

by Eileen Sullivan, Ed.D.
Program Coordinator
Physical Education, Health, and Coaching
Boston University
Curriculum and Teaching Department
School of Education

If you work or want to work with middle school-aged adolescents, you will benefit greatly from reading, digesting and implementing the activities in this book.

Dr. Katie Kilty's experience as an adventure facilitator, health educator, physical educator and teacher with diverse populations, from young athletes to Native American students has allowed her to capture the needs of our middle school students. Dr. Kilty's guide is grounded in well-established theory, that she clearly explains and integrates. She has created activities that are innovative, creative, and fun—ensuring that students enjoy as well as learn from them. Reinforcing cognitive health content and concepts with hands-on activities that are engaging, all-inclusive, and standards-driven provides cutting-edge health instruction in the six priority risk areas of the National Health Education Standards.

- Intentional and unintentional injury prevention
- Mental and emotional health
- Nutrition
- Physical fitness
- Substance abuse prevention
- Personal and consumer health

The book provides the reader with everything they need to implement this exemplary guide:

- A theory into practice approach
- Lesson plans that are detailed and easy to follow
- Lesson plans that guide professionals in the how-tos of capitalizing on those "teachable moments' the activities will create
- Lesson plans designed by grade level—appropriate to the needs and development of each grade

- Lesson plans that are sequential—building upon children's learnings
- Tear out guides for use on the go

Creating Healthy Habits: An Adventure Guide to Teaching Health and Wellness enhances and enriches what and how our adolescents learn about health. Katie Kilty has successfully compiled a teacher manual that can and will be used by everyone who works with adolescents. Whether the students are playing Bear, Salmon, Mosquito to learn about the fight or flight response to conflict, Triangle Tag to discuss substance abuse and peer pressure, or Food Pyramid Juggle to reinforce planning a healthy meal, they are involved, active, and learning essential concepts that matter and help them to develop and maintain a healthy lifestyle. Students and teachers will be smiling as they learn and complete the activities in the book. This book is the most up to date and complete resource activity guide in the Health Education field today. The activities are original and they will never become obsolete because who would ever not want to move as they learn? Thank you Katie for providing a manual that should not be on the bookshelf, but in the hands of everyone working with sixth through eighth graders.

II

Dear Reader:

I met Katie in December of 1999. In 1994 I went through a major change in my professional life which brought me to the invigorating position of Recreation Specialist in Arizona for the Navajo Nation. I left the world of coaching women's tennis, which I had spent my high school, college and education years pursuing. Coaching and a four-year stint as a recreation programmer for the Department of Defense at the Naval Air Weapons Station brought me to the Indian Health Service in Tuba City, Arizona (on the Navajo Nation)…to be exact…and life has never been the same…only better! It is through this work that I met and formed a close collaborative working relationship and long lasting friendship with Katie.

I became a Recreation Specialist with the Health Promotion/Disease Prevention Program (HP/DP), under the guidance of Dr. Christian Hill (HP/DP Prevention Officer). He believes it is possible to help teens overcome childhood obesity and, further, to effectively do so requires not being centered on a clinical-based medical model. That is really 'out of the box' thinking from a medical provider working in a clinical setting! And because of his vision we challenged ourselves and our program as we began a journey to realize Dr. Hill's vision. We learned how to 'facilitate' as opposed to 'instruct', we moved out of the classroom setting and into the wrestling room, we invited our students to define how they would like to be treated and in turn how they would like to treat others and we moved into our 'stretch zone—sometimes panic' when it came to authenticity. For the next two years our HP/DP program delivered the 'Teen Wellness Series' helping sophomores learn health principles and overall teen health and wellness; "recognizing that the behavior change necessary to promote healthy behaviors cannot be taught, but must be learned through individual and group experience" Katie and Project Adventure were our vital partners in this transition supporting us in and teaching us all of the above as well as working with us to design a curriculum which suited the cultural and health and wellness needs of our youth.

Looking back these past four years the Adventure-based activities (provided in this book—created by Katie) has enabled Tuba City HP/DP program to accomplish much. With Katie's help our program has offered local Adventure workshops to help other organizations learn the, 'What? So What? and Now What?' We have also used Adventure to host an adolescent camp and had a wonderful time working with girls ages 9–14 with our own Adventure Girls Camp. The most amazing part of all this work is the supportive reception our other Navajo Nation Service Unit HP/DP programs have given our Adventure programming. Because of their support—thank you HP/DP Coordinators and Programs: Marge, Donna, DeAnne, Shirley, Nancy, Marie and Karen—the 'Adventure Approach to Wellness' has become a reality to all middle schools throughout the Navajo Nation. Tuba City has always been known for being a little different and non-conventional when it comes to programming for health and wellness. Because of the Navajo Coordinated School Health Initiative, Dr. Hill's vision, Katie's dedication and her natural ability to make Adventure a truly personal experience, along with a little bit of luck on my part, the Navajo Nation, its community, schools, and HP/DP programs are enriched and better equipped to acquire the tools necessary to help the Navajo People advance their journey towards wellness.

Thank you Katie for all of your support with my own paradigm shift and journey to wellness...my life and professional endeavors will always contain The Full Value Contract, Challenge by Choice, GRABBS, Name Card Exchange, Chicken Tag, Everybody's It!, Elevator Air, People To People and my new favorite...Name 5. This book reflects our work with Katie and Project Adventure. As such it is sure to energize and bring relevant skills to you and the children with whom you work.

Sincerely,

Michelle Archuleta
Health Promotion Director
Tuba City Service Unit
Navajo Nation

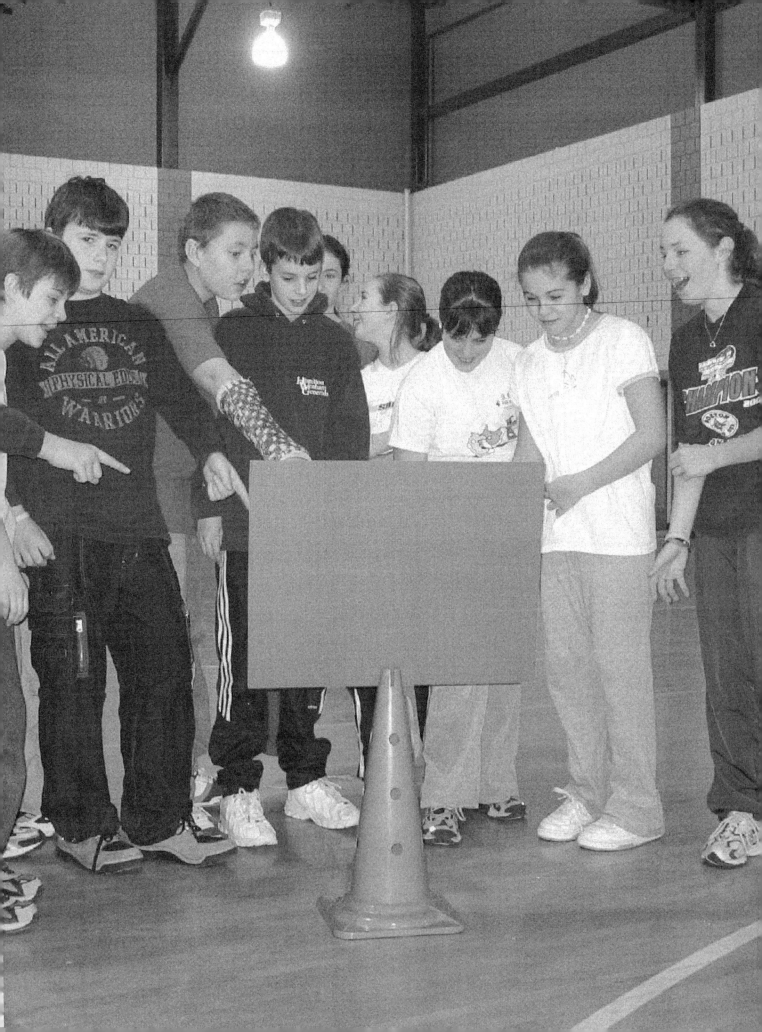

Introduction

CREATING HEALTHY HABITS: AN ADVENTURE GUIDE TO TEACHING HEALTH AND WELLNESS

"I thought it was going to be like when we sit down and tell each other health things we eat and stuff like helping each other out with problems like drugs, family help. Until we started running around then I started to look forward to the class. Everybody participated and everyone cared about what was going on in the class."

—A student's comments after experiencing a semester of activities from *Creating Healthy Habits*

A human being is a vibrant combination of body, mind, and energy. Any program intended to improve personal health must address all of these components. Until now, conventional health and physical education programs have focused primarily on the physical aspects of personal health. Although there is a large and growing body of research connecting stress to illness and the interplay of emotions with the immune system, practitioners and researchers continue to look to physical causes and treatments almost exclusively to promote and maintain health (Weil, 1997). Adventure learning brings the concept of health and wellness to a multidimensional level, incorporating mental, emotional, interpersonal, spiritual and cultural aspects. It builds on self-knowledge in a way that allows us to connect with the whole person, integrating different learning styles rather than trying to fit a specific diet or exercise plan to individual needs. This guide helps students gain the skills necessary to think, choose and act as they develop sustainable healthy habits for life.

Obesity has become a significant problem in the United States. An overriding concern is that health education and physical education programs in schools are in danger of becoming obsolete. This is in response to a perceived need to increase test scores in more academically-oriented classes. Teachers tend to feel that the existing health curriculum is repetitive. Administrators believe that the delivery of the curriculum takes too much time away from other subject areas. The Creating Healthy Habits guide was created with these concerns in mind.

This standards-based guide uses Adventure learning philosophies and techniques in conjunction with more traditional classroom strategies to teach critical thinking skills and to promote personal responsibility and positive behavior change in the areas of health and wellness. The model is predicated on awareness of self within the context of community and provides an experiential base from which students learn to make healthy decisions. After creating a safe learning environment within the class, the model focuses on six priority risk areas:

- Intentional and unintentional injury prevention

- Mental and emotional health
- Nutrition
- Physical fitness
- Substance abuse prevention
- Personal and consumer health

The primary goal of *Creating Healthy Habits* is to teach students to routinely "think, choose and act" for health within each of the priority risk areas. By addressing health skill standards, students: learn core concepts, access information, and analyze influences applying these to important health issues. They make decisions, set goals and communicate about their health choices. Students act in healthy ways when they demonstrate self-management skills to promote and protect health for themselves and advocacy skills to promote and protect health for themselves and others (Building Blocks for Health Literacy: The Hawai'i Health Education Standards). This goal is achieved by participation in Adventure activities that support the more didactic classroom activities.

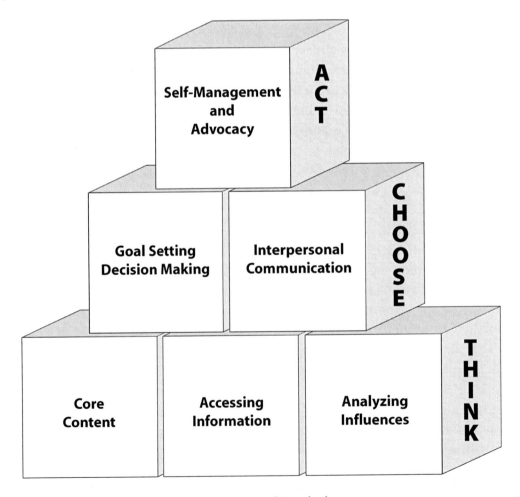

Think, Choose and Act For Health within National Standards

WHAT IS ADVENTURE LEARNING AND HOW DOES IT RELATE TO HEALTH AND WELLNESS?

Adventure learning is founded on experiential learning. Prevention, intervention and educational research suggest three levels of learning: memorization, content mastery and experiential. The first two emphasize gaining knowledge while the third emphasizes gaining and applying knowledge. Promoting health and wellness depends on students being able to make healthy choices—not just knowing, but being able to apply what they know. The guide offered here, built on experiential learning, does just that, enables students to translate knowledge into action.

EXPERIENTIAL LEARNING AND THE EXPERIENTIAL LEARNING CYCLE

The Experiential Learning Cycle (Kolb) provides a cornerstone for understanding experiential learning. It expresses the principle that helping students to experience a seemingly isolated event within the context of a series of events provides students with the opportunity to learn, understand and apply knowledge. Learning is greatly enhanced when accompanied by a complementary reflective process. Kolb's model consists of four phases (see illustration):

- Concrete Experience
- Reflection (What?)
- Generalization (So What?)
- Application (Now What?)

This process is dynamic in that the cycle of experience builds on itself encouraging higher levels of learning and application.

The Adventure Integrated Model, developed by Project Adventure, enhances the ELC by:

1. highlighting the importance of aligning activities with goals (Goal Setting)
2. identifying the need to promote group development—norms and the ability to care for one another—as vital to effective experiential learning (Full Value Contract)
3. expanding the reflective process (debriefing) to broader life experiences (see diagram).
4. empowering students to be active and participatory learners by asking them to define their own stretch zone—for optimal learning (Challenge by Choice)

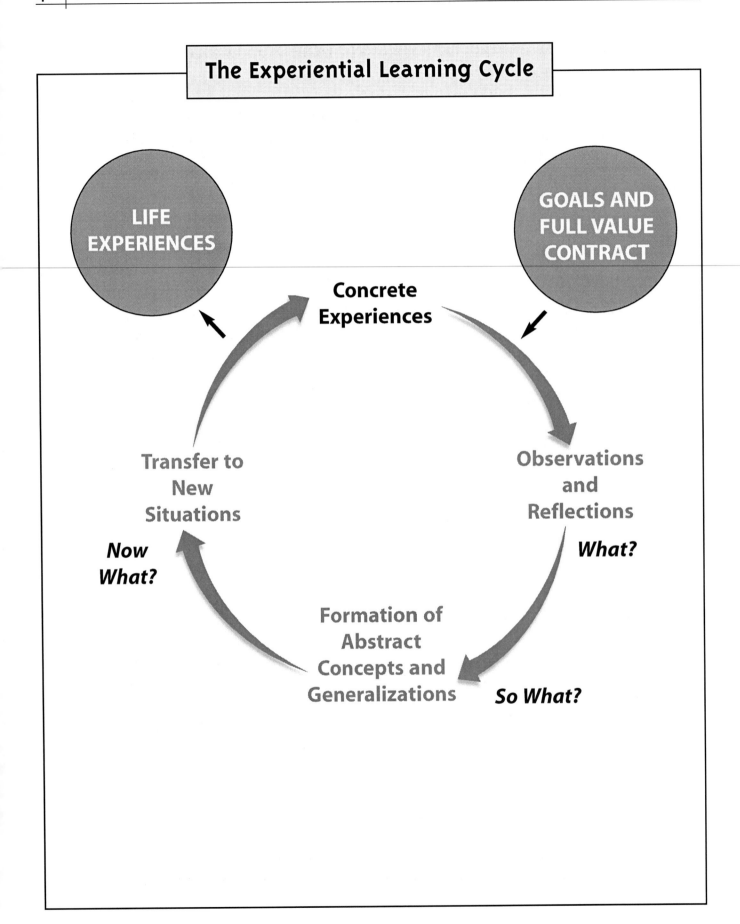

The Experiential Learning Cycle

GOALS AND FULL VALUE CONTRACT

LIFE EXPERIENCES

Concrete Experiences

Transfer to New Situations

Observations and Reflections

What?

Now What?

Formation of Abstract Concepts and Generalizations

So What?

CREATING A LEARNING COMMUNITY IN THE CLASSROOM

The *Creating Healthy Habits* guide begins with creating a safe learning community in the classroom. This is accomplished by taking time at the start of the semester to allow students to get to know one another and by developing relevant guidelines for behaviors that encourage physical and emotional safety. Once a safe environment is established, students are much more willing to take risks, ask questions and share insights, all very important elements of effective health education. The Full Value Contract and Challenge by Choice are integral partners in helping you create a learning community.

Full Value Contract (FVC)

The Full Value Contract is a dynamic behavioral agreement that students commit to maintain throughout the lifetime of their class or group. It is not a set of rules—students identify their own norms or guidelines for behaviors. Rather than describe behaviors that are unacceptable and will be punished, FVC describes the behaviors groups will be using when they attain their ideal. They agree on behaviors that will create and sustain an environment that is physically and emotionally safe as well as growth oriented. It can be helpful to think of rules as predetermined, non-negotiable safety parameters and the Full Value Contract as a fluid agreement that serves as a reference point for discussion and skill building around specific behaviors. *It is important that once the Full Value Contract has been created it remains a living part of the class—something that is readdressed weekly, daily or more often.* The ultimate goal of the Full Value Contract is to help students become responsible to themselves and each other for exhibiting positive and confronting negative behaviors.

The FVC should support work towards group and individual goals. Goals may be task or behavior oriented. For example, the students, as a group, may have a goal of getting the props and classroom space ready for activities more efficiently, while at the same time an individual student may have a goal of speaking up more during reflections.

Every grade in this guide begins by developing community in the health classroom. This is crucial to the success of the unit, because it creates an environment where students feel safe enough to take risks. The Full Value Contract serves as a structure for creating behavioral norms that everyone in the class agrees to follow, and that everyone in the class agrees to work on maintaining throughout the life of the class. The norm-setting process establishes an atmosphere of caring, of feeling connected and of feeling valued. This atmosphere is critical to students' abilities to participate fully in Adventure activities.

There are many ways to develop a Full Value Contract. A number of different methods are included in the lessons in this book. (These are: Lesson Six for grade six, Lesson Four for grade seven and Lesson Three for grade eight.) However, feel free to create your own unique way of representing this critical agreement in your class.

The Full Value Contract cannot be a voting activity—the group must achieve consensus on each behavioral norm. Otherwise, it won't work. Determine a method to symbolize consensus around and commitment to the agreed upon norms. Some group leaders begin by having their students make a verbal or thumbs up/down agreement followed by signing the Full Value Contract to formalize the commitment.

The norms and values created in the Full Value Contract are the ideal for which the group will strive. None of us are perfect; therefore the ideal will not always be met. There will be times when people do not follow the norms or "mess up." Once norms and values have been agreed upon, systems to reinforce them need to be developed. Develop these systems for reinforcing the norms and values with your group.

Perhaps the most common misuse of the Full Value Contract is when it is employed as a punitive rather than developmental tool. For example, pointing to the FVC on the wall and saying "Full Value Contract! You wrote down listening and no one is listening right now!" is punitive. A more effective approach for maximizing this powerful tool is to acknowledge when people are listening, or actively exhibiting the behaviors cited on the contract. For example, "everybody freeze, I want to acknowledge what a great job you all are doing listening to one another" is positive. It is important to stop the class to address unsafe behavior immediately. As well as preventing physical and emotional injury, this models an effective intervention – one that your students can use as they develop more skills. Remember to intervene in a manner that will set the tone for the continued development of a community of learners in your classroom. This approach is supported by Alfie Kohn's work which encourages educators to consider "working with" students versus "doing to" students—demonstrating what we expect of one another in our classroom.

Challenge by Choice (CBC)

Challenge by Choice is another tool for "working with" students—helping them to be partners in learning, not simply recipients of information. Challenge by Choice is an approach in which students decide how they would like to participate or challenge themselves within a given assignment or activity.

A way to understand this concept is by looking at the optimal learning zone. Most of us can recognize three different zones: comfort, stretch and panic, within which we function (see graphic).

Challenge by Choice lives in the stretch zone. In their book *Making Connections: Teaching and the Human Brain*, Renate and Geoffrey Caine describe the stretch zone as a place of "relaxed alertness" where students are able to process information and make good decisions while fully engaged. When students are in the comfort zone they are often bored or disengaged. Students in the panic zone are frequently hyper-vigilant, anxious and willing to do anything to remove themselves from the anxiety-provoking situation. It is very difficult to be open to learning and to process information when your body is saying "get me out of here!" As teachers, it is our responsibility to present learning opportunities that have the potential to actively engage every student by presenting viable options. For example, when inviting students to present a song as part of a tag game the teacher can say, "There are at least three ways you and your partner can present your songs to the group…you can say the words, you can sing the words or you can "perform" the words…you and your partner decide how you would like to challenge yourselves today." This is very different from "once everyone has come up with a song, you and your partner will sing it in front of the class."

STRETCH ZONE:
Relaxed Alertness
Optimal Learning Zone
Fully Engaged
CHALLENGE BY CHOICE

COMFORT ZONE:
Safe
Secure
Potential Boredom
Apathy

PANIC ZONE:

Limited Processing Ability
Fight or Flight Response

Poor Decision Making Ability
"Back To Comfort Zone" Mentality

Coaxing young people into doing a difficult task or element teaches them only that they can be talked into doing something. On the other hand, helping students see that they have the right and ability to choose their level of challenge, and how to assess what is and isn't an appropriate level of challenge, teaches them how to make positive decisions for life. This is critical to a well-taught Adventure program.

So, CBC like the Full Value Contract should be present in all your Adventure work. (You may want to have a lesson or two behind you before you introduce the CBC concept to students—*although you're applying it!*) Some find it easy to understand and explain Challenge by Choice in the following way:

• Students have the right to choose when to participate and in what way.

• Students are asked to add value to the experience at all times. Sitting out is rarely an appropriate option.

• Students are asked to respect and value the decisions of their class members.

There are some activities in this book that will help you specifically teach this key concept. Educators who keep the concept of Challenge by Choice in mind in each moment of their Adventure work will meet with much more success than those who approach their work with the attitude that everyone must do everything!

As educators, our language and the behaviors we reinforce will send a powerful message. As we offer activities and hold students to behavioral norms, we must model the Full Value Contract and Challenge by Choice. Doing so will demonstrate to your students that you are committed to them, that they are important and effective models. Granted, this is more work than telling your students what to do, but the results are well worth it. Students will actively take responsibility for their learning and support their peers in doing the same. By fully embracing Challenge by Choice and the Full Value Contract, you will help your students become independent, engaged and happy learners. It is the interdependence of the Full Value Contract and Challenge by Choice that creates the Adventure learning environment.

Adventure learning is holistic in that it addresses students in their entirety "as thinking, feeling, physical and emotional beings." It permits students to practice making choices they might not ordinarily make as well as observe peers practicing behaviors that might not ordinarily seem possible. "If we create a classroom community, we can then learn what it means to be members of that community. If we want students to act responsibly, we must give them responsibility. This microcosm of "the real world" is at the core of experiential education: to learn by doing, and to gain insight from the experience." (Frank, 2001) This is particularly relevant when attempting to impact health behavior in young people and is aligned with the new directions in school health education.

CHECK-INS

A check-in consists of taking a few minutes at the start of the class to invite students to express what they are thinking or feeling using a variety of techniques. The purpose of the check-in is to provide students time to transition together and focus their attention and behavior. A check-in can really help a student stay or become aligned with the parameters of their Full Value learning community. Check-ins also provide teachers with invaluable information about what is happening with their students and how to modify lesson plans for optimal engagement. The only steadfast rule for conducting a check-in is that it must be absolutely safe. Students need to feel free to appropriately acknowledge what they are thinking or feeling in the moment. For example, a student may select the distracted Feeling Marketplace card and say "I am feeling very distracted because I am going to a baseball game with my family after school and I can't wait! I am so excited! I need help concentrating!" The student is not saying, "I don't want to be here, but rather, "Help me be here." Check-ins help to develop the foundational health skill of being able to appropriately express one's self and one's needs.

The format for check-ins is most often a circle where people can see one another and have the opportunity to speak to the whole group. Students who are not ready to check-in or do not wish to talk may say "Pass." It is important that these students verbalize the word "Pass" so that their voices are heard as valuable members of the learning community. Because students aren't required to say anything, this approach also allows students the freedom to really listen to what others are saying without worrying about what they are going to say when it is their turn. There are several variations below that will help students develop the skill of self-expression. Each check-in variation gives students a method of expressing their thoughts or feelings by relating them to different objects, colors, types of weather and so on. Check-ins do not need to happen at the beginning of every class but work well during the first and last class meeting of each week. Creating Healthy Habits suggests doing a Challenge Circle check-in at the start of each new priority risk area unit as well as Full Value check-ins periodically throughout the semester.

The time invested in the check-in is well worth the resulting group transformation in which students begin to appreciate and anticipate the opportunity to express themselves and to be heard. The check-in is a very powerful tool in establishing healthy, safe learning communities.

- **Animal**

   Students identify an animal that describes what they are feeling. For example, quiet as a mouse or like a horse—strong and fast.

- **Beanie Baby®**

   Students select a Beanie Baby® to represent what they are feeling.

- **Bull's Eye Check In**

   Create a large target on the floor with a few circles of ropes. Ask students to position themselves somewhere on the target in response to a series of statements. For example, "Today I am feeling energized and ready to go." If that statement is right on target for some students they would stand in the center. If that statement is somewhat true for some students they would stand in the middle ring. If the statement is completely false for some students they would position themselves on the outside edge of the target.

- **Bumper Sticker**

   Students cite a saying from a bumper sticker or make up their own bumper sticker phrase which describes what they are thinking or feeling.

- **Challenge Circles**

   As you did in the Bull's Eye Check In, create three concentric circles on the floor with rope. The inner circle will represent the comfort zone, the middle the stretch zone and the outer the panic zone. Ask students to stand in the appropriate zone in response to a variety of questions. For example, running a mile without stopping; talking about alcohol and other drug use; eating a balanced diet; expressing anger appropriately. This type of check in works well to explain the concept of Challenge by Choice and is also recommended for use at the start of each new priority risk unit.

- **Color**

  Students name a color that describes how they are feeling.

- **Color Chips**

  Students choose a color chip to represent what they are thinking or feeling. Color or paint chips can usually be obtained from your local hardware store for free.

- **Deep Breath**

  Ask students to stand in a circle, close their eyes and take a few slow, deep breaths. Tell them to open their eyes when they are ready to be present and begin the class.

- **Facial expressions and personal sculpture**

  Ask students to stand in a circle facing away from the center. At the count of three have students turn around and show either a facial expression or a full body expression of what they are thinking or feeling.

- **Feelings Marketplace Cards**

  Students choose an emotion which represents how they are feeling at the beginning of class.

- **Fist to Five**

  On the count of three, students hold out the number of fingers, zero to five, that describes how they are feeling (no fingers meaning very bad and all five fingers meaning very good).

- **Full Value Check-In**

  Have students stand in a circle. Place the Full Value Contract in the center of the circle and ask each student to identify either when they saw a behavior listed happening in the last class or what behavior they would like to focus on for this class. This check-in is recommended for use very soon after the Full Value Contract has been formalized and then periodically throughout the remainder of the semester. It can also be used as a reflection or closure activity.

- **I Am About Cards**

  Students select a visual representation of what they are thinking or feeling from a variety of photographs.

- **Piece of Clothing**

  Students identify a piece of clothing that represents how they are feeling at the moment. For example: comfortable like a soft flannel shirt or ready to take anything on like a new pair of blue jeans.

- **Partner Check-In**

  Students find a partner to discuss what they are thinking about; how they are feeling or what happened to them on the way to class.

- **Readings**

  You or your students select and read some short writing that is relevant to that day's lesson or a current event.

- **Scales: 1–10 rating lineups**

  Clear a space in your classroom and create parameters for a continuum. Invite students to position themselves along the continuum in response to a variety of questions. For example, "today I am feeling very optimistic/pessimistic; I am really motivated/unmotivated about participating in class today."

- **Sound Check**

  Students make a noise that exemplifies how they are feeling.

- **Thumbometer**

  Have students create a "thumbs up" position with one hand and rotate it all the way around to a "thumbs down" position. Explain that the full range of movement represents a rating system for how you are feeling. Ask students to close their eyes and on the count of three show their thumbometer. Group members can open their eyes and look around to see how their classmates are feeling.

- **Type of Weather**

  Students describe a type of weather that explains what they are thinking or how they are feeling. For example, "Would you describe how you're thinking as stormy, sunny or snowy?"

HOW DOES ADVENTURE LEARNING LINK TO HEALTH BEHAVIOR THEORIES?

There are three types of health behavior:

- **Prevention:** Prevention is defined as behaviors that one engages in or ceases to engage in to prevent or reduce future health risk.
- **Promotion:** Promotion consists of engaging in behaviors to maintain or enhance current state of good health.
- **Detection:** Detection provides information about the presence or absence of an unhealthy condition. For example, standardized fitness tests.

Creating Healthy Habits addresses all three types of health behavior. Importantly, the guide recognizes the significance of understanding the motivation behind participation in prevention, promotion and detection. Not only is motivation recognized, it is used to create and sustain behaviors. Often there is a transition from initiating behaviors to maintaining behaviors in terms of life-long health and wellness activities. The following theories help us understand some of the thinking behind health behavior change.

Social Cognitive Theory (Bandura)

Self-efficacy is the perception of one's ability to perform a task successfully. In other words, it is situation-specific self-confidence. Self-efficacy theory states that initiation and persistence of behaviors is determined by judgments and expectations around skills, capabilities and the likelihood of success.

The process involves:

- Self-efficacy expectancy: "Can I do this?"
- Outcome expectancy: "What is the probable outcome?"
- Outcome value: "What is the reinforcement/incentive?"

Key points of Bandura's theory are:

- Self-efficacy alone is not enough to be successful. A student must have the desire to succeed as well as the ability.
- Self-efficacy affects the student's choice of activities, level of effort, and persistence in participating. Students who believe in themselves will tend to persevere especially under adverse conditions.
- Although self-efficacy is task-specific, it can generalize to other similar skills and situations.
- Self-efficacy is related to goal setting. Students who exhibit high self-efficacy are more likely to set challenging goals. (stretch zone)

This process is interwoven with students' perceptions of control over their environment and reasons for their success or failure. For example, students will perceive exercise as having a stronger impact on their health if they feel empowered to control the types of workouts in which they are able to participate. Conversely, stereotypical physical education or health classes in which activities and participation in them are dictated by the teacher, create situations in which the student is "done to" rather than worked with." Students in this learning environment find it easy to be passive and blame the teacher for lack of participation or failure. Consequently, they do not accept responsibility for and acquire healthy behaviors.

The following graphic demonstrates the flow of factors contributing to efficacy and healthy behaviors.

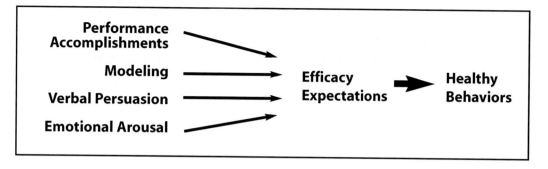

Performance Accomplishments:

Performance accomplishments are the most dependable basis for self-efficacy judgments because they are based on one's mastery experiences. If experiences are generally successful, they will raise the level of self-efficacy. However, repeated failures will result in lower efficacy expectations.

Modeling:

Modeling is the use of demonstration to help learn new skills. Seeing the task completed alleviates anxiety and opens the door for the possibility of completing the task.

Verbal Persuasion:

Positive verbal feedback, encouragement and belief statements influence student behavior. The feedback must be relevant and grounded in the experience versus non-specific and general in order to have a positive impact on self-efficacy.

Emotional Arousal:

A student's perception of the environment, task at hand and their physiological response affect their behavior by influencing efficacy expectations. If students perceive the environment as judgmental and threatening, the task too complex for their skill sets, and are feeling anxious, they will not believe in their ability to be effective.

The Adventure learning environment intentionally uses Bandura's contributing factors to bring forth self-efficacy. Strategies for promoting activities include skill building, setting achievable goals, identifying benefits and social support (Marcus, 2003). The creation of a safe learning community founded on the interdependence of the FVC and Challenge by Choice helps students gain confidence in their knowledge and skills thus reinforcing their desire to make healthy choices. For example, changes identified by students who have participated in a curriculum that based on the *Creating Healthy Habits* guide include:

"I started peeling the skin off a chicken and started drinking more milk."
"I stay outside longer and run every evening."

"I walk more, am friendlier now. We're helping each other and the days are better."

"I am trying to reach my goals and ignore everything bad around me."

One of the best examples of increased self-efficacy is reflected in one student's response to being called "fat" while walking down the hall at school. She calmly and firmly turned to the person and said, "You need to take the Adventure Wellness class and learn how to respect yourself and other people!" and continued on her way.

Behavioral Choice Theory (Epstein)

The Behavioral Choice Theory relies less on performance expectations and more on social perceptions and the perception of choice.

Key points of the Behavioral Choice Theory are:

- Comparison of perceived benefits versus the perceived costs of participating in healthy behavior
- Perception of choice
- Availability of behavioral options

The Behavioral Choice Theory incorporates the Decisional Balance Theory (Janis & Mann) in which the students choose behaviors by weighing the possible gains versus the challenges or losses that will be a consequence of each behavior. This deliberation leads to action. Epstein expands this decisional balance beyond perceived benefits and costs, to include other factors such as availability of physical activities, reinforcement and degree of effort. For example, making the options for after school physical activity obvious and accessible to all students before they go home and perhaps sit in front of computers or televisions is a way to ensure they know physical activities are available. The Behavioral Choice Theory elucidates the importance of having more community-based physical activities than just traditional sports programs. Epstein also highlights the importance of students' abilities to choose how to participate in healthy behaviors (CBC) and to experience rewarding consequences as a result of their own choices. Challenge by Choice gives us a method for creating choice and allowing students to own/be responsible for behaviors and their consequences (both positive and negative). Strategies for promoting health behavior change within this theoretical framework are: 1) increasing awareness of healthier options and 2) developing student participation in planning and decision making (Marcus, 2003).

The Adventure learning environment is the perfect place for students to explore healthy risk-taking as well as making choices that will lead to a healthier life in a supportive learning community. Students are frequently asked to identify multiple community resources as part of the content for activities—helping them understand and identify how they can maintain healthy behaviors. For example, in Wellness Tag, students must stop and call out different types of wellness behaviors to avoid being tagged or to literally create a Wall of Support for staying away from alcohol and other drugs. Students are also encouraged to consciously choose their level of challenge throughout each lesson, experiencing the positive and negative consequences of risk-taking in a safe environment. For example, in Turn Over A New Leaf, students state a healthy behavior they would like to keep or improve and an unhealthy one they would like to leave behind as they work together to turn the tarp they are all standing over without anyone stepping off! These experiences provide the foundation for healthier behavior choices in the "real world."

Habit Theory (James)

Habit Theory suggests that a habit is a behavior that is performed repeatedly and has become an automatic cognitive process.

Key points of Habit Theory are:

- A Healthy Habit is a behavior that is performed automatically; for example, brushing your teeth before going to bed.
- The goal is to make the transition from a controlled decision-making process to an automatic response to situational cues.

The Healthy Habit behavior is performed without conscious thought or consideration of an alternate behavior. For example, students will automatically buckle their seatbelts each time they get into a vehicle versus weighing the pros and cons or odds of getting into an accident without wearing them.

Cultivating the Habit of Thinking, Acting and Choosing Healthy Behaviors

It is important to note that the goal of Habit Theory is to move from a decision making process to an automatic response in a given situation. As health educators it is our responsibility to help students process health information and develop the skills to make thinking, acting and choosing for health a habit. Developing a habit is not the same as modifying behavior. In behavior modification one behavior, such as quitting smoking, is the focus of change and a plan is made to change it. Developing a habit requires supporting students through each step required to complete a healthy behavior. Using the *Creating Healthy Habits* guide educators can help students move from knowledge acquisition to decision making to proficiency and finally maintenance. Creating a health class learning environment where daily practice and ritual, consistency of action and opportunity make the process of cultivating a healthy habit attainable is the goal of *Creating Healthy Habits*.

ABOUT THIS GUIDE

Creating Healthy Habits combines traditional health education methodologies with Adventure learning. It is not intended to be a stand alone program but rather to supplement existing health curricula. Included in the following pages are activities that bring health concepts and skills to life, providing students with ample opportunities to think, choose and act on healthy behaviors. This approach differs from many health textbooks and curricula because the initial focus is on developing community in the classroom. This is accomplished by understanding peer and family relationships and cultural assumptions in ways that are valuing and promote respect versus immediately addressing body systems, nutrition and fitness. We have found that spending immediate quality time creating such an environment allows for more honest discussions among students when delving into the different priority risk areas. It is through community building that students transition from knowing what is healthy to doing what is healthy. FVC and CBC set the stage for habit development. The guide follows a recommended sequence. Teachers may choose to change the flow of topics to suit their needs; however, it is highly recommended that the initial community-building piece stay intact.

Connection to Standards

The *Creating Healthy Habits* guide is informed by the integrated thematic instruction model and aligns with national and general state health education, physical education, and family and consumer sciences education standards. The fundamental purpose of this comprehensive guide for health curriculum is to facilitate student development of habits of thinking, choosing and acting in the healthiest way. The guide is organized around the guiding principles, national health skills/standards and priority risk areas.

The **Guiding Principles** direct and inform health education and the building of school communities that promote the health and well being of students, families, teachers, and staff. The guiding principles of the activities found in this guide are adapted from the Massachusetts Health Curriculum Frameworks and are as follows:

1. Comprehensive health education teaches students fundamental health concepts and skills that foster habits and behaviors for the student as well as others through the coordinated teaching of health, physical education and family and consumer sciences education at each grade level.

2. Comprehensive health education teaches students to use fundamental health concepts to assess risks, to consider potential consequences, and to make health-enhancing decisions.

3. Comprehensive health education teaches skills that assist students in understanding and communicating health information clearly for self-management and health promotion.

4. Comprehensive health education contributes to the capacity of students to work with families, school staff, peers and community members to enhance personal health and create a safe and supportive environment where individual similarities and differences are acknowledged.

5. Comprehensive health education is strengthened through collaboration and partnerships among all components of the coordinated school health program and other subjects.

Creating Healthy Habits is a skills-based approach intended to empower all students to promote and protect their own health and that of others in six priority risk areas.

National Health Skills/Standards

Health Skill/Standard 1:

All students will apply health promotion and disease prevention concepts and principles to personal, family and consumer health issues. (*Core Concepts*)

Health Skill/Standard 2:

All students will access valid health information and appropriate health-promoting products and services. (*Accessing Information*)

Health Skill/Standard 3:

All students will practice health-enhancing behaviors and reduce health risks. (*Self Management*)

Health Skill/Standard 4

All students will analyze the influence of cultural beliefs, media, and technology on health. (*Analyze Influences*)

Health Skill/Standard 5

All students will use goal setting and decision-making skills to enhance health. (*Goal Setting/Decision Making*)

Health Skill/Standard 6

All students will demonstrate effective interpersonal communication and other social skills which enhance health. (*Interpersonal Communication*)

Health Skill/Standard 7

All students will demonstrate advocacy skills for enhanced personal, family, and community health. (*Advocacy*)

Priority Risk Areas

1. **Intentional (Violence) and Unintentional (Safety) Injury Prevention Safety:**

   Violence Prevention

   Students will:

   - learn how their actions affect others
   - understand the power that positive character traits can have in preventing violence
   - gain skills for reporting incidents of violence and hurtful behavior to adults in the school and community
   - avoid engaging in violence
   - identify constructive alternatives to violence, including how to discourage others from engaging in violence.

   Injury Prevention

   Students will:

   - gain the knowledge and skills to avoid and recognize verbal, physical, and emotional abuse
   - assess the factors that contribute to intentional and unintentional injury, including environmental safety

   Benchmark Examples:

   K–2 Explain how to handle disagreements without fighting.
   State rules to keep safe.

   3–5 Name kinds of violence such as bullying, fighting, homicide.
   Describe the ingredients for a healthy family.

   6–8 Explain how to prevent injuries at home and at play.
   Examine attitudes toward risk taking behaviors.

   9–12 Identify and use community resources and services that promote a safe and healthful environment.
   Examine different family structures, customs and values.

2. **Mental/Emotional Health:**

   Students will:

   - Acquire knowledge about emotions and physical health, the management of emotions and social awareness.
   - Learn skills to promote self-acceptance, make decisions, and cope with stress.

   Benchmark Examples:

   K–2 Demonstrate the expression of feelings in a healthful way.
   Discuss handling feelings of sadness.

   3–5 Describe kinds of stressors and their effects.
   Describe how to show anger in healthful ways.

6–8   Describe responsible decision-making and its benefits
Identify life skills for health.

9–12   Examine personal health attitudes and the steps that may be taken to affect change.
Develop and maintain interpersonal relationships.

3. Nutrition:

Students will gain the knowledge and skills needed to select a diet that supports health and reduces the risk of illness and future chronic diseases.

Benchmark Examples:

K–2   Identify healthful and unhealthful snacks.

List the food groups in the food pyramid.

Name sources of meats, vegetables, fruits and dairy products.

3–5   Identify different kinds of convenience foods.

Place a variety of foods in their food groups.

6–8   Explain the misconception of normal body size and shape.

Describe signs of eating disorders.

9–12   Apply knowledge of sound nutritional concepts to patterns of behavior and personal choice.

Select weight control programs based on accurate information.

4. Physical Fitness:

Students will comprehend basic physical activity principles and concepts that enable them to make decisions, solve problems and become self-directed life-long learners who are informed physical activity consumers.

Benchmark Examples:

K–2   Describe the effects of exercise on the heart.

Explain the importance of exercise and play.

3–5   List examples of aerobic activity.

Explain the importance of muscular endurance, strength, flexibility and fitness skills.

6–8   Analyze social pressures from peers, adults, and the media which affect nutrition and fitness behaviors.

Describe the cultural aspects of fitness and nutrition.

9–12   Select exercise and programs based on accurate information.
Describe how socio-cultural factors, peer relationships, and values have an impact on health behaviors.

5. **Tobacco, Alcohol, & Substance Use/Abuse Prevention:**

   Students will:

   - Acquire the knowledge and skills to be competent in making health-enhancing decisions regarding the use of medications and avoidance of substances.

   - Acquire the knowledge and skills to be competent in communicating about substance use/abuse prevention for healthier homes, schools, and communities.

   Benchmark Examples:

   K–2   Identify different kinds of drugs.

   Explain how medicine can be helpful or harmful.

   3–5   Identify factors which protect a person from drug use.

   Discuss drugs and passive, assertive, aggressive and violent behaviors.

   Describe tobacco and the hazards of its use.

   6–8   Define drug use, misuse, abuse and dependence.

   Analyze common advertising techniques used to promote health and drug products.

   9–12   Examine the effects of drug use and abuse on family dynamics.

   Develop and apply skills to resist pressures to use drugs.

6. **Personal and Consumer Health:**

   Students will:

   - Develop sound personal health habits.

   - Be appropriately informed and supported by health care information, services and community resources.

   Benchmark Examples:

   K–2   Demonstrate sitting and standing with correct posture.

   Explain importance of good hygiene.

   Describe the functions of the lungs.

   3–5   Identify consumer appeals with positive and negative messages.

   6–8   Describe how health is portrayed in advertising and in the media.

   Examine community resources that provide health care products and services.

   Evaluate personal health habits.

   9–12   Recognize the impact of media and cultural influences on health care and consumer decisions.

HOW TO USE THIS GUIDE:

Lesson Outcomes

Each lesson begins with specific outcomes that have been developed from the National Health Standards. These provide the teacher with an overview of the types of activities and general expectations of each lesson.

Grade Specific Sections and Lessons

Creating Healthy Habits is divided into sixth, seventh and eighth grades. Each grade level has specific lessons that are organized by the six priority risk areas. The first section in each grade creates classroom community by learning about injury prevention and the emotional health priority risk areas. This section is followed by the nutrition, physical activity and substance abuse prevention priority risk areas. Personal and consumer health is integrated into the other priority risk area lessons.

Differences within each grade include a specific focus on tobacco use prevention in the sixth grade; a greater emphasis on conflict resolution in the seventh grade; and a more intense exploration of cultural awareness in the eighth grade. Activities within each priority risk area are sequenced with group and student skill development in mind.

The lessons are based on 45-minute class periods and are intended to be completed in classrooms, unless otherwise specified, of about 20–25 students. Lessons may be modified to accommodate length of class periods as well as class size. Hints for how to adapt an activity to a particular class size are included.

The format for the lessons is as follows.

HOW TO USE EACH LESSON

The components of each lesson are:

Activity:	Name of activity
Lesson Objectives:	Goals for the activity
Time:	Approximate time needed to complete each activity
Props:	Materials needed for the activity
Health Skills:	National Health Standard focus
Set-up:	How to prepare the space and get the class ready
Framing:	What to say to the class to set the stage for the activity
Procedure:	Rules and sequence for doing the activity
Reflections:	Specific debriefing approaches related to the activity objectives
Other Thoughts:	Safety considerations, other ideas and variations

The following diagram describes the overlay of the health learning objectives with Experiential Learning Cycle.

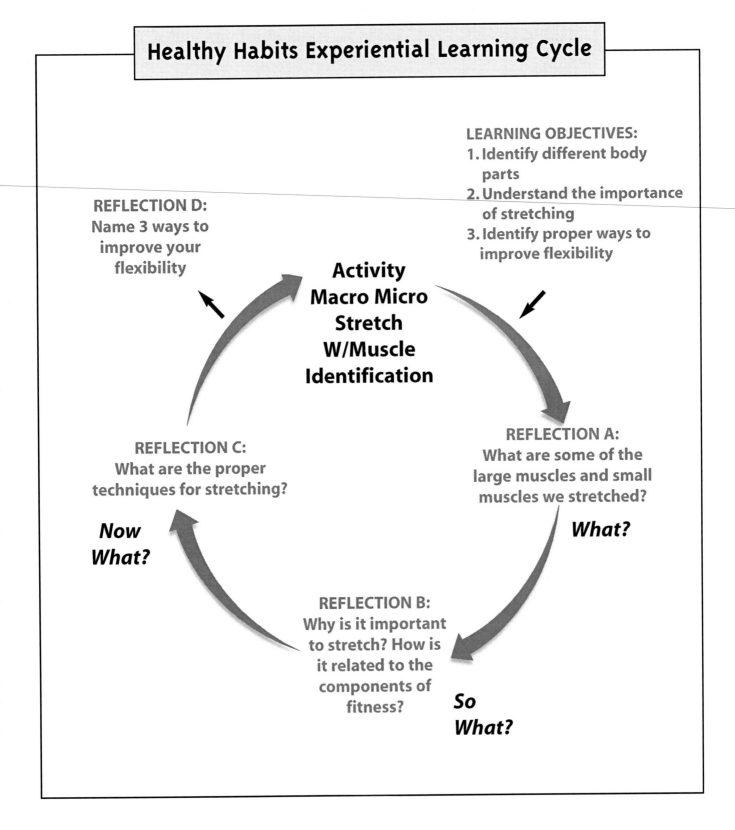

Healthy Habits Experiential Learning Cycle

LEARNING OBJECTIVES:
1. Identify different body parts
2. Understand the importance of stretching
3. Identify proper ways to improve flexibility

Activity Macro Micro Stretch W/Muscle Identification

REFLECTION D:
Name 3 ways to improve your flexibility

REFLECTION C:
What are the proper techniques for stretching?

Now What?

REFLECTION A:
What are some of the large muscles and small muscles we stretched?

What?

REFLECTION B:
Why is it important to stretch? How is it related to the components of fitness?

So What?

Each grade begins with a scope and sequence followed by specific activity descriptions for each lesson. Each lesson begins with a chart that provides an overview of the lesson outcome as the header, followed by activity names, learning objectives, time requirements, props and health skills addressed. There is a second chart for teacher notes regarding framing, set-up/procedure and reflections. These charts are intended to provide teachers with a page they can tear out or copy as an easily accessible guide for delivering lessons. The charts are followed by specific descriptions of each lesson's activities which include framing, set-up, step by step procedures and reflection questions directly connected to that activity's objectives. An example of a lesson chart is shown on the following page.

LESSON 20

In this lesson students will identify sources of nutrients and foods that energize and learn the benefits and concepts of eating a healthy, balanced diet.

ACTIVITY	LEARNING OBJECTIVE	TIME	PROPS	HEALTH SKILLS
Dinner Call	**At the conclusion of this activity, students will be able to:** • Identify nutrients found in different foods. • Learn about making the best possible choices among unhealthy alternatives.	15 minutes	• None	• Core content • Self-management • Interpersonal communication
Gobart Tag	• Identify foods that are energizing. • Recognize the symptoms of unhealthy eating habits. • Describe healthy eating habits.	15 minutes	• Boundary markers	• Self-management • Advocacy • Core content

TEACHER'S NOTES:

FRAMING	SET-UP PROCEDURE	REFLECTION

IMPORTANT ASSUMPTIONS

Training

Implementing the activities in this guide requires proper training. Project Adventure suggests a comprehensive training plan that addresses the following key areas:

- Learning the basic theory of Adventure and experiential education
- Experiencing activities including warm-ups, ice breakers, initiatives
- Learning facilitation and debriefing skills
- Learning safety and risk management skills appropriate for each grade being taught

Project Adventure offers a variety of workshops and site-specific program consultation to meet these needs and help you effectively implement your program.

Safety

This guide does not include a safety manual. Some of the activities in this guide can be dangerous if conducted without proper training on the facilitator's part.

Props and Equipment

Each lesson details the props that are necessary for its related activities. This guide does assume that specialty props not typically found in the traditional health education classroom will be purchased. Project Adventure offers a number of prop packages that make acquisition of the necessary materials cost effective.

Use of Assessment

Assessment is an integral part of education. Because *Creating Healthy Habits* is a guide to supplement your curriculum, standard health education assessment methods work well. The adventure activities and debriefing process provide ample opportunities to assess content knowledge as well as skill application.

Grade 6

INJURY PREVENTION / MENTAL EMOTIONAL HEALTH

CREATING COMMUNITY

Lesson 1:
In this lesson, students will begin to develop a healthy classroom community by learning each other's names and acknowledging similarities and differences.

Activities:	Name Go Round with Favorite Movie, Book or Video Game
	What Do You Know?
	Categories

Lesson 2:
In this lesson students will reinforce and expand on developing a healthy classroom community by distinguishing between safe and risky or harmful behaviors and developing nonviolent communication.

Activities:	Fill Me In
	Commonalities

Lesson 3:
In this lesson students will learn to identify and practice safety behaviors in a physically active environment and begin to define concepts of health and wellness.

Activities:	Moving Without Touching
	Healthy Behavior Tag

GOAL SETTING

Lesson 4:
In this lesson students will be introduced to goal-setting for health and wellness.

Activities:	Full Value Check-In
	Pairs Tag with Exercise
	Moonball

Lesson 5:
In this lesson students will identify how to support one another in achieving their goals.

Activities:	In Anticipation of Learning
	Kaizan: The Art of Continuous Improvement

HEALTHY RELATIONSHIPS

Lesson 6:
In this lesson, the class creates a visual representation of behavioral norms necessary for a safe and challenging health class learning community. Students also set individual goals for the health class.

Activities:	Circle of Strength (FVC)

Lesson 7:
In this lesson students will explore concepts of healthy and unhealthy peer and family relationships.

Activities:	All Aboard
	Out of Kilter

Lesson 8:
In this lesson students will work together to construct bridges of communication.

Activity:	Bridge It

EMOTIONAL EXPRESSION

Lesson 9:
In this lesson students will recognize and identify feelings.

Activities:	Gotcha!
	Feelings Market Place Relay

Lesson 10:
In this lesson students will learn how to appropriately manage anger (within an emotionally safe environment).

Activity:	Emotions Pass

STRESS MANAGEMENT

Lesson 11:
In this lesson students will explore self-management and advocacy skills for coping with stress.

Activities:	Tai Chi Stretch
	I Need…

Lesson 12:
In this lesson students will learn to differentiate between eustress and distress and then learn to apply stress management strategies.

Activities:	Measured Breath
	It's All Happening

CONFLICT RESOLUTION

Lesson 13:
In this lesson students will experience different approaches to conflict and conflict resolution.

Activities: Let's Win
Rock, Paper, Scissors into Anticipation
Bear, Salmon, Mosquito

Lesson 14:
In this lesson students will practice problem-solving and conflict management strategies.

Activities: 7,11,21
Pick n' Pack...The Case of the Kaytees

PHYSICAL FITTNESS

Lesson 15:
In this lesson students will identify multiple ways to be fit, options for accessing fitness in different environments and practice active stretching.

Activities: Fitness Speed Rabbit
Co-op Competition

Lesson 16:
In this lesson students will explore the concepts of cardiovascular fitness and measure and track their heart rate in response to different environmental stressors.

Activities: Instant Impulse
Swat Tag

Lesson 17:
In this lesson students will identify anatomically correct body parts, discover the five components of fitness and identify the range and availability of fitness resources as well as principles of exercise adherence.

Activities: People to People
Be the Best/Share The Health

NUTRITION

Lesson 18:
In this lesson students will practice their interpersonal communication skills and knowledge of the food pyramid.

Activities: What Food am I?
Food FFEACH and MOOCH

Lesson 19:
In this lesson students will identify multicultural health and wellness practices—focusing primarily on nutrition.

Activities: Mapping
Multicultural Food Find

Lesson 20:
In this lesson students will identify sources of nutrients and foods that energize and also name the benefits and concepts of eating a healthy, balanced diet.

Activities: Dinner Call
Gobart Tag

Lesson 21:
In this lesson students will work in small groups and create visual representations of a variety of body types and healthy diet plans to match.

Activity: A Day in the Life

SUBSTANCE ABUSE PREVENTION

Lesson 22:
In this lesson students will test their knowledge of the risks and health effects of tobacco use.

Activity: Be Smart Don't Start

Lesson 23:
In this lesson students will challenge themselves to manage the influences of advertising techniques used by tobacco companies.

Activity: Tobacco Field

Lesson 24:
In this lesson students will strengthen their understanding of the effects of stress-related decision making and need for support in substance abuse prevention.

Activities: Zip, Zap
Lifeline

Lesson 25:
In this lesson students will learn to recognize the effects of substance abuse and work together to identify resources for substance abuse prevention.

Activities: Substance Scrabble Babble

CLOSURE

Lesson 26:
In this lesson students will work together to reinforce the concept of continually practicing healthy behaviors and leaving unhealthy behaviors behind as they commit to not using substances.

Activity: Turn Over A New Leaf

Creating Community

LESSON 1

In this lesson students will begin to develop a healthy classroom community by learning each other's names and acknowledging similarities and differences in their group.

ACTIVITY	LEARNING OBJECTIVE	TIME	PROPS	HEALTH SKILLS
Name Go Round	At the conclusion of this activity, students will be able to: • Identify and name their fellow group members. • Identify and verbally communicate some of their own personal preferences.	15 minutes	• None	• Interpersonal communication
What Do You Know?	• Identify and name their fellow group members again. • Begin building healthy relationships. • Identify and begin to carry out cooperation skills.	20 minutes	• None	• Interpersonal communication • Self-management
Categories	• Demonstrate some interpersonal communication skills. • Acknowledge similarities and differences among peers. • Discuss some of the ways which diversity strengthens a group.	8–10 minutes	• None	• Interpersonal communication • Self-management • Analyze influences

TEACHER'S NOTES:

FRAMING	SET-UP PROCEDURE	REFLECTION

Name Go Round with Favorite Movie, Book or Video Game

Set-Up:

Clear a large open space in your classroom.

Framing:

"The first step to building a healthy learning community is to find out who is in our class and what they like."

Procedure:

1. Ask students to stand in a circle inside the open space.
2. Tell the students that they will each have the opportunity to say their name and favorite movie, book or video game. For example, "My name is Sarah and my favorite movie is Harry Potter."
3. Ask for a volunteer to start the process and then tell the class which direction the progression around the circle will go (i.e., left or right).
4. Students may pass if they are not ready and can contribute after the first round is complete.

Reflection:

1. None needed.

. . . .

What Do You Know?

Set Up:

Identify the boundaries of the space in which you would like students to line up between (points A and B), one boundary space per group. Students will be divided in groups of four to eight people.

Framing:

Ask the students: "What do you know about your own name? What do you know about the names of your friends? What could you learn about other students that will help you get to know them better?"

Procedure:

1. Divide the students into clusters of four to eight people. A small class group can participate as one cluster.

2. Tell them they will have several challenges to work on. Each challenge involves performing a task and may be limited by time.

3. For the first task, ask the students to line up in their clusters by the number of letters used to spell their first names, longest to shortest, as quickly as they can.

4. Keep track of time and let students know how quickly they completed the task.

5. For the second task, ask the students to line up by the number of letters in their first and last name.

6. Finally ask the students to line up by the number of letters in all of their names (i.e., First, last, middle, nicknames, etc).

7. After each round ask the students to say their name(s) and the number of letters in them.

8. For additional challenges you can ask each cluster to determine any of the following:

   • Whose name uses the most different letters?

   • How many letters in the alphabet are used by all of your names?

   • Combining the letters from all your names (i.e., all of the clusters) are all the letters in the alphabet used?

   • What single letter is used most in all of your names; in each of your names?

   • Using only the letters in your own names, (i.e., those in your cluster) how many other names of students not in your cluster, but in this class, can you spell?

   • Using only the letters in your own names (by cluster or by entire class), how many words related to health and wellness can you spell?

Reflection:

Questions for Discussion:

1. "Can anyone name all the students?"

2. "Can you identify some of the skills you used to complete the various challenges?"

3. "Can you tell us something about where your name came from? Were you named after your great aunt or your father's favorite author?"

4. "Tell me some new things you learned about yourself and one another during this activity."

5. "Name something you learned that will be helpful during the health and wellness class."

Categories

Set Up:

Clear a fairly large open classroom space.

Framing:

"Part of building community in the classroom involves knowing how we are alike and how we differ. Knowing people are like us makes it difficult to be hurtful to them. This will help us prevent violence in our classroom—knowing how much we are like one another."

Procedure:

1. Have students stand in a circle while you explain instructions.
2. Say to students: "I am going to call out a variety of topics. For example, a topic might be 'favorite kind of cheese.' For each topic your challenge is to find other people who have a similar response to the topic. So if your favorite kind of cheese is Swiss, call out 'Swiss' until you find all the other people who share Swiss as a favorite."
3. Have each group say what category they represent and then present another topic.
4. Sample Categories:
   - Favorite ice cream
   - Favorite type of music
   - Favorite type of dessert
   - Places you would like to visit
   - Number of siblings (define in whichever way makes sense to you)
   - Types of pets
   - School activities/clubs

Reflection:

Questions for Discussion:

1. "What did you learn about one another?"
2. "Can you name three examples of why it is important to know what people have in common and how they differ?"
3. "What do you think about the statement 'our differences make us stronger?'"
4. "Tell us about some situations related to being healthy where groups and friends may be helpful."

 Additional Thoughts

You can also have a basket of cards with different categories printed on them so that students may present a category to the group.

LESSON 2

In this lesson, students reinforce and expand on healthy classroom community development by distinguishing between safe and risky or harmful behaviors and nonviolent communication.

ACTIVITY	LEARNING OBJECTIVE	TIME	PROPS	HEALTH SKILLS
Fill Me In	At the conclusion of this activity, students will be able to: • Recall each other's names. • Demonstrate an ability to cooperate. • Distinguish between safe and risky or harmful behaviors. • Begin to identify community norms.	20 minutes	• Flip chart • Markers	• Interpersonal communication • Self-management
Commonalities	• Identify classmates with common interests and backgrounds. • Demonstrate some communication skills that build and maintain healthy relationships.	20 minutes	• 1 pencil • 1 piece of paper per team	• Interpersonal communication • Self-management • Analyze influences

TEACHER'S NOTES:

FRAMING	SET-UP PROCEDURE	REFLECTION

Fill Me In

Set Up:

1. Create a large, open space in your classroom.

Framing:

"We are going to practice remembering each other's names while moving safely in and out of a circle. How do you think this relates to creating a safe and healthy learning environment in our classroom?"

Procedure:

1. Ask students to line up in a circle about 30 feet across.
2. Begin the action by stepping into the circle, announce the name of the person directly opposite you and then walk toward that person.
3. The person whose name was called immediately duplicates your action by saying another person's name and walks toward their spot in the circle. Each named person begins heading toward another student's position.
4. It is helpful to establish eye contact with the person you named to get them started.
5. After the activity has been going for awhile, introduce an additional challenge: ask two moving students to meet as they cross the circle, shake hands, and exchange names.
6. Emphasize the need for safe movement and occasional need for bumpers (hands open and raised in front of torso to serve as buffer between students).

Reflection:

Questions for Discussion:
1. "What happened when the first person whose name was called, called another and started moving?"
2. "What did the class do to be able to move in and around each other safely?"
3. "What are some of the times that we will have to be safe with one another in this class? Physically? Emotionally? Intellectually?"
4. "What are some things that we can do to prevent violence and keep each other safe in our classroom?"

Reflection Activity:
5. Have a student record these ideas on flip chart paper and ask the class to agree to try to exhibit such behaviors in future classes.

Commonalities

Set Up:
NONE

Framing:
"As you look at the other people in your class, think about some of the things you have in common. In this activity we are going to try to find out what our hidden and learned commonalties are. A hidden commonality is something we cannot see. Learned commonalties are those things we've seen since we met each other."

Procedure:

1. Divide the students into groups of three and give each team a piece of paper and a pencil.
2. Ask one student from each group to be the recorder.
3. Say to the students: "Each group will have ten minutes to find as many hidden commonalties as they can. A "hidden" commonality is something all members have in common that is not visible or obvious and not known to participants prior to the activity. For example, "We are all in sixth grade" would not be allowed, but "We all like cherries" might be allowed.
4. The recorder in the group will write down all of the hidden commonalities and then the students will report these out to the entire class.

Reflection:
Questions for Discussion:
1. "Can someone volunteer to introduce the members of your small group and share your commonalities? Who's next?"
2. "Can a member of each small group tell us about one thing they had in common that surprised them?"
3. "Is there something the whole class has in common?" (You may need to give them a minute to figure this out.)
4. "Can you tell us about some situations when it is important to be connected with others? Are there other times when it is not important?"
5. "Can you name some strategies which help people connect with one another?'

LESSON 3

In this lesson students will identify and practice safety behaviors in a physically active environment and begin to define concepts of health and wellness.

ACTIVITY	LEARNING OBJECTIVE	TIME	PROPS	HEALTH SKILLS
Moving Without Touching	**At the conclusion of this activity, students will be able to:** • Demonstrate an age appropriate ability to care for, be considerate of and respect self and others. • Begin to apply self management skills. • Develop guidelines/rules for working together in the health classroom.	20 minutes	• Spot markers	• Interpersonal communication • Self-management • Analyze influences
Healthy Behavior Tag	• Identify different ways to be healthy. • Begin to measure changes in heart rate through activity. • Explore how the environment and personal health are related. • Analyze influences affecting personal activity levels.	20 minutes	• Spot markers • 2–3 fleece balls • Stop-watch	• All

TEACHER'S NOTES:

FRAMING	SET-UP PROCEDURE	REFLECTION

Moving Without Touching

Set Up:

1. Set the spot markers in a square or rectangular shape, large enough to just fit around the perimeter of the entire class.
2. Have the list of behaviors from Lesson Two (the flip chart paper from Commonalities) visible.

Framing:

"We have already begun the process of creating a safe learning environment. Now we are going to increase the challenge and see how we do with moving at a variety of speeds in a smallish space. Remember, our goal is to practice physical and emotional safety and reinforce the behaviors we identified in the last lesson."

Procedure:

1. Ask the students to step inside the marked-off space.
2. Explain to the class that they are going to practice moving around each other within the boundaries without touching or bumping into one another.
3. Tell them that there will be four speeds…1=SLOW MOTION, 2=STROLL or GLIDE, 3=REGULAR WALKING and 4=FAST WALKING. Bumpers up while moving! Stop immediately if you hear the word STOP!
4. The goals are 1) to move without touching anyone and 2) to practice the behaviors identified in Lesson Two.
5. Begin to move at speed one, SLOW MOTION, with bumpers up and without touching anyone. (Demonstrate what Slow Motion looks like.)
6. Gradually increase and decrease the speed of the movement by saying different numbers, then say, "STOP!" (Demonstrate all speeds to help manage safety.)
7. For fun you can tell the class that if they choose to speak or laugh they need to do it at the current movement speed. (Demonstrate a slow motion laugh as an example!)

Reflection:

Reflection Activity:

1. Have students circle up. Introduce the "Thumbometer" concept where you create a "thumbs up" position with one hand and rotate it all the way around to a "thumbs down" position. The full range represents a rating system for how the group performed—students do not have to choose up or down (excellent or rotten), but can choose anywhere in between.

2. Next, ask students to rate how well they accomplished one of the safe behaviors identified in Lesson Two with their "Thumbometers." If you see a range of thumb positions, ask the group what they could have done to exhibit this behavior more obviously.

3. Repeat for other behaviors on the list.

Questions for Discussion:

4. "What did you observe about the group's movement patterns (i.e., people began to move in a circular pattern along the outside of the space when the speed increased)? "Why do you think this may have happened?"

5. "Is there anything you want to add to the list of ways they can support one another?"

Knowledge Review:

6. Have students sign off on the list as a sign of commitment to try to exhibit the behaviors in future classes.

 Additional Thoughts

• *The play area is related to the level of challenge: A larger space is less challenging, and a smaller space is more challenging.*

• *This is a great way to assess the class's ability to care for each other.*

• *Use the "Stop!" phrase any time you feel the group bordering on or being unsafe (for example, purposely bumping into one another).*

• *The different speeds may be applied to other movement activities throughout the guide.*

• *Some students will mimic hitting one another in slow motion…this is a great opportunity to discuss violence prevention and inappropriate physical interaction.*

Healthy Behavior Tag

Set Up:

Set out the four boundary markers in a fairly large, rectangular or square space.

Framing:

"Often times we think there is only one way to be healthy or that we don't have the resources to do the things we want to do to be healthy. Health and wellness involves not just the physical aspects of our beings, but our minds, emotions, relationships, etc. Let's see how many different ways we can identify to be healthy. Then we will figure out how we can access some of them in our environment."

Procedure:

1. Ask students to stand in a circle inside the boundaries.

2. Tell the students that they are going to play a tag game that brings out many different ways to be healthy, practice safe behaviors and elevate their heart rates.

3. This tag game is a little different in that players cannot be tagged if they state a healthy behavior. For example if Ian was "the tagger" and was chasing Maddie, Maddie could squat down and say "running" and Ian would not be able to tag her.

4. Students need to state a new healthy behavior each time they are trying to avoid being tagged.

5. If someone gets tagged, they become the "tagger."

6. The "tagger" carries a fleece ball to identify him or herself as "the tagger." The ball is not intended to be thrown at anyone.

7. Use more than one "tagger" depending on the size of the group. For example, one tagger for every 12 students works well.

8. Finally, before beginning the game, ask the students to locate their pulse in their wrist or carotid artery and count the number of beats in six seconds. Tell the students to multiply the resulting number by ten and that is their heart rate. (Time the six seconds with your stop watch so students can concentrate on counting.)

9. Remind the students that you will be asking them to check their pulse periodically throughout the game and try to keep track of any changes. Periodically stop the action so they can measure their heart rate.

10. A tagger can hand off the fleece ball after two minutes if tired of being it.

Reflection:

Questions for Discussion:

1. "What happened to your heart rate during this activity?"

2. "When was it the highest? The lowest?"

3. "What are some of the different ways we discovered to practice wellness/being healthy?"

4. "How can some of the activities we identified be used to increase/decrease our heart rates?"

5. "What prevents us from doing those activities both in class and out of class? How can the Full Value Contract prevent us from doing those things?"

6. "What helps us to do those activities both in class and out of class? How can the Full Value Contract help us to do those things?"

7. "How can we help each other to be healthy this semester?"

Goal Setting

6.4

GOAL
SETTING

LESSON 4

In this lesson students will be introduced to the concept of goal-setting for health and wellness.

ACTIVITY	LEARNING OBJECTIVE	TIME	PROPS	HEALTH SKILLS
Norms Check-In (FV check-in on p. 10)	At the conclusion of this activity, students will be able to:	5–8 minutes	• Norms list	
Pairs Tag with Exercise	• Identify some of the health benefits of physical activity. • Describe how we can be influenced to choose different physical activities. • Demonstrate a beginning understanding of the concept of achieving the goal of fitness.	15 minutes	• Cones	• Interpersonal communication • Self-management • Core concepts
Moonball	• Describe steps for setting goals. • Demonstrate goal-setting skills. • Identify influences on achieving goals.	20 minutes	• 2 earth balls 24–26 inches in diameter	• Goal setting • Decision making • Interpersonal communication

TEACHER'S NOTES:

FRAMING	SET-UP PROCEDURE	REFLECTION

Pairs Tag w/ Exercise

Set Up:

1. Create a large open space with four cones to mark the boundaries.

Framing:

"Exercise and physical fitness are important aspects of being healthy. You may have a goal to workout at least five times a week but something always gets in the way of your ability to achieve this goal. This activity will help you identify many different ways to exercise as well as things that impact your choice of where and how to exercise."

Procedure:

1. Have students congregate within the boundaries.
2. Ask students to find a partner and stand next to their partner.
3. Tell the class "We are going to play a fun tag game where each partnership needs to come up with a fitness activity that can be modeled now; for example, jumping jacks, cross country skiing, stretching."
4. Give them a couple of minutes to plan what their partnership's exercise will be and how they will model it.
5. When the class is ready, have them come back to a circle. Ask the partners to show the rest of the class their exercises by going around the circle.
6. Now comes the tag game. Ask the partners to decide who will be "tagger." Explain that the person who is "tagger" will chase only their partner.
7. When a partner is tagged, that person will stop wherever they are, say something that prevents them from exercising and then perform their exercise to the count of ten. For example, watching television, and then do ten jumping jacks or lunges, etc.
8. This person is now the "tagger" and can begin chasing their partner after they perform their exercise so the original tagger better get out of there fast!
9. Partners switch back and forth for the duration of the activity.
10. Be sure to do a heart rate check before, during and at the end of the game.

Reflection:

Questions for Discussion:

1. "What was it like to perform your exercise to the count of 10 while thinking about trying to tag your partner?"
2. "What did you notice about your heart rate during this game?"

3. "What are some reasons you don't exercise?"

4. "What are some of the health benefits of physical activity?"

5. "What are some ways to make time for exercise, play, friendship, and rest in your daily life?"

 Additional Thoughts

• *This is a good opportunity to refer to the speeds practiced in Moving Without Touching as a way to manage safety.*

• *Do not allow players to crouch behind other team members as this can create dangerous collisions.*

. . . .

Moonball

Set Up:
NONE

Framing:
"We have a very important job and that is to care for our earth by keeping it up and moving in the atmosphere. This is a huge responsibility and therefore needs to be shared by everyone in the class. Fortunately, our earth is still very forgiving so if it hits the ceiling, walls or floor, she will let us try again."

Procedure:

1. Ask the students to form a circle.

2. Use two balls and two separate circles for a large class.

3. Explain that the object is to hit the ball in the air as many times as possible before the ball strikes the ground, ceiling or walls.

4. A player may not hit the ball twice in succession.

5. Touching the ground/floor, ceiling or walls and hitting the ball two or more times in a row means the count starts again.

6. Keep track of the number of hits quietly at first. After a couple of attempts, introduce the concept of goal setting by asking "How many taps do you think we can make to keep the earth in the air" or "How long do you think we can work together to keep the earth safe?"

7. Have the group set a goal (number of hits/taps or time) and then work toward achieving that goal within the same guidelines.

8. Be sure to have the students share strategies and helpful information with each other between attempts to achieve the goal.

Reflection:

Questions for Discussion:

1. "How did you support one another in this process?"

2. "How did you make adjustments so you could make more hits or keep the ball in the air longer?"

3. "What are the steps of effective goal setting?"

4. "How did you set and achieve goals throughout this activity?"

5. "How can we support one another in achieving our personal or group goals for healthier lifestyle choices?"

 Additional Thoughts

• *By unobtrusively asking the groups to set a goal for the number of hits they can manage or by interjecting an arbitrary goal into the class, the leader is planting the seed of goal setting.*

• *Often students will ask what the "record is" or "How long did the other class do it?" Redirect the focus to the group that is working together now and what their highest possible achievement may be.*

• *If students feel that the guidelines are too "easy," encourage them to come up with ways to adapt the rules of play to increase the level of challenge.*

• *This activity may be adapted to the classroom by having students begin by sitting in a circle. The same guidelines apply with the addition of having to keep your bottom on the chair at all times. If anyone lifts their bottom off of the chair or hits twice in a row, hits the ceiling, floor or walls then stop and restart play.*

6.5

GOAL
SETTING

LESSON 5

In this lesson students will recognize how to support one another in achieving their goals and learn about stages of task/content mastery.

ACTIVITY	LEARNING OBJECTIVE	TIME	PROPS	HEALTH SKILLS
In Anticipation of Learning	**At the conclusion of this activity, students will be able to:** • Explore and normalize different stages of learning new skills. • Identify some support systems available in the school environment.	10–15 minutes	• None	• Interpersonal communication • Self-management
Kaizan: The Art of Continuous Improvement	• Demonstrate responsibility and cooperation as needed to accomplish group goals/this initiative. • Demonstrate ability to support peers in achieving group and individual goals/this initiative. • Demonstrate communication skills needed to build and maintain a healthy learning environment.	30 minutes	• Keypunch kit or 30 poly-spots numbered 1–30 • Boundary rope • Boundary line • Stop-watch	• Goal setting • Decision making • Self-management • Interpersonal communication

TEACHER'S NOTES:

FRAMING	SET-UP PROCEDURE	REFLECTION

In Anticipation of Learning

Set Up:
NONE

Framing:

"As a learning community it is important that we all recognize that we learn at different speeds and in different ways. It is also important that we recognize when we might want to offer each other help or when and how to ask for help."

Procedure:

Preparation for the Game:

1. Have students stand in a circle. Ask them to show you what it looks like when someone is trying very hard to learn something and is having trouble "getting it."

2. Mirror a few of the responses and then pick an expressive gesture for the difficult stage of learning. Together, the whole group should practice that expression.

3. Next ask for a demonstration of what it looks like when someone is starting to understand a concept but still has some things to learn.

4. Mirror a few of the responses and then pick an expressive gesture for the second stage of learning.

5. Have the group repeat both gestures.

6. Finally, ask students to demonstrate what it looks like when you "get it" – when you completely understand the concept and are confident in your ability to perform the task.

7. Mirror a few of the responses and then pick an expressive gesture for the mastery stage of learning.

8. Have the group repeat all three gestures.

9. Ask students to find partners and stand near them.

The Game:

10. Explain to the group that they are going to have the opportunity to practice their ability to communicate with each other without talking.

11. Have partners stand with their backs to one another and explain that on the count of three both of you will turn and show one of the three gestures the group chose that represent levels of learning. Your objective is to match your partner without talking or non-verbally signaling one another beforehand.

12. For the first couple of rounds you should count to three and ask the students to face each other with their gesture. Students can perform their own count down for the remaining rounds.

Reflection:

Questions for Discussion:

1. "What was it like to try to connect with your partner without being able to talk or signal one another before turning around (verbal or non-verbal communication)?"

2. "Are there times when you feel as though you "should know something" and just don't have enough information?"

3. "Can someone give us ideas on how we can support each other through the different phases of learning in health class this semester? In the larger school environment?"

. . . .

Kaizan: The Art of Continuous Improvement

Set Up:

1. Place a large rope in a circle. Randomly place poly spots numbered 1 – 30 inside the circle.

2. Set up a short rope as a line approximately 25 feet from the circle (so that students standing at the rope cannot clearly see the spots in the circle).

Framing

"Today we are going to practice the art of continuous improvement and supporting one another so we can achieve our goals. In Japan the Art of Continuous Improvement is known as Kaizan. You will have five opportunities to continuously improve your performance in speed and efficiency as well as in demonstrating skills in creating healthy interpersonal relationships."

Procedure:

1. Tell students that: "The challenge is to touch the spots in order, 1-30 as quickly as possible. You will have five attempts to improve on the overall time that this task takes you."

2. There are a few rules, and a few opportunities for learning (penalties) if the rules are broken.

3. Ask the students to gather behind the starting line and show them the circle

of spots in the distance. Explain that their goal is to touch the numbers in sequence from one to thirty as quickly and efficiently as possible.

4. Tell the group that their speed is measured by timing each trial and that the time begins when the first person crosses over the start line and ends when the last person crosses back over the start line—returns to the group.

5. There are some important rules to follow:
   - Only one person at a time is allowed within the boundary containing the spot markers.
   - Each numbered spot needs to be touched in sequence.
   - Only one number may be touched at a time.

6. A ten-second penalty will be assigned to any rule infraction; if there is more than one person in the boundary, if a number is touched out of sequence or if more than one number is touched at a time.

7. All planning is done behind the start line.

8. Watch the "trample factor" during the race to and from the start line.

9. Be sure to give the group their time, including penalties after each trial and encourage them to set a goal for improvement for the next round.

Reflection:

Questions for Discussion:

1. Ask students to fill in the blank in response to this statement:

   My group continually improved by _____. Ask for specific examples of when some of the sited responses occurred.

2. Next ask students to fill in the blank in response to this statement:

   I contributed to the team's continuous improvement by _____. Ask the rest of the group for specific examples of times when they saw the sited contributions happening.

3. "How are individual and group contributions important for creating healthy learning environments?

4. "What are some behaviors you will need to apply as you continuously strive to reach your goals while learning about health and wellness?"

Healthy Relationships

LESSON 6

In this lesson students will create a visual representation of behavioral norms necessary for a safe and challenging health class learning community—their Full Value Contract. Students also set individual goals for the health class.

ACTIVITY	LEARNING OBJECTIVE	TIME	PROPS	HEALTH SKILLS
Circle of Strength	**At the conclusion of this activity, students will be able to:** • Formalize guidelines/rules for working together in the health classroom. • Describe the difference between put downs and positive messages. • Provide positive messages in a group activity setting. • Demonstrate some communication skills that convey respect.	40 minutes	• Large piece of paper • Markers • Construction paper • Glitter • Feathers • Glue • Cut-out shapes • Scissors	• Goal Setting • Decision Making • Interpersonal communication • Self-management • Advocacy

TEACHER'S NOTES:

FRAMING	SET-UP PROCEDURE	REFLECTION

Circle of Strength

Framing:

"We know that creating a classroom environment that is safe and challenging will help us practice and learn about health and wellness in the real world. We have been doing a great job of …(site behaviors from previous activities, i.e., listening to each other, cheering each other on, making sure everyone participates, etc). Let's strengthen our commitment to those behaviors by creating a circle of strength with our hands and identify specific goals for each of us to work on this semester."

Procedure:

Step One: (20 minutes)

1. Have each student trace their hand on a piece of paper, cut it out, and decorate it in a way that represents who they are and what goal they have for the class.
2. Then, if time allows, have students connect their hands into a large circle and tape or glue them to the large sheet of paper.

Step Two: (20 minutes)

1. Gather all the students around the circle of hands and ask them to reflect on the norms identified in Fill Me In and Moving Without Touching. What behaviors and attitudes have been helpful to the class so far? Have students write those words in the middle of the circle of hands.
2. Ask the group if there are any other behaviors or attitudes they might want to add to the list. Have the students write the new words or draw pictures that express these positive things inside the outline of the hands.
3. Have students explain what they meant by the words they chose. Even if the words were the same, the meaning may be different for different people.
4. Ask the class if they think they can agree to use this Circle of Strength as a set of guidelines for their behavior during the health and wellness class. Once everyone has agreed, have each person sign the Full Value Contract on their hand and post the Circle of Strength in a place where it can be readily referenced for check-ins and debriefing.

Reflection:

Questions for Discussion:

1. "What do you notice about the words that are inside the Circle of Strength?"
2. "In what ways are these attitudes and qualities important to healthy relationships and taking care of yourself and others?"
2. "How do put downs affect our ability to achieve our goal?"
3. "How can positive messages help us to achieve our personal and group behavioral goals?"

LESSON 7

In this lesson students will explore concepts of healthy and unhealthy peer and family relationships.

ACTIVITY	LEARNING OBJECTIVE	TIME	PROPS	HEALTH SKILLS
All Aboard	**At the conclusion of this activity, students will be able to:** • Explain the importance of assuming responsibility for personal health behaviors in the areas of physical safety. • Demonstrate some communication skills that convey respect. • Display some behaviors that encourage group participation.	20 minutes	• 3 feet x 3 feet All Aboard platforms • Extra poly-spots as needed • Colored dots • Circle of Strength	• Interpersonal communication • Goal setting • Decision making • Self-management
Out of Kilter	• Describe some of the positive and negative aspects of family and peer connections. • Describe how friendships can involve positive and negative risks. • Demonstrate an age appropriate ability to respect, care for and be responsible to self and others.	15 minutes	• Paper • Markers • Boundary marker(s) – rope, traffic cones, poly spots, etc.	• Interpersonal communication • Analyzing influences • Core concepts

TEACHER'S NOTES:

FRAMING	SET-UP PROCEDURE	REFLECTION

All Aboard

Set Up:

1. Place the platforms in the center of a large open space in your classroom. Be sure to leave at least five feet of space between each platform.

2. There should be one platform for 10–12 students. Place an extra poly-spot per extra student around the perimeter of the platform or for a physically larger student population.

3. You want to make the area small enough to present a challenge for everyone to get on board, but large enough so that it is possible to get everyone on board.

Framing:

"We have made an agreement to build a safe learning environment in this class. Our environment is represented by the platform and surrounding spots. Your task is to support one another in getting everyone safely on board into this environment we've built. Before you start, what are the qualities that might help accomplish this task? Thinking back to the Circle of Strength, what behaviors do you think will be the most useful in making this attempt?"

Procedure:

1. The object is simply to get your whole group on a platform at one time without touching the floor or ground.

2. In order to be counted as "on the platform," each person needs to have both feet off the ground or on a poly-spot.

3. The group's challenge is to hold a balanced position for at least eight seconds; i.e., no one touches the ground for eight measured seconds.

4. Proper spotting as necessary must be monitored by the teacher and any method that appears to be unsafe (stacking people on top of one another, etc.) should not be allowed.

Reflection:

Questions for Discussion:

1. "What was it like when you got the whole group on board into the healthy environment?"

2. "What kind of communication was necessary for everyone to get safely on the platform?"

Reflection Activity:

3. Ask students to place colored dots next to the behaviors on the Circle of Strength that were accessed during this activity.

Question for Discussion:

4. "How are these behaviors related to encouraging emotional, mental and physical health in this community? In the school community?"

Out of Kilter

Set Up:

1. Create a fairly large open space in your classroom. Be sure to stay away from hard surfaces and protruding edges. Define the boundaries with poly spots, traffic cones, rope, etc.

Framing:

"Our friends can either bring us down or help hold us up as we move through the many changes of adolescence. Supporting one another while we grow, without letting go or holding on too tightly is perhaps the best gift we can give one another."

Procedure:

1. Ask students to find a partner who appears to be their "total opposite."
2. Explain to the class that this is an activity about balance, yours and your partner's. The object is to always be physically unbalanced.
3. Tell the partners to grab one another's hands or wrists, lean backwards, away from each other, until they find that if it were not for the support of their partner, they would topple over.
4. Explain that of course while they are in the process of putting themselves out of balance their partner is doing the same.
5. Tell the partners to move around a bit and try different positions, all the while regaining a sense of balance to the point of imbalance. As they get more comfortable with one another they can get a bit more daring.
6. Now find another pair and make your duo a quadruple. Be careful! Four unbalanced people can lead to a heap of falling bodies.
7. Again, the task is to create a point of imbalance that won't work without the support of your partners. If you feel that you are going to fall take a step backward/forward.

Reflection:

Reflection Activity:

1. Remind the group that we have been talking about the importance of relationships in being healthy. Have the groups of four brainstorm and describe times when family and/or peer relationships are in balance and when they can get out of balance (healthy/unhealthy; positive/negative).

2. Ask them to write their responses on the piece of paper provided. Ask them to define the skills needed to manage each situation in a healthy manner. For example, a friend might be pushing someone to smoke cigarettes or engage in other unhealthy behaviors. A way to manage this might be to clearly communicate that you want to be friends, but you won't smoke and the way he or she is pushing you to smoke makes you not want to be friends.

3. Have the groups of four come back together and share their responses.

4. Observe that during the activity it seemed as though it took a lot of trust and support to take different kinds of risks. (Give examples, if possible.) How can families and peers trust and support one another as they face the many challenges of being healthy?

LESSON 8

In this lesson students will work together to construct different bridges of communication.

ACTIVITY	LEARNING OBJECTIVE	TIME	PROPS	HEALTH SKILLS
Bridge It	**At the conclusion of this activity, students will be able to:** • Begin to describe how people interpret words differently and how misunderstandings occur because of unclear verbal communication. • Demonstrate some effective listening skills. • Begin to explore friendships between people who have differences. • Describe people who influence their choices.	30–40 minutes	• balls • 16 plastic cups • 16 pieces of paper • 16 straws • 8 balloons • 4 rolls of tape • 4 index cards with "new language" on each	• Interpersonal communication • Accessing information • Self-management • Analyze influences

TEACHER'S NOTES:

FRAMING	SET-UP PROCEDURE	REFLECTION

Bridge It

Set Up:

1. Create four separate spaces within your classroom. Try to find or create spaces where students from other groups may not see one another.

2. Place four balls, four plastic cups, four straws, four pieces of paper, two balloons and a roll of tape in each separate space.

3. Each group also gets a card with their "language" on it. (See sample language cards at the end of this activity.) The challenge is for the group to use the language on the card when communicating with other groups. They can use common language when in their smaller group.

Framing:

"Have you ever been in a situation where you thought you knew what your friends were talking about or you were sure you explained yourself so well that everyone got it only to discover that no one was on the same page? How about a time when you didn't understand what another person was saying whatsoever but had to accomplish something together? We are going to recreate that type of situation and try to build some bridges for communication and understanding."

Procedure:

1. Ask the students to divide themselves into four equal groups and move to one of the four spaces.

2. Explain that the objective is for each small group to build a bridge that looks as much like the other bridges as possible and is able to connect with the other bridges.

3. Tell students that they have scheduled meeting times (similar to school gatherings, holiday celebrations, family events, etc.).

4. The sequence begins with a five minute meeting with a chosen representative from each small group. Refer to communication rules below.

Communication Rules:

- A new representative from each small group should be chosen each time.
- The groups work independently of each other, but are allowed three planning/negotiating meetings together as an entire class.
- During the planning/negotiation sessions, only one spokesperson from each small group can talk.
- Communication between groups is guided by the language cards (each small group has a separate language card).

5. Next there is a seven minute discussion and building back at the site.

6 Then another five minute planning/negotiating session (new representatives from each group).

7. Followed by a five minute discussion and building time back at site.

8. Then another five minute planning/negotiating session (new representatives from each group).

9. Then a five minute building time.

10. Finally, the "unveiling" takes place with each small group bringing their bridge to the center of the room or have students rotate through each construction site and come together in one large group for the debrief.

Reflection:

Reflection Activity:

1. Have each small group describe their process to the other groups.

Questions for Discussion:

2. "What was it like to try to communicate with the other groups?"

3. "What were the differences between what it was like in the collaborative meetings versus the "home base" meetings?"

4. "Have you ever had similar communication challenges in 'the real world'?"

5. "What are some effective strategies for managing such communication difficulties without violence?"

 Additional Thoughts

• *It is up to you to manage the time efficiently for this activity!*

Sample Language Cards:

Group 1	Group 2
Ball = Taco	Ball = Big Mac
Cup = Dog	Cup = Truck
Paper = Milk	Paper = Hogan
Straw = Basketball	Straw = Book
Balloon = Dress	Balloon = Mesa
Tape = Sister	Tape = Brother

** Basically they are words that are relevant to the topic, but make no sense in terms of connections to the actual objects.

Emotional Expression

LESSON 9

In this lesson students will begin to recognize and identify feelings through physiological response and emotional expression.

ACTIVITY	LEARNING OBJECTIVE	TIME	PROPS	HEALTH SKILLS
Gotcha!	**At the conclusion of this activity, students will be able to:** • Identify some stress triggers. • Describe some reactions helpful to stress management.	10 minutes	• None	• Self-management • Analyze influences
Feelings Marketplace Relay	• Demonstrate some ability to recognize and express feelings. • Identify some cultural differences in the expression of feelings. • Identify and describe the experience of different feelings and how feelings affect daily functioning. • Apply the expression of emotions in positive ways.	10 minutes	• Feelings Marketplace Cards	• Interpersonal communication • Core concept • Analyze influences

TEACHER'S NOTES:

FRAMING	SET-UP PROCEDURE	REFLECTION

Gotcha!

Set Up:
NONE

Framing:
"Our ability to respond to stressors depends on what we are paying attention to, how the stressor is introduced to us and how our emotions play into our response. Let's explore our response to stress by assessing our reaction time and ability to focus. The challenge is simple—we can avoid getting caught by the stress or we can grab it and deal with it, or we can do both at the same time! No pressure…let's see how we do!"

Procedure:

1. Have students stand in a circle and place their left hands in front of the person to their left, palm up and flat.
2. Ask them to take their right index finger and place it straight down into the palm of the person to their right.
3. Tell the class you are going to challenge their reaction time.
4. Tell the students: "At the count of three, try to quickly, but gently, grab the finger in the left hand, while avoiding having your finger grabbed in the right."
5. After a couple of rounds, switch hands with right hand flat and left finger down.
6. As soon as possible encourage others to count by saying anyone wearing blue can count, anyone with glasses can count, etc.

Reflection:
Questions for Discussion:

1. "Can you describe what happened in each round?
2. "Did you react too quickly? Only use one hand, instead of both?" etc.
3. "Would you have been better at catching your classmate's finger if you didn't have to worry about your finger being caught too?"
4. "Can you name some events that cause stressful reactions?

Knowledge Reinforcement:

5. Have them identify some helpful strategies for reacting to stress drawing on strategies that some more successful participants used in this activity.

Feelings Marketplace Relay

Set Up:
NONE

Framing:

"The funny thing about feelings is that we all express similar emotions in very different ways. Also, there are so many ways of feeling, and yet we often describe the way we are feeling at a given time as simply 'fine' or 'good' which really doesn't tell anyone anything. In this activity, which is kind of like the old game Charades we are going to explore a wide range of feelings words and in a fun way, start exploring how we each express certain feelings. Here's how it will work...."

Procedure:

1. Divide the class into smaller groups, each of an even number (two, four or six etc.) if possible.

2. Spread the groups out so that they are equidistant from each other and so that each group is about twenty feet from you (a wheel pattern works well with more than two groups).

3. You should be in the middle with the Feelings Marketplace Cards

4. The activity begins when each small group sends a representative to you to see a Feelings Card.

5. Once the card is viewed, the representative returns to their small group and as in Charades, acts out the feeling on the card without speaking.

6. The rules are:
   - The person may only physically act out the word.
   - The person may not speak or use noises while acting out the word.
   - The person may use the "sounds like" motion, tugging at one's ear, from Charades, as well as motions for the number of syllables in the word.

7. Instruct the groups to send a different person up each time, rotating through the group.

8. If the small groups are really small (four people or less) have each person go twice instead of once.

9. The activity will end when all the representatives from a small group have had the opportunity to act out one or two feelings.

Reflection:

Questions for Discussion:

1. "What was it like to act out the different feelings?"

2. "What was it like to guess what emotion someone was acting out?"

3. "How do you know what someone else is feeling?"

4. "What do we know about emotional expression in different cultures?"

5. "When is it appropriate to talk about feelings with someone else?"

6. "How do feelings affect our daily interactions?"

7. "What are some ways we can encourage each other to express our feelings appropriately in this class? After school? At home?"

LESSON 10

In this lesson students will learn how to manage anger within a positive emotional climate.

ACTIVITY	LEARNING OBJECTIVE	TIME	PROPS	HEALTH SKILLS
Emotions Pass	**At the conclusion of this activity, students will be able to:** • Differentiate between angry feelings and angry behavior. • Identify some ways to manage anger positively. • Describe actions/situations that make students display anger. • Contrast the difference between helpful and non-helpful behaviors when they are angry.	40–45 minutes	• Mass Pass Kit • 2 containers • 24 balls • 1 long boundary rope/s (60–80 feet or 2 x 20 feet and 2 x 15 feet lengths) • red fleece balls • Masking tape • Markers	• Self-management • Analyze influences • Goal setting • Decision making • Core content

TEACHER'S NOTES:

FRAMING	SET-UP PROCEDURE	REFLECTION

Emotions Pass

Set Up:

1. Ask the students to label each of the foam balls with as many constructive emotions, other than anger, that they can think of. For example, joy, curiosity, etc.

2. Create a large square/polygon of 15–25 feet per side. It is helpful to use the boundary markers to enclose the square.

3. Place one container in one corner of the square and place the other container at the opposite corner. Place all of the foam balls (feelings) inside one of the containers as the starting point.

4. A typical set up is to have 10–15 objects for a team of 15 and four red fleece balls.

Framing:

"Now that we have identified the many different emotions we are capable of feeling, let's spend some time managing all of them at once. Once we get a positive emotional environment going we will see how anger changes the atmosphere. For our purposes the four red fleece balls will represent anger. What do we know about anger? During this activity we will help each other manage angry emotions as they come up with other emotions."

Procedure:

1. Have students line up equally on all four sides of the square/polygon (i.e., three on each side).

2. Tell the students that the object of the activity is to create a positive emotional environment by transporting the balls ("feelings") around the perimeter of the square/polygon without passing them directly to the person to their left or right. The more balls that end up in the final container, the more positive the environment.

3. Explain to the class that they will have four 90 second rounds to develop a strategy to manage the feelings and that they will have at least five to ten minutes of planning time between each round.

   Rules for the first round are:

   • All objects start inside one of the containers at the beginning of every round.

   • Time for each round starts when the first object is removed from the container.

   • All sides of the square (or polygon) need to be occupied by at least one participant.

- Once a person has chosen a side, s/he may not switch sides within a round.
- Each participant needs to touch the object after it leaves the container and before it lands in the customer container.
- Objects may not be passed to anyone to your immediate right or left. In other words the object needs to "skip" at least one person when it is passed.
- Any time an object is dropped, it should be returned to the originating container to be recycled, if it is to be used in the round.
- If an object is dropped inside the boundary markers, it may not be retrieved and is lost for the duration of that round.
- No member of the team may step inside the perimeter boundary during a round. If such a touch occurs, all the objects need to be returned to the start.

4. After the first round, ask the class to review their process and apply any changes they would like to the second round. Second round has the same guidelines as first.

5. After the second round ask the group what happens when anger comes into the mix of emotions? How do people respond/act out? Let them know that for the next two rounds they will be managing angry feelings among all of the other emotions.

6. Angry feelings are represented by the red fleece balls and will start at the opposite container from the other emotions and pass through the positive emotional environment system in reverse. Start with one and give students time to plan. Add balls as appropriate.

7. After the third round, review their experience with attention to dealing with anger. Give them time to adjust and apply learnings to help manage for a final, fourth round.

Reflections:

Reflection Activity:

1. Ask students to form small groups with one person from each side represented in their group and discuss the following:
   - Describe some actions that make young people display anger.
   - Describe the difference between angry feelings and angry behaviors.
   - Identify three ways to express anger appropriately and three ways to manage another's angry feelings.

Stress Management

LESSON 11

In this lesson students will explore self-management and advocacy skills for coping with stress.

ACTIVITY	LEARNING OBJECTIVE	TIME	PROPS	HEALTH SKILLS
Tai Chi Stretch	**At the conclusion of this activity, students will be able to:** • Experiment with roles of leader and follower. • Discuss internal and external influences that affect role choice. • Discuss proactive strategies for coping with stress.	15 minutes	• None • Relaxation music optional	• Interpersonal communication • Self-management • Analyze influences
I Need...	• Describe passive, assertive and aggressive communication. • Demonstrate some assertive communication skills. • Begin to identify when to access health services for self and others.	20 minutes	• Soft toss-able objects *(half as many as number of students)* • Masking tape • Markers • Boundary markers	• Self-management • Advocacy • Interpersonal communication • Core content

TEACHER'S NOTES:

FRAMING	SET-UP PROCEDURE	REFLECTION

Tai Chi Stretch

Set Up:

1. Clear a fairly large, open space in your classroom.
2. Play relaxation music in the background if you choose.

Framing:

"Ask the class if anyone has ever heard of or practiced Tai Chi? Tell them that this is a 'unique version' of Tai Chi and that it is really about energy management and body movement. It is important to know how to manage our energy and help others manage theirs particularly in response to unhealthy stress. With this in mind, sometimes we need to lead and sometimes we need to follow."

Procedure:

1. Ask participants to find a partner and stand in a circle next to him or her, with about a foot of space between them.
2. Ask them to begin to breathe slowly and deeply.
3. Ask them to begin moving and stretching their bodies at a Level One speed (from the Moving Without Touching activity) (p.), while continuing to breathe slowly and deeply.
4. Have them stop and find a separate space with a partner. (Ask them to find a partner.) Tell the students that they are going to practice mirroring their partner's movements and part of the challenge is to do the activity as silently as possible. One will start as the leader, the other as follower.
5. After a few minutes, say to students: "Now switch leadership with your partner" and continue moving.
6. After a few minutes, say to students: "Now continue your movements with no identified leader or follower, just let it ebb and flow". For example, if Sally moves her hand up, then Joan does, but then Sally responds as Joan moves her hand back down, without even planning!
7. End the activity by asking students to finish the last move, acknowledge their partner and form a large circle.

Reflection:

Questions for Discussion:

1. "Can you tell us how you are feeling right now?"
2. "Did you have different feelings when you were leading than you had when you were following? Which was more comfortable for you?"
3. "What did it feel like to have no identified leader or follower?"

4. "Have there been times in your life when you were unsure whether to lead or follow?"

5. "What thoughts, feelings or behaviors, yours or someone else's, influenced your choices to lead or follow?"

6. "What did you learn from this activity that can help you productively manage your own emotions and feelings of stress when deciding to lead or follow?"

 Additional Thoughts

• *This activity is best done in silence. Expect a few giggles in the beginning. Gently remind students to be as silent as possible.*

• *Concepts of appropriate stretching techniques may also be integrated into this activity.*

. . . .

I Need...

Set Up:

1. Mark off a large open space with boundary markers.
2. Have enough objects to equal about half the number of students playing.

Framing:

Have the group identify and label each object so that it represents what sixth graders need in a support system that promotes good mental health and prevents unhealthy choices. Some examples are love, friendship, discipline, support.

Procedure:

1. Assign two to three people to be the taggers.
2. Tell students: "You will be playing a tag game in which you will be safe when you are holding a specific object. The way to get the object is to say 'I need …' asking for the object by name from the person who is holding it. For example, 'I need friendship."
3. The play begins with the two or three taggers attempting to tag the rest of the students.
4. Distribute the objects to half of the class.

5. A player is immune from a tag when holding an object. Remind students that to obtain an object and be free from being tagged a participant needs to call the name of someone who has an object and yell, 'I need _____' whatever label is appropriate.

6. An object cannot be thrown to the same person twice in succession.

Reflection:

Questions for Discussion:

1. "Tell us about some of the ways you asked for what you needed and how people got tagged."

2. "Can you describe how it felt to ask for what you needed; to not get what you needed or to not be able to ask for what you needed?"

3. "How did people's communication change in the different situations (passive, aggressive, assertive)?"

4. "Can you identify a specific situation where you needed or might need help and what health services you would go to for support?"

6.12

STRESS
MANAGEMENT

LESSON 12

In this lesson students will differentiate between eustress or good stress and distress or bad stress and then apply a stress management strategy.

ACTIVITY	LEARNING OBJECTIVE	TIME	PROPS	HEALTH SKILLS
The Measured Breath	At the conclusion of this activity, students will be able to: • Apply a proactive strategy for managing one's own feelings. • Analyze social and emotional influences.	10 minutes	• Flip chart • Markers	• Self-management • Core content
It's All Happening	• Begin to recognize how the combination of many small stressors affects our ability to make healthy decisions. • Identify some home, school and community activities that elicit stress. • Demonstrate some skills that promote personal well-being in response to stress needed to complete this initiative.	30 minutes	• 1 fleece ball per two students	• Self-management • Advocacy • Interpersonal communication

TEACHER'S NOTES:

FRAMING	SET-UP PROCEDURE	REFLECTION

The Measured Breath

Set Up:

1. Clear an open space in your classroom.

Framing:

"What is the first thing we forget to do when we get scared, excited, stressed out? Breathe! Breathing is the least expensive most powerful but most often ignored skill we can use to help us manage just about any situation. In order to be able to use breathing effectively though, we need to understand how to do it properly and to practice breathing in different situations."

Procedure:

1. Ask students to stand or lie in a circle and close their eyes if they feel comfortable doing so.
2. Tell the class that you are going to ask them to practice taking deep breaths.
3. Tell them that you are going to ask them to inhale to a count of six, hold that breath for a count of seven and then exhale to a count of seven.
4. Practice this a few times while you count.
5. Next tell them to try to take a few breaths themselves, at their own tempo, as they count inhaling for six, holding for seven and exhaling for seven.

Reflection:

Questions for Discussion:

1. "Can you describe what difference you noticed in your body while you were breathing?"
2. "Can you name some of the challenges of a structured breathing/breathing in this activity like this one? Did you feel self-conscious (impatient, distracted, etc.)?"

Knowledge Review:

3. Explain that they can use this tool anywhere at any time and that the more they practice, the more effective it is.

Further Questions for Discussion:

4. "What are some internal and external factors that contribute to your feelings of stress?"
5. "How would you put structured breathing into practice as a coping strategy for stress management?"

It's All Happening

Set Up:

1. Create a large open space in your classroom. Be sure there is enough ceiling clearance to toss the ball about ten feet into the air.

2. Have several balls near you.

Framing:

"Stress is an important aspect of our health and well-being. We often associate stress with negative situations. 'I am so stressed out.' 'This test, paper, friend is really stressing me out.' The truth is that we need some level of stress to motivate us and get us going in a forward direction. The key is in knowing what is enough to help us and what to do when it gets to be too much."

Procedure:

1. Have everyone stand in a loose group.

2. The fleece balls represent stressors. Start the action with someone throwing one fleece ball up in the air and have someone else catch it. Be sure it goes up at least ten feet, but not more than fifteen.

3. The person who catches it then throws it up and another person catches it.

4. No one may catch the ball twice in a row. Names may not be called out instructing a particular person to catch the ball.

5. Continue the activity until everyone has had a chance to catch and throw the ball. Count the number of times the ball hits the ground.

6. Start the second round the same way. Have one person throw one fleece ball into the air and someone else catch it. If the ball is caught, add another ball.

7. Now two balls will be thrown into the air and caught by someone other than the person who threw the ball.

8. Anyone can catch the ball, except the person who threw it even if they have caught one previously.

9. Once again, names may not be called out. This is a random process.

10. Each time the balls are thrown and caught, add another ball to the activity.

11. Keep track of how many balls the group can catch before one is dropped.

12. About midway through the activity ask students to notice their breathing patterns, verbal communication changes and body tension as more balls are added

13. Stop the process once all of the "stressors" have been in play. Tell students you are going to repeat the last round with all of the balls and they will have three

minutes to come up with a plan to manage all of the "stressors" accessing themselves as resources.

Reflection:

Questions for Discussion:

1. "How did your body, thoughts, actions change when working with one ball (or stressor) versus many?"

2. "What are some of the feelings you experienced when more stressors were added?"

3. "How did you decide what to do when stressors kept being added?"

4. "How did the opportunity to plan affect your ability to manage all of the stressors?"

5. "What are some of the positive stressors in your life?"

6. "When do these common stressors begin to be too much to handle?"

7. "What are some of the things you can do (without help) to reduce stress?"

8. "What are some resources you can access to reduce stress?"

Conflict Resolution

LESSON 13

In the next two lessons students will focus on conflict resolution and problem solving. In this lesson students will experience different approaches to conflict and resolving conflict.

ACTIVITY	LEARNING OBJECTIVE	TIME	PROPS	HEALTH SKILLS
Let's Win!!!	**At the conclusion of this activity, students will be able to:** • Define and discuss some conflict resolution strategies. • Begin to understand the win-win approach to conflict resolution.	15 minutes	• Numerous pieces of healthy snacks • Flip chart paper • Markers	• Self-management • Goal setting • Decision making
Rock, Paper, Scissors into Anticipation	• Explore different approaches to managing conflict used in this activity. • Explore possible causes of conflict among students in schools and communities.	10–15 minutes	• Chart from previous activity	• Self-management • Advocacy
Bear, Salmon, Mosquito	• Recognize fight or flight response to conflict. • Describe some ways to avoid and reduce threatening situations.	20 minutes	• 15–20 foot length of rope • 4 cones	• Advocacy • Self-management • Analyzing influences

TEACHER'S NOTES:

FRAMING	SET-UP PROCEDURE	REFLECTION

Let's Win!!!

Set Up:

NONE

Framing:

"When we are trying to support our friends or resolve conflicts we want to try to find a solution that is not harmful to anyone. Some solutions are better than others." Ask the group to list some ways to have good solutions to conflict. Post this list during Let's Win.

Procedure:

1. Generate a list of good solutions to conflict and post so it is visible to the entire class.
2. Have students partner up with someone they want to thumb wrestle with for healthy snacks.
3. Students may sit at desks or on the floor as long as there is an even space between partners.
4. Tell the students that each partnership is going to try to win as many healthy snacks as possible in 30 seconds. Every time the partner's thumb touches the other person's hand, they win a healthy snack.
5. Review that a win-win situation means that the solution worked for both people versus a win-lose situation where someone misses out.
6. Time a couple of rounds and keep track of the progress, passing out healthy snacks as you go.

Reflection:

1. Ask students to rate their performance in terms of practicing some of the good ideas generated on a scale of zero to five using the fist to five approach. (described in the Check-Ins section page 8)
2. Acknowledge the range and highlight positive responders.
3. Explain the win-win approach to conflict resolution and demonstrate with a thumb wrestling partner.

 Additional Thoughts

• *The win-win approach shifts the conflict resolution approach from one person being right and the other wrong to "I want to win and I want you to win too." This changes disagreements from "right and wrong" situations to cooperative agreements. This approach works because both parties get more of what they want and are committed to the solution.*

Rock/Paper/Scissors into Anticipation

Set Up:
NONE

Framing:
"Does anyone remember the game Rock, Paper, Scissors? Great!"

Procedure:

1. Have participants find a partner and stand in a circle next to their partner.

2. Ask students if they remember the game Rock, Paper, Scissors. If so, review it. If not, explain it.

3. The game is a win-lose scenario in which each person, after the count of three, represents one of the three symbols. Rock is represented by a closed fist, paper a flat hand and scissors are two fingers opening and closing. Rock crushes scissors, scissors cut paper and paper covers rock.

4. This time we are going to SUPERSIZE rock, paper, scissors and try to match our partner. Here's how...

5. After reviewing Rock, Paper, Scissors, ask the class to try to create a winner in a "best of five series" with their partners.

6. When the class comes back together, "play up" the notion of the winners.

7. Next say "we are going to revisit the win-win concept from the previous activity by changing this activity just a bit!"

8. In this instance, Rock is represented by curling your body over your knees in a solid stance. Paper is represented by raising your arms above your head, stretching your body out flat. Scissors are represented by making giant cutting motions with your arms.

9. Have the group repeat all three gestures.

10. Explain to the class that they are going to have the opportunity to practice win-win approaches to conflict and remind them of the earlier activity In Anticipation of Learning where they modeled different stages of learning.

11. Ask students to stand back to back with their partners and on the count of three, both turn toward each other and show one of the three supersized gestures they just learned.

12. The goal is to try to match the gestures without talking to each other. It is a best of five series...five tries to connect with each other. Ask the students if they have any questions.

13. Teacher counts to three for the first round, students count the remaining five.

Reflection:

Questions for Discussion:

1. "What were the differences between the first and second versions of the game?" Give examples of the differences you saw in laughter, energy, involvement, etc.

2. "Can you tell us about specific situations in which resolving conflict would have been more fun and energized if both people were interested in working together?"

3. "Does anyone have a real life example of a win-win solution?" Follow up with "How did you achieve this?"

4. "How do you create a win-win situation when someone is pressuring you to do something you know is bad for you or that you don't want to do?"

Knowledge Review:

5. Review list from previous activity. Record other approaches to managing conflict.

. . . .

Bear, Salmon and Mosquito

Set Up:

1. Place the long rope in the center of a large, open space.

2. Create two safety zones by placing two cones on each side of the center line, about twenty yards away from it.

Framing:

"Have you heard of the fight or flight response? I thought so. Well this activity will give us the opportunity to practice our fight or flight response and to understand how we anticipate and manage conflict. We will be working in two small groups and this center line is our point of conflict."

Procedure:

1. Divide the students into two small groups.

2. Tell the class that they need to know how to represent three creatures: bear, salmon and mosquito.

3. Tell them as you demonstrate how to create each creature. "Bears are very tall, with their hands straight up over their head and give a great big 'ROOOAAAR.'"

4. "Salmon are formed by placing your two hands together in prayer fashion, pointing away from your body and then swishing them forward while making a swooshing water sound."

5. "Mosquitoes are formed by spreading you arms out to your side, wiggling your fingers whilst making a loud buzzing noise."

6. Bears eat salmon, salmon eat mosquitoes and mosquitoes bite bears on the nose. This is important. Have the group repeat it back to you.

7. The goal is for each small group to win members from the other group.

8. Each small group goes back to their safety line (the area 20 feet away from the center line you marked with cones) and decides what creature they would like to be. The group then comes back to the center line where at the count of three, all members will show the decided upon bear, salmon or mosquito.

9. The group that shows the stronger creature become the chasers and the other group, the runners. The runners try to run past their cones to safety without being tagged.

10. If the runners are tagged, they become members of the other team, and each team gets another planning session.

11. If each side shows the same creature, participants shake hands, return to their small groups and try again.

12. Ask students to try to identify what they are thinking or feeling right before they show their creature and immediately after.

13. Play a few rounds or until most of the group is on one side.

Reflection:

Questions for Discussion:

1. "Can you recall and describe what you were feeling when they stepped up to the line to show their creature?"

2. "Can you recall and describe what you were feeling when the other team showed their creature and you had to decide whether to chase or be chased?"

3. "Can you recall and describe what you were feeling when you showed your creature and it was the same as the other side's?"

4. "How do you think these feelings relate to the "fight or flight" response to conflict?"

5. "Do you feel your response was helpful or harmful in this activity?"

6. "Can you describe some ways to avoid and diminish threatening situations?"

 Additional Thoughts

• *This activity may be best played in a large space, outdoors or in a gymnasium.*

LESSON 14

In this lesson students will practice problem solving and conflict management strategies.

ACTIVITY	LEARNING OBJECTIVE	TIME	PROPS	HEALTH SKILLS
7, 11, 21	**At the conclusion of this activity, students will be able to:** • Demonstrate use of some communication skills to solve problems and avoid conflicts. • Define and describe some criteria for responsible decision-making.	20 minutes	• None	• Interpersonal communication • Self-management • Analyze influences
Pick N Pack...The Case of the Kaytees	• Demonstrate effective communication skills. • Demonstrate assertiveness and self-control. • Demonstrate listening to and appreciating the views of peers. • Demonstrate some strategies for managing conflict in healthy ways. • Apply responsible decision-making strategies.	30–40 minutes	• Game Frame or Spider's web • 10 Fleece balls (Kaytees) • Boundary markers	• Goal setting • Decision making • Interpersonal communication • Self-management

TEACHER'S NOTES:

FRAMING	SET-UP PROCEDURE	REFLECTION

7, 11, 21

Set Up:
NONE

Framing:
"Sometimes we make decisions based on what we think other people will do and sometimes we make decisions based on what we want to do. Clear communication can be very helpful when trying to solve problems. It can also be very challenging particularly when more people are involved. This is a fun activity in which we try to solve a problem with one or more other people without officially communicating with them. Let's see how we do…"

Procedure:

1. Ask the students to find a partner.

2. Explain that this activity is very much like Rock, Paper, Scissors in that someone will count to three and each member of the group will display their fingers but instead of rock, paper or scissors, they will be trying to come up with the sum of a predetermined number.

3. Give the partnerships one minute to see how many times they can come up with the number seven between them. No discussion beforehand. For example, one student displays three fingers and the other student displays four. Check in on results.

4. Ask the students to get into teams of three. Same rules apply except now the goal is 11.

5. Next ask the students to get into teams of five. Same rules apply except now the goal is 21.

6. Finally ask the students to get into teams of seven. Each team is now going for the number 30. Give them 30 seconds to plan how to make it happen.

Reflection:
Questions for Discussion:

1. "How challenging was it to throw number 7? 11? 21? 30?"

2. "How did the different number of people in your groups change your decisions as to how many fingers to throw?"

3. "Did having planning time make a difference in how you worked together?"

4. "Why is clear communication so important in problem solving?"

5. "What happens when we do not have clear communication?"

6. "Describe a situation where unclear communication caused a problem for you or a friend."

7. "What are steps that we can take to be sure to communicate more clearly?"

. . . .

Pick N Pack: The Case of the Kaytees

Set Up:

1. Set up the Game Frame or Spider's Web.

2. Place a boundary marker on each side of the web, approximately 12-24" away from the frame.

3. Place all the balls on one side of the web.

Framing

"You are harvesting "kaytees" an exotic, delectable and very perishable fruit from the Planet J. Once these fruits are picked, the goal is to have them transported as quickly as possible to the refrigeration unit to preserve their freshness and appearance. Any delay in the harvesting and packing process causes the fruit to lose its nutritional value. Your group purchased the contract guaranteeing a monopoly on the harvest this year. Your success depends on how quickly you can manage the harvest, as well as how carefully you pack the fruit since they are very delicate and susceptible to damage. Customers will not buy them if they are blemished in handling or have turned color indicating that they were not picked and packed promptly. Your task involves creating an efficient process for picking and packing the fruit."

Procedure:

1. Divide the class in half. Ask each half of the group to go to opposite sides of the Game Frame or Spider's Web.

1. Explain the following rules.

   - No one may stand or touch the ground inside the "zone" outlined by the boundary markers. Any touch by a person adds 10 seconds to the group's time.

   - No "kaytee" may touch the web while it is being tossed. Any touch adds five seconds to the group's time for each infraction.

   - No "kaytee" may touch the ground inside the zone. Any fruit touching the ground is lost and the infraction adds 20 seconds to the group's time.

   - While tossing and catching the "kaytees," people need to remain behind the boundary lines.

- The goal is to pass each "kaytee" back and forth through the web until each person has thrown and caught it once. The passes always occur through the web (a person may not pass to someone on the same side of the web).

- Each opening in the web can be used twice – one pass from each side. Once a pass has been made from side A, the opening is closed from that side. Someone from side B can still use it. If an opening is used more than once per side, the group has to start over again.

- When the last person receives the "kaytee," he or she places it on the ground to complete the process and finish the cycle for that object. Once the last "kaytee" has been received and put on the ground, the problem is finished.

3. Before timing an attempt to solve the problem, it may be helpful to give the class some planning time to create a pattern for passing so that each person catches and throws. The pattern can change, but every student participates by catching and throwing at least once for a solution to be acceptable.

4. If there are more students than openings in the web, it may be necessary to allow more than one pass through each opening.

Reflection:

Questions for Discussion:
1. "How were you able to successfully deliver the "kaytees"?"
2. "What were the critical decision making points?"
3. "What strategies did you use to manage conflict in healthy ways?"
4. "How can these strategies be used in real life situations?"

Physical Fitness

LESSON 15

In this lesson students will identify multiple ways to be fit, options for accessing fitness in different environments and practice active stretching

ACTIVITY	LEARNING OBJECTIVE	TIME	PROPS	HEALTH SKILLS
Fitness Speed Rabbit	**At the conclusion of this activity, students will be able to:** • Increase their ability to identify what is available for them to become fit. • Identify community resources for fitness activities.	20 minutes	• None	• Self-management • Interpersonal communication • Analyze influences
Co-op Competition	• Comprehend the principles and importance of proper stretching. • Identify ways to support peers in practicing injury prevention through proper stretching.	15 minutes	• None	• Decision making • Self-management • Interpersonal communication

TEACHER'S NOTES:

FRAMING	SET-UP PROCEDURE	REFLECTION

Fitness Speed Rabbit

Set Up:

NONE

Framing:

"Today we will think about the many ways to be fit. As a group we are going to create three-person sculptures which represent different ways to be fit. We will start with three—yoga, swimming, and bench pressing. Does anyone have an idea what components of fitness they relate to? OK, let's get started. The yoga sculpture looks like this…"

Procedure:

1. Ask the students to stand in a circle.
2. The starting fitness sequences are as follows and should be amended and added to as play continues: Yoga—The center person stands very straight and takes a deep breath. The players to the right and left of that person put their outside arms straight out to the side and bend their outside legs, with their outside foot placed on the knee of the inside leg.
3. Swimming—The center person places his/her hands together with arms straight over his/her head in a diving position. The people on either side do a swim stroke with their outside arms.
4. Bench Press—The center person puffs up his or her chest with a deep breath and the outside people push their outside arms forward, bent at the elbow as if they were lifting a barbell. Sound effects are always fun.
5. Demonstrate the fitness sequences to the class by having everyone do the middle position followed by the side positions together. (For example, the whole group demonstrates the middle swimming position by bringing their hands together over their heads. Then the whole group demonstrates the side position by stroking with one hand. Go through all the positions this way.)
6. One student should stand in the center of the circle.
7. His/her job is to point to a person on the outside circle and say either: Yoga, Swimming or Bench Press. The signified individual, and the two people to that person's immediate right and left, are challenged to perform one of the fitness sequences before the person in the middle can count to 10.
8. If the sequence is not done correctly or in time, then the center of the trio will take the place of the person in the middle of the circle. He or she then points to a new person and starts the sequence again.
9. If the sequence is performed correctly, the person in the middle points to another person until someone eventually makes a mistake.
10. Invite the class to come up with additional fitness poses!

Reflection:

Questions for Discussion:

1. "What are some of the different ways we identified to be fit?"

2. "How does working together help people maintain a fitness routine?"

3. "What are some places in our community where we could access the different fitness activities we discovered?"

. . . .

Co-Op Competition

Set Up:

NONE

Framing:

"Let's review the important parts of proper stretching (i.e., no bouncing, stretch to point of tension not pain, etc.) Great! Everybody find a partner—someone you are fairly comfortable with—and stand facing each other with one foot in front of your partner's, toe to toe and one hand connected to your partners. Great! Your challenge for the next three to five minutes is to move your bodies into as many proper stretches as possible, while staying connected. Ready, go!"

Procedure:

1. Ask students to find a partner. Someone they feel comfortable working with and stand facing their partner.

2. Ask students to connect with their partners by aligning one toe to one toe and one palm to one palm.

3. Tell the students that the goal is to move their bodies into various stretching positions while maintaining connection.

4. For the second round, have partners change positions so that they are standing face to face, toe to toe squarely.

5. Have partners switch positions and continue the activity.

Reflection:

1. Ask students to identify the basic principles of proper stretching.

2. Ask students to name three things that worked well in their partnership and three challenges they encountered in their partnership.

3. After reviewing responses ask students to relate the importance of balance/body awareness and flexibility in overall fitness.

4. Ask students to identify resources and specific times that they can help each other implement flexibility into their fitness routines.

6.16

LESSON 16

In this lesson students will explore the concepts of cardiovascular fitness and measure and track their heart rate in response to different environmental stressors.

ACTIVITY	LEARNING OBJECTIVE	TIME	PROPS	HEALTH SKILLS
Instant Impulse	**At the conclusion of this activity, students will be able to:** • Begin to acquire knowledge about the concept of cardiovascular fitness. • Identify ways to exercise the heart and lungs.	5–8 minutes	• None	• Core content • Self-management
Swat Tag	• Recognize the changes in heart rate in response to movement, anticipation and stress. • Begin to identify components of fitness.	15–20 minutes	• Boffer • Poly spot	• Core content • Self-management • Interpersonal communication

TEACHER'S NOTES:

FRAMING	SET-UP PROCEDURE	REFLECTION

Instant Impulse

Set-Up:

NONE

Framing:

"Can anyone tell me what cardiovascular fitness is? Cardiovascular fitness involves exercising the heart and lungs. One way to measure that is by tracking our heart rates. Let's get a sense of what it takes to keep a steady pulse or heart rate going for our group."

Procedure:

1. Have the group organize themselves into a circle and hold hands.
2. Students may either stand or sit in a circle.
3. Tell the students that they will be sending a wave impulse around the circle as quickly as possible by squeezing each other's hands.
4. Practice sending an impulse in one direction around the circle. Stop and then send it around in the other direction.
5. Explain that you can reverse the direction of the impulse by double squeezing. Play a few rounds.
6. It is not unusual to "lose" the impulse or to suddenly have more than one going.

Reflection:

Reflection Activity:
1. "With a fist to five rating, five fingers being the highest, how did we do on keeping the pulse going consistently?"
2. Reflect on some of the differing ratings.

Questions for Discussion:
3. "What are some things that we could have done to maintain the pulse?"
4. "Can you define the concept of cardiovascular fitness?"
5. "Tell us about some of the strategies identified in this activity that will keep your pulse/ heart rate up for 20 minutes at a time."

SWAT Tag

Set Up:

Clear a large space in your classroom.

Framing:

"Today we are going to learn how our heart responds to different situations and identify some ways to be fit. We are going to play a fast-paced tag game in which both reflexes and endurance will come in handy. I will ask you to take your heart rate before we start, a couple of times during the activity and at the end. Try to remember what was happening when you took your heart rate, were you tagging, watching, just been tagged? We will check in afterwards to see what happened. Ready…"

Procedure:

1. Have the class stand in a circle, facing the center where you've placed a Boffer on top of the spot marker.

2. Designate one player to start.

3. The action starts when the first player walks to the marker, picks up the Boffer, and commences to move around the inside perimeter of the circle. Being careful not to telegraph his/her intentions, he/she suddenly swats another below the knee with the Boffer and then hurries to return the Boffer to the center spot.

4. The "swattee" then heads for the marker to claim the Boffer.

5. The swatter, after replacing the Boffer on the spot, returns to the marker, lays the Boffer on it and returns to the swatted person's place in the circle. He/she does this before the person they swatted can recover the Boffer and tag her with it.

6. If the "swattee" succeeds in swatting the "swatter," the "swattee" drops the Boffer back on the marker and returns to his/her original place in the circle before the swatter can recover the Boffer and tag him/her again.

7. This action continues with the Boffer always returned to the marker between swats until one of these two players does manage to get back into place before being tagged. The person left holding the Boffer becomes the new swatter and begins stalking the circle for another victim.

8. Demonstrate a safe tag and explain that the Boffer is made of foam and while it may make a loud noise, it will not hurt if used properly.

Reflection:

Reflection Activity:

1. Have students monitor their heart rate before, during (stop the game for a few seconds) and post activity.

Questions for Discussion:

1. "What differences did you notice in your heart rate?"

2. "Can you tell us what made those differences?"

3. "What components of fitness did this activity bring out?"

 Additional Thoughts

• *Make sure that the same player isn't the swatter all the time, getting exhausted and becoming less and less likely ever to succeed in tagging another player. This self-governing is part of the caring restraint we use when we agree not to play too rough.*

LESSON 17

In this lesson students will identify anatomically correct body parts, discover the five components of fitness and identify range and availability of fitness resources as well as principles of exercise adherence.

ACTIVITY	LEARNING OBJECTIVE	TIME	PROPS	HEALTH SKILLS
People to People	At the conclusion of this activity, students will be able to: • Identify anatomically correct body parts. • Apply interpersonal communication skills.	15 minutes	• None	• Core content • Self-management • Interpersonal communication
Be the Best Share the Health	• Identify the five components of fitness. • Demonstrate knowledge about the five health-related components of fitness. • Identify principles of exercise adherence.	30 minutes	• 5 Hula-Hoops ™ • 20 Fleece balls	• Core content • Goal setting • Decision making • Advocacy

TEACHER'S NOTES:

FRAMING	SET-UP PROCEDURE	REFLECTION

People To People

Set Up:
NONE

Framing:

"For our warm up today we are going to try to identify different body parts by their anatomically correct names. The way we are going to do that is I will start as the caller and ask you to connect different parts of your body...for example toe to toe. You and your partner will connect toes to toes. And then I will call again. When you hear 'People to People', you need to change partners as quickly as you can. After a few rounds I will change to the anatomically correct body parts...for example if I were to say patella to patella, what would you do? Great! Ok let's start moving a bit..."

Procedure:

1. Have the class find a partner or create pairs and form a large circle with all of the partners. Do not choose a partner yourself as there needs to be one person out. (If you have an odd numbered group, you will have one partnership of three.)

2. Have the group start bouncing lightly up and down on their toes/feet and clapping their hands.

3. Tell the students they need to follow your directions and connect a part of their body to part of their buddy's body. For example say "foot to foot." Each member of the pairs should each put one foot next to his/her partner's foot.

4. Keep the body parts the same initially and then you can change to more complex commands such as "elbow to knee."

5. After five or six command sequences, yell "PEOPLE TO PEOPLE" and everyone finds a new partner. There will be some chaos as they find new partners. If the group is not able to manage the change you can just keep going with the same partners.

6. If you decide to join the exchange, one person will be left out and will then become the "caller."

7. To increase the level of challenge, use the anatomically correct names of different body parts; for example, patella to patella (kneecap to kneecap).

Reflection:

Questions for Discussion:

1. "What are some of the body parts you came up with?"

2. "How did you communicate with one another when connecting different body parts?"

3. "Where can you find a chart of all the different body parts?"

4. "What are some times that it might it be important to know the proper terms for your body?"

. . . .

Be the Best/Share the Health

Set Up:

1. Place the Hula-Hoops in each corner of a large square shape and also one in the middle. On four sets of five fleece balls write one component of fitness on each ball and then place all 20 balls in the hoop in the middle.

Framing for Be The Best:

"Ok everybody, who can tell me what the five components of fitness are? Excellent! Your goal for the first part of this activity is to be the best/most fit by getting all five components of fitness, represented on the different fleece balls, into your hoop before any other group does. Here are the guidelines."

Procedure:

1. Ask the class to divide into four equal teams. Have each team stand near a Hula-Hoop in each of the four corners.

2. Tell the class that their goal is to "be the best" – the first team to have all five components of fitness in their nest.

3. The way to get balls is to send one representative at a time to the middle hoop and take only one ball at a time. Balls also may be retrieved from neighbors' nests and only one at a time and carried by one representative.

4. More than one person may leave the nest at a time; however, they can only go to one destination.

5. The game is over when the first team has the five components of fitness in its hoop. The team group declares their victory by shouting and making poses reflecting the five components of fitness.

6. Students may not physically protect their hoops, e.g., forming a circle around their hoop that other students can't penetrate.

7. Play several rounds and then switch the concept to Share The Health

Framing for Share The Health:

"Now as you are catching your breath, let's switch this around and share the health. Your goal for this round is to empty your hoop as quickly as possible. Share the health with your peers or with the community hoop in the center. The guidelines are the same as the previous rounds."

Procedure:

1. Each group starts with the five components of fitness in their hoops and needs to be the first to empty their hoops by sharing resources with others.

2. Same rules apply in terms of one object at a time, one person per destination and objects may be placed in the center of other hoops.

3. The first group to empty their hoops is proclaimed the best team of advocates for health and they declare their victory by shouting and making poses reflecting the five components of fitness.

Reflection:

Knowledge Review:

1. Review the components of fitness and identify what components were accessed during this activity.

2. Ask the small groups to identify the ways that they are fit or unfit within the five components of fitness.

Questions for Discussion: (back to the large group)

3. "Did you notice which situation lasted longer being the best or sharing the health?"

4. "Can you tell me some of the reasons people maintain fitness programs and how they might help each other stay fit?"

 Additional Thoughts

• *This activity may be best played in a large space, outdoors or in a gymnasium.*

Nutrition

LESSON 18

In this lesson students will apply their interpersonal communication skills and knowledge of the food pyramid.

ACTIVITY	LEARNING OBJECTIVE	TIME	PROPS	HEALTH SKILLS
What Food Am I?	At the conclusion of this activity, students will be able to: • Identify some dietary guidelines. • Analyze food choices. • Identify some internal and external influences that affect food choices. • Discuss healthy and unhealthy weight management practices. • Set goals to improve eating habits.	20 minutes	• Post-its ® or Paper and tape instead of Post-its • Markers • 2 giant Food Pyramids (found on page __ in the appendix)	• Core content • Interpersonal communication • Accessing information
Food FFEACH and MOOCH	• Recognize influences impacting food choices.	15 minutes	• List of different fast foods, advertisement slogans and healthy foods • Feelings Marketplace Cards	• Core content • Interpersonal communication • Analyzing influences

TEACHER'S NOTES:

FRAMING	SET-UP PROCEDURE	REFLECTION

What Food Am I?

Set Up:

1. Tape one food pyramid or the shape of a food pyramid to the floor per 14-16 students. Be sure to allow for some space between pyramids if you need more than one.

Framing:

"I think it is safe to say that we all have heard about or seen a food pyramid. I think it is also safe to say that it would be a good idea to review what foods are healthy. We are going to start with the standard USDA Food Pyramid and then adapt the food pyramid to age, activity level and cultures."

Procedure:

1. Pass out one Post-it and marker to each student.
2. Say: "Everyone write a type of food from one of the food groups on your Post-it, but don't show anyone! Keep the foods basic. For example, if you were going to write spaghetti with meatballs, write either spaghetti or meatballs, not both."
3. Have students stick their Post-it on another student's back.
4. Have students ask yes and no questions of each other until they guess what food is taped to their back. For example…Bart has a Post-it that says Celery on his back, and he asks MB if he is a vegetable, and she says, 'Yes.'
5. Limit the questions to 20 per person.
6. After students figure out what food they are, have them stand in the section of the food pyramid that they believe matches their food, with their Post-it note attached to their front.
7. Once they get there, have students converse with others in their food group about how many servings per day are recommended for a healthy diet.

Reflection:

Questions for Discussion:

1. "What kinds of questions were helpful in determining what type of food you were?"
2. "How did you determine where to stand on the pyramid and how many servings you should have in one day?"
3. "How does the US pyramid change for different cultures, ages, activity level?"
4. "What are some strategies to make sure you eat a balanced diet each day?"

Reflection Activity:

5. Have students find a partner and state one goal about changing food choices for a healthier lifestyle.

 Additional Thoughts

• *Be sure to discuss healthy and unhealthy weight management practices as students identify numbers of servings, etc.*

FOOD FFEACH (Fast Food, Emotions, Advertisements & Choices for Health)

Set Up:

1. Clear a large open space in your classroom.

Framing:

"Food brings out the best in us. What we choose to eat is influenced by many things—advertising, emotions, setting. We are going to try to express ourselves in ways that allow people to figure out what it is we are craving."

Procedure:

1. Divide the class into two smaller groups and separate them by a few yards.
2. Situate yourself somewhat apart and between the groups.
3. Announce to all the players that you will secretly and separately reveal a word (fast foods: 'quarter pounder,' 'fries', etc.) to one player from each group.
4. That player will then swiftly return to act out the word to their team members. (No talking, but supportive sounds can be made such as whistling).
5. As soon as the word is guessed, another member of the group races up to verbally receive another word and returns to his or her team and repeats the process.
6. The first team to guess the individual words that each member is given wins the Nutrition Oscar.

Reflection:

Questions for Discussion:

1. "What are some of the things you represented during this activity?"
2. "What were some of your reference points for acting out the different words?"
3. "What were the most challenging words to act out? The easiest?"
4. "How does advertising influence our food choices?"
5. "How do emotions and other people influence our food choices?"

 Additional Thoughts

• *If winning seems inappropriate ask the first team that finishes to hurry over to whatever group is still charading and join in. In this way, the groups are not competing against one another, but eventually cooperating until all are finished, with everyone cheering on each other.*

LESSON 19

In this lesson, students will identify multicultural health and wellness practices, with a primary focus on nutrition.

ACTIVITY	LEARNING OBJECTIVE	TIME	PROPS	HEALTH SKILLS
Mapping	**At the conclusion of this activity, students will be able to:** • Describe some of the ways family and peers influence the nutritional practices of adolescents. • Describe some of the influence of cultural beliefs on health behaviors and the use of health services with relation to nutrition.	15 minutes	• Spot marker or cone	• Accessing information • Core content • Interpersonal communication • Analyze influences
Multicultural Food Find	• Explain some ways in which society and diversity influence students' food choices. • Give examples of how advertising, fad diets, and behavioral patterns influence food choices.	40 minutes	• Food Pyramid Charts (samples found in the appendix page___) • Food cards • Stopwatch • Extra blank cards • Markers • 5 Hula-hoops ™	• Analyze influences • Interpersonal communication

TEACHER'S NOTES:

FRAMING	SET-UP PROCEDURE	REFLECTION

Mapping

Set Up:

1. Place a spot marker or cone in the center of a large, open space in your classroom.

Framing:

"Wellness and healthy behaviors are practiced differently all over the world. Let's say this cone represents our school in _____. It will be our point of orientation as we create our own imaginary map of the world on the rest of the floor."

Procedure:

1. Ask your students to form a circle around the spot marker or cone.

2. Explain to the students that the cone represents geographically where you are at the moment and that the rest of the room represents the world. The cone or spot marker is the point of reference in response to the following questions.

3. Say "I am going to ask you a series of questions and you need to decide in which country or place in a country you need to be to answer my question. You can help each other figure out where different countries are and what are some good responses to the questions."

4. "Go to the place where you were born." Each person figures out where their birthplace is 'on the map' and stands there.

   Sample Questions:
   • Go to the place where your parents were born.
   • Go to the places where people drink coffee for breakfast.
   • Go to the places where meditation is practiced faithfully.
   • Go to the places where rice is the main source of food.
   • Go to the places where walking is the main form of transportation.
   • Go to the places where children speak more than one language.
   • Go to the places that have the most fit young people.
   • Go to the places that have the healthiest older people.

5. Ask students to identify the places they chose and why. Correct any misinformation, generalizations or stereotypes. For example, the United States does not have the most fit young people. Finland does.

6. Reinforce the notion that there are many ways to practice health and wellness.

Reflection:

Questions for Discussion:

1. "What did you learn about your own and the group's world perspective?"
2. "How do you think family heritage influences health behaviors, particularly around nutrition and eating?"
3. "What did you notice about people's awareness of different health customs in the world?"
4. "What can we learn about other cultures' health and wellness practices that will help us make healthier lifestyle choices?"

. . . .

Multicultural Food Find

Set Up:

1. On an index card write a different food from each food group for different ethnic groups (see appendix page>>>). Keep the cards sorted by ethnic groups. Be sure to include food from each ethnic group in your class; e.g., burritos, pizza, couscous.
2. Place food cards in a hoop in the middle of the open space, and have the students form four groups, one in each corner of the classroom. Each group will have their own hoop in their own corner.

Framing:

"Think about some of your favorite foods...where did you learn about them? Are there foods you only have at family gatherings, holidays? Family traditions and culture influence many of our preferences."

Procedure:

1. Give students extra blank index cards and markers. Have them write down one or two of their favorite foods that are related to their family's ethnicity on a card and place the cards in the center hoop.
2. Have students write their favorite foods on separate cards and place them in the middle hoop. Be sure there is only one food identified per card.
3. Give each group a pyramid that represents a different culture to place in the center of each hoop.
4. The goal of the activity is for each small group to complete their food pyramid as quickly as possible. (You should quantify this. An example might be to have three servings in each area of the food pyramid.)

5. Each member of the group runs to the center hoop, collects a food card, and places the food in the correct category on the pyramid back at their home hoop.

6. Groups will be moving at once. Only one member may leave their hoop at a time and only one food card may be collected.

7. Not all cards will be used.

Reflection:

Reflection Activity:

1. Have each group identify the ethnicity or culture of the foods selected for their pyramid. Make any necessary adjustments together.

2. Select a food category and have students name foods from at least four different cultures that fall into that category.

3. Read the foods listed on the remaining cards in the center hoop. Ask students to identify ways they have seen foods advertised and how that influences their desire to eat it or not.

Question for Discussion:

4. "How do the diets of different cultures relate to body composition?"

 Additional Thoughts

• *There are several different culturally appropriate graphics for healthy food intake (such as the pagoda, palm frond and rainbow) which are fun to integrate into this activity as well.*

• *Be sure to help students dispel myths or stereotypes about cultural nutrition practices and body composition.*

LESSON 20

In this lesson students will identify sources of nutrients and foods that energize and also learn the benefits and concepts of eating a healthy, balanced diet.

ACTIVITY	LEARNING OBJECTIVE	TIME	PROPS	HEALTH SKILLS
Dinner Call	**At the conclusion of this activity, students will be able to:** • Identify the nutrients found in different foods. • Evaluate making the best possible food choices among unhealthy alternatives.	15 minutes	• None	• Core content • Self-management • Interpersonal communication
Gobart Tag	• Identify foods that are energizing. • Recognize the symptoms of unhealthy eating habits. • Describe healthy eating habits for sustainable energy.	15 minutes	• Boundary markers	• Self-management • Advocacy • Core content

TEACHER'S NOTES:

FRAMING	SET-UP PROCEDURE	REFLECTION

Dinner Call

Set Up:

1. Clear a large open space in your classroom.

Framing:

"Did you know that Vitamin D helps build healthy bones? What foods do you think Vitamin D can be found in? Nutrients are an important part of a balanced diet. Each nutrient has a specific role in keeping us healthy so we need to know where to find them!"

Procedure:

1. Ask the students to get into two lines facing one another inside the open space.

2. Ask students to reach one hand out to the person across from them in order to form pairs.

3. Each pair needs to come up with two food words, one that is the name of the food and the other that is a nutritional component of that food. For example, potassium and banana, or calcium and milk. Each person in the pair takes one of the two words

4. The pairs should now split up, returning to their lines. Ask one line of people to go to one end of the classroom or gym and the other line to the other end.

5. If the two members of the pairs are lined up directly across from each other, you may want to have a line "scramble up" before proceeding with the directions.

6. Ask all students to close their eyes and put their hands up in front of their chests (bumpers up). On "Go" the lines begin walking toward one another as players yell their partner's words, while at the same time listening for their partners, who are calling out their other words.

7. Students continue calling their partners' words until they find each other. Once they have found each other, they can open their eyes and watch the other students as they search for their partners.

Reflection:

Questions for Discussion:

1. "What did it feel like to do this activity?"

2. "What skills did you use to be able to find your partner?"

3. "How do you know what nutrients are in different foods when you can't "see" them?"

4. "What is it like to try to make good choices about food in different settings?"

5. "How can the skills you used during this activity help you make the healthiest possible food choices in different situations?"

 Additional Thoughts

• *No running!*

• *Be sure to reinforce the concept of Challenge By Choice by encouraging students to stop, evaluate their perceived levels of risk, take a quick look if they need to and then move on.*

Gobart Tag

Set Up:

1. Set the boundary markers out for a fairly large open space.

Framing:

"Some foods energize us and some foods make us sluggish. When, what and how much we eat also has an impact on our ability to sustain energy throughout the day. Sometimes we just need a healthy pick-me-up to keep ourselves going. This tag game will do just that!"

Procedure:

1. Have class circle up inside the space as you explain the activity.

2. Explain to students that it is important to eat a nutritious diet to maintain a consistent level of energy to get through the day. This tag game will represent what it is like to run out of energy.

3. Players will place one hand behind their backs, palms facing out. A hand, so presented, represents the On/Off Button for the lower half of that person's body.

4. When tagged on the back, players will stop and slump over as if fatigued and un-energized.

5. Each player's objective is to re-energize the other player by tagging their On/Off Button while not getting tagged themselves.

6. Once the On/Off button is tagged a player may get back in the game by having another player touch their On switch, while citing the name of an energizing food.

7. If a player removes their On/Off switch while trying to touch someone they freeze from the waist down.

8. Everyone is It – at the same time students are It, they can unfreeze others. (Yes, this game is a little bit of contained chaos.)

9. The game ends when everyone is energized and moving around.

Reflection:

Questions for Discussion:

1. "What were some of the energizing foods we came up with to switch back 'on'?"

2. "What is the difference between slow and fast-burning carbohydrates?"

3. "Which is better for sustainable energy?"

4. "What is an effective dietary plan for maintaining energy throughout the day and where can you find that food?"

LESSON 21

In this lesson students will work in small groups and create visual representations of a variety of body types and healthy diet plans to match.

ACTIVITY	LEARNING OBJECTIVE	TIME	PROPS	HEALTH SKILLS
A Day in the Life	**At the conclusion of this activity, students will be able to:** • Plan a healthy meal, using info from the dietary guidelines and the food guide pyramid. • Describe nutritious diets for different groups of people. • Differentiate healthy weight management practices from fad diets, weight loss or gain advertisements and use of supplements.	40 minutes	• Flip chart paper • Markers	• Goal setting • Decision making • Self-management • Analyze influences

TEACHER'S NOTES:

FRAMING	SET-UP PROCEDURE	REFLECTION

A Day In The Life...

Set Up:

NONE

Framing:

"We have talked about the basic food pyramid and its relationship to healthy diets. Not only is it important to know what foods are in the food pyramid, it is also important to know how much of those foods are needed to provide healthy diets for different types of people. Let's try to figure out what an Olympic athlete might need, what a twelve year old young man would require, a vegetarian, etc."

Procedure:

1. Divide the class into four small groups.

2. Give each group a piece of flip chart paper and markers. Assign each group one of the following: athlete, vegetarian, pregnant female or obese person.

3. Explain to the students that they are going to spend the class creating a nutritional day in the life of four different groups of people.

4. Specifically, each small group needs to describe or draw their person and create a healthy menu for one day in that person's life. Tell the groups that they can expand and include activities but should be sure to state where their person will get their food and at what times they will be eating, etc.

5. Have each small group creatively present their person to the larger group.

Reflection:

Questions for Discussion:

1. "Can you tell me the difference between healthy weight management practices and fad diets/weight loss or gain advertisements/the use of supplements?"

2. "Can you summarize the modifications you made in the basic food pyramid to meet the healthy diet needs of each of the four people? Why did you make these changes?"

 Additional Thoughts

• *This is a good time to dispel myths about proper diets for different people.*

• *Be sure to reflect on and "correct" the body images of the drawings presented as well.*

Substance Abuse Prevention

6.22

SUBSTANCE
ABUSE
PREVENTION

LESSON 22

In this lesson students will test their knowledge of the risks and health effects of tobacco use.

ACTIVITY	LEARNING OBJECTIVE	TIME	PROPS	HEALTH SKILLS
Be Smart Don't Start /Be Fit It's Time To Quit	At the conclusion of this activity, students will be able to: • Identify negative health effects of tobacco use. • Identify short and long-term effects of tobacco use. • Identify risks of different types of tobacco. • Identify diseases caused by smoking.	30 minutes	• 1 Be Smart Bingo Card per student • Be Smart answer list • Pens or pencils	• Core content • Decision making • Analyze influences • Interpersonal communication

TEACHER'S NOTES:

FRAMING	SET-UP PROCEDURE	REFLECTION

Be Smart Don't Start /Be Fit It's Time To Quit

Set Up:

NONE

Framing:

"Using tobacco is a personal choice. Unfortunately this choice is often made without the benefit of reliable information. Before you decide to start using tobacco it is important to know the facts about how tobacco use affects your personality, your body and the people around you."

Procedure:

1. Pass out one Be Smart Bingo Card (found on page ...) and one writing utensil to each student.
2. Flip chart and post the Be Smart answer list so that everyone is able to see it.
3. Explain to the class that the goal is to get as many different answers to the questions in the box as possible in 20 minutes.
4. The boxes are filled in by asking each other the questions in the boxes and writing the responses in the spaces provided.
5. Only one student answer per box is allowed. In other words, a student must talk to a different student in getting a response for each box.
6. When someone completes a line, they should shout out "Bingo" and then keep trying to fill in the rest of their sheet.
7. Reinforce that this is a group effort and that they need to talk with each other to complete the Bingo card.

Reflection:

Reflection Activity:

1. Collectively review the answers to the questions so that students are sure to have accurate information.

Questions for Discussion:

2. "What surprised you about the information you learned during this activity?"
3. "Can you tell me about one thing you learned that will help you stay smoke free or to quit smoking?"

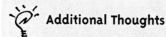 **Additional Thoughts**

• *The Be Smart answer list can also be written on the board.*

• *If you would like to increase the level of challenge do not post the answer list.*

LESSON 23

In this lesson, students will challenge themselves to manage the influences of advertising techniques used by tobacco companies through strong interpersonal communication and creation of their own counter messages.

ACTIVITY	LEARNING OBJECTIVE	TIME	PROPS	HEALTH SKILLS
Tobacco Field	**At the conclusion of this activity, students will be able to:** • Describe health effects of tobacco that aren't depicted in advertising. • Develop effective antismoking messages targeted toward their peers. • Identify ways to stay smoke free. • Demonstrate ways to maintain relationships while safeguarding personal health.	40 minutes	• Boundary markers • Assorted objects (tossables) • 80 foot long boundary rope • Masking tape • Index cards • Markers	• Core content • Interpersonal communication • Self-management • Accessing information • Analyze influences

TEACHER'S NOTES:

FRAMING	SET-UP PROCEDURE	REFLECTION

Tobacco Fields

Set Up:

1. Clear a large open space in your classroom.
2. Create a large rectangular shape with the boundary rope leaving about three feet of space on the outside perimeter.

Framing:

"Advertisers use many different strategies to get you to buy cigarettes but they don't tell the whole story. Peers, siblings, friends and even parents can also have a great influence on your decision to use tobacco. As we learned in the last activity, the most common situation for taking a first smoke is with a friend. The best defense against using tobacco then is in understanding what the advertisements are not saying and support one another by creating your own advertisements for staying tobacco free."

Procedure:

1. Ask students to stand around the rectangle and select two tossables.
2. Pass out tape and markers to students.
3. Have students find partners.
4. Ask students to identify different advertising strategies that promote tobacco use, write them down on the tape and tape one strategy to each object.
5. Ask students to then identify the health effects of tobacco that aren't depicted in advertising, write and tape one on their second object.
6. Randomly disperse objects throughout the inside of the rectangle or tobacco field. Be sure the tobacco field is full of advertisements so that it is a challenge to walk from one end to the other without stepping on an object. (Ask students to make more as needed.)
7. Have students pair-up.
8. Pass out index cards to each partnership. Ask each student to write down an antismoking message that they would say to their peer on their index card. Tell students to keep the message to themselves for right now.
9. Explain to the group that they are going to be working with their partner to walk safely from one side of the tobacco field to the other. Their goal is to remain tobacco free by not "buying" (meaning touching) any of the objects on the floor.
10. Tell the students that the challenge is that one person in their partnership will be unable to see and the other will act as a guide.

11. There are three ways to be guided through the tobacco field:

    a. Your partner is in the field with you both verbally and physically guiding you.

    b. Your partner is in the field with you verbally guiding you.

    c. Your partner is on the outside of the field verbally guiding you.

12. If an object is touched, the partnership needs to stop and the guide needs to state their effective antismoking message to their partner loudly and clearly before they can continue moving through the tobacco field.

13. After the first partner is finished, the pair has a brief discussion as to what was or was not effective about the guide's strategy.

14. Partners change roles and repeat above.

15. Students must exit directly across from where they entered.

Reflection Activity:

1. Ask students to gather around the perimeter of the tobacco field, standing next to their partners. Have students close their eyes and respond with the fist to five method to the following question:

2. "What level of challenge was it to move through the tobacco field and not be influenced by the advertising and negative health effects (touching the objects)?"

3. Have students put their hands down and open their eyes while you comment on the range of response students had to that question.

4. Ask: "What strategies did you use to avoid "buying" the advertisements to smoke?"

5. Ask students to read their antismoking messages aloud and post them in a visible place for the remainder of the semester.

 Additional Thoughts

- *This activity takes a bit of preparation so it may be helpful to have the students sit down around the perimeter of the tobacco field while writing on objects and index cards.*
- *Offer a blindfold to students who choose to use one.*
- *Watch this activity very carefully for safety issues.*
- *Remind students that they are responsible for the safety of their partner.*
- *Ask blindfolded students to move with "bumpers up" if it is crowded.*

LESSON 24

In this lesson students will review the effects of stress-related decision making and the need for support in substance abuse prevention.

ACTIVITY	LEARNING OBJECTIVE	TIME	PROPS	HEALTH SKILLS
Zip Zap	**At the conclusion of this activity, students will be able to:** • Attend and respond to appropriate cues while acknowledging physiological responses to stress. • Explain when risk taking is appropriate and inappropriate.	10 minutes	• None	• Self-management • Goal setting • Decision making • Analyze influences
Life Line	• Explain the steps for solving problems and making decisions. • Explain why people do and do not need drugs. • Describe how to use decision-making skills to make healthful decisions around substance abuse prevention.	30 minutes	• 2-3 fifty foot lengths of rope/ webbing	• Core content • Self-management • Interpersonal communication • Goal setting • Decision making

TEACHER'S NOTES:

FRAMING	SET-UP PROCEDURE	REFLECTION

Zip Zap!

Set Up:
NONE

Framing:
"Risk taking is a funny thing. Sometimes it is appropriate and sometimes it is not. We need to pay attention to what is happening around us and inside of us when we decide to take a risk, particularly with our health and well being."

Procedure:

1. Ask the class to stand in a circle and explain that one person will be in the middle of the circle when the game begins.
2. Play begins when the person in the middle points to someone on the outside of the circle with their elbow and says ZIP!
3. The person pointed to needs to duck down or step back as quickly as possible.
4. The two people on either side of that person then quickly point to each other with their elbows and say ZAP!
5. Whoever is distracted or responds out of sequence then takes the middle person's place and the game continues.

Reflection:
Questions for Discussion:

1. "What did it feel like when someone pointed to you and yelled ZIP!"
2. "What kinds of changes did you notice in your body and thinking while playing this game?"
3. "How do these changes relate to deciding when to take risks?"

. . . .

Life Line

Set Up:

1. Tie simple overhand knots in the rope so that there is one space between knots for each person in the group.
2. The knots should be about five feet apart. There should be enough spaces for all the students.
3. Spread the rope out on the floor so that there are no overlaps, etc.

Framing:

"We all need sources of support to help us through life. The rope before you represents your lifeline. As you can see there are several knots in your life path. The knots represent times when you may be pressured to use or want to use drugs or tobacco. With support we know that we can move through many challenges or knots in our path to a healthy life. In that way support may also include the appropriate use of drugs or medicines."

Procedure:

1. Have students stand near the rope at a space between two knots. Be sure no one is at the very ends of the rope and that there is a knot between them and the ends.

2. Tell students that the rope before them represents their life line of support and in a moment you are going to ask them to reach down and grab the rope with one hand in between two knots.

3. Explain that when they grab the rope their hand will be super-glued to that spot so choose their hand and position wisely.

4. The group's task is to untie all of the knots on the rope without taking their hand off of it.

5. They can use their other hand, talk to one another, etc. They just can't remove the hand that is super glued onto the rope.

Reflection:

Questions for Discussion:

1. "How were you able to make decisions and solve the problems so you could untie all the knots?"

2. "How important is it to stay super-glued to your lifeline of support when dealing with pressure to use drugs or tobacco?"

3. "What are some examples of when your lifeline of support includes the use of drugs or medicines?"

4. "What are some helpful guidelines for deciding when people are using over-the-counter drugs or medicines as healthy supports versus unhealthy coping strategies?"

6.25

SUBSTANCE
ABUSE
PREVENTION

LESSON 25

In this lesson students will begin to recognize the effects of substance abuse and work together to identify resources for substance abuse prevention.

ACTIVITY	LEARNING OBJECTIVE	TIME	PROPS	HEALTH SKILLS
Substance Scrabble Babble	**At the conclusion of this activity, students will be able to:** • List different types of drug abuse. • Describe short and long term consequences of substance use and abuse. • Identify appropriate sources for information about the effects of drugs. • Identify ways to help others promote and protect their health in preventing substance abuse.	40 minutes	• Alphabet Soup Kit • Two 25 foot long boundary ropes	• Core content • Accessing information • Interpersonal communication • Self-management • Analyze influences

TEACHER'S NOTES:

FRAMING	SET-UP PROCEDURE	REFLECTION

Substance Scrabble Babble*

Set Up:

1. Separate letter inserts from frames and randomly disperse into two piles at the far end of an open space.
2. Set up a boundary rope about thirty feet away from the letters with enough open space behind it to allow students to lay the foam letters on the floor in a Scrabble type format (typically a 10–15 foot square is adequate).

Framing:

"The effects of substance use and abuse are widespread. It is important to get accurate information about the effects of drugs as well as to know where to go for help. Sometimes we need to understand the negative impact substance abuse has on everyone before we can appreciate ways to promote and protect our health by substance abuse prevention."

Procedure:

1. Divide the class into two teams.
2. Explain to the class that they will have 20 minutes to form words using letter inserts and frames similar to a Scrabble board. The theme of the words is the short and long term consequences of substance use and abuse. Remind students that the focus is on "what happens" when people use versus how to "prevent" use.
3. Participants may pick up to two letters at a time and may choose from either resource pile. Encourage creativity with the use of the letters, inserts and foam blocks.
4. Remind students of the time. After twenty minutes, have students view one another's Scrabble board creations reading the different words out.
5. Ask students to reflect on the social, emotional and physical implications of the words they come up with in relation to substance use and abuse.
6. Next tell the group that their new goal is to combine their Scrabble creations to form one puzzle that focuses solely on words related to substance abuse prevention.

Reflection:

Questions for Discussion:

1. "Can you tell me how using the words you came up with can help prevent substance use?"
2. "Can you identify some social, emotional and physical implications of accessing the resources you found?"
3. "Tell me about one way you can support yourself and each other to promote and protect your health by preventing your own substance use or abuse."

*Thanks to Topaz Terry for enhancing the original version of this activity!

Closure

6.26

CLOSURE

LESSON 26

In this lesson students will work together to reinforce the concept of continually practicing healthy behaviors and leaving unhealthy behaviors behind as they commit to not abusing substances.

ACTIVITY	LEARNING OBJECTIVE	TIME	PROPS	HEALTH SKILLS
Turn Over A New Leaf	**At the conclusion of this activity, students will be able to:** • Identify helpful versus harmful health management behaviors. • Demonstrate the ability to influence and support others in making healthful choices. • Identify components necessary for permanent health behavior change.	30–40 minutes	• One 3 X 5 foot tarp per 12 students • Post-Its® • Pens or pencils	• Goal setting • Decision making • Self-management • Analyze influences • Advocacy

TEACHER'S NOTES:

FRAMING	SET-UP PROCEDURE	REFLECTION

Turn Over A New Leaf

Set Up:

1. Place the tarp on the floor and fold it to a size that will be challenging. Typically you can do this by ensuring that once the group is standing on it you do not see a large amount of open space. Too much open space makes the activity too easy, but err on the large side.

Framing:

"We have explored many aspects of wellness this semester and identified lots of different ways to have a healthy lifestyle. Let's each think of one healthy behavior we would like to take with us and one unhealthy behavior we would like to leave behind as we move on and reinforce our goals of not abusing drugs and maintaining a healthy lifestyle."

Procedure:

1. Ask the class to stand around the perimeter of the tarp.
2. Pass out two Post-its and a writing utensil to each student.
3. The class will begin the process by standing, as a group, on the tarp.
4. Ask students to write a healthy behavior that they have currently and would like to continue on one Post-it and an unhealthy behavior they would like to stop on the second Post-it.
5. Go around the tarp and have students state their unhealthy behaviors and then stick their Post-its anywhere on the tarp.
6. Go around the tarp and have students state their healthy behaviors and stick them to themselves like a name tag.
7. Finally, ask students to step onto the tarp and explain that the goal is to have the group turn the tarp completely over while remaining on it. Demonstrate what you mean.
8. Every member has to be within the three dimensional boundaries of the tarp. This rule means that students cannot hang a leg, or other body part, out into the space beyond the tarp for balance or to create space on the tarp.
9. If anyone steps off the tarp and touches the ground, the class starts the activity again.
10. Prohibit people from stacking on backs, shoulders, etc. and caution people about lifting members or standing on other people's feet. Spot the students as necessary to insure safety.

Reflection:

Questions for Discussion:

1. "What strategies did you access to support each other in turning over a new leaf?"

2. "How was your communication affected by your physical closeness?"

3. "How was your decision making affected by your physical closeness and the task at hand?"

4. "How does the closeness of support impact your decision to practice helpful versus harmful health management behaviors?"

5. "What are the challenges that you think you face in committing to not abusing drugs and living a healthy life-style?"

6. "Name three components necessary for permanent health behavior change."

Grade 7

INJURY PREVENTION / MENTAL EMOTIONAL HEALTH

CREATING COMMUNITY

Lesson 1:
In this lesson students will begin to establish a healthy learning community by learning one another's names and practicing behaviors that promote belonging and respect.

Activities: Name Time
Pairs Sequence
Three Things In Common
The Last Detail
FV Anticipation

Lesson 2:
In this lesson students will continue to apply and expand skills for creating the healthy classroom community by acknowledging and supporting individual strengths and approaches to problem solving.

Activities: Name Roulette
Transformer Tag
Circle The Circle

Lesson 3:
In this lesson students will develop positive peer relationships, by recognizing physical and emotional safety parameters through participation in active problem-solving.

Activities: Don't Touch Me
Mergers

Lesson 4:
In this lesson students will create a visual representation of the behavioral norms necessary for a safe and challenging health class learning community.

Activities: Full Value Check In
House of Health

GOAL SETTING

Lesson 5:
In this lesson students will experience the principles of goal setting and peer support.

Activities: L/R Pairs Tag
Help Me

Lesson 6:
In this lesson students will reinforce their understanding of the importance of support and feedback in overcoming barriers to goal achievement.

Activity: In The Basket

HEALTHY RELATIONSHIPS

Lesson 7:
In this lesson students will explore the concept of positive peer role models and begin to understand how effective communication skills influence positive peer interactions.

Activities: Have You Ever?
Back Talk

Lesson 8:
In this lesson students will solidify and support a positive sense of self-esteem by participating in activities designed to encourage healthy risk taking.

Activities: Measured Breath with Visualization
Human Camera
Go For It

STRESS MANAGEMENT

Lesson 9:
In this lesson students will define the concept of stress and recognize the importance of stress management in lifelong health.

Activities: Pi Chart Stress
Stress Reduction Stations

Lesson 10:
In this lesson students will experience the difference between healthy stress and unhealthy stress and identify how to access appropriate sources of support.

Activities: Balloon Frantic
What Did You Do That For?
FVC closure

CONFLICT RESOLUTION

Lesson 11:
In this lesson students will apply conflict resolution and problem-solving strategies while working together in small groups.

Activities: Make the Right Choice
Cooperative Carpet Ride

Lesson 12:
In this lesson students will explore the impact of verbal and nonverbal responses in the prevention, promotion or resolution of conflict.
> Activities: Quick Line Up
>   Negotiation Square

Lesson 13:
In this lesson students will identify the impact of culture on conflict management and discover how to be effective allies.
> Activities: Sea of Diversity
>   Everybody Up!

Lesson 14:
In this lesson students will identify and apply strategies to access quality health information and analyze influences on health behaviors.
> Activities: Trash Relay
>   It's Knot My Problem

NUTRITION

Lesson 15:
In this lesson students will access nutritional information and identify principles of healthy eating habits.
> Activities: Name 5
>   Nutrition Golf

Lesson 16:
In this lesson students will work together to access healthy food choices and consider the effect media has on nutrition and body image.
> Activities: Eyes, Body, Mouth
>   Media Messages

Lesson 17:
In this lesson students will create and support representations of healthy "bodies" on different diets.
> Activity: Model Citizens of Nutrition and
>   Fitness

Lesson 18:
In this lesson students will identify and validate a healthy body image for themselves.
> Activity: Passport To The Future

PHYSICAL FITNESS

Lesson 19:
In this lesson students will identify anatomically correct muscle groups and reinforce principles of cardiovascular fitness.
> Activities: Macro/Micro Stretch
>   Striker

Lesson 20:
In this lesson students will apply aspects of four components of physical fitness and identify activities that promote each of those four components.
> Activity: Fitness Baseball

Lesson 21:
In this lesson students will expand their understanding of cardiovascular fitness.
> Activity: Heartbeat Stations

Lesson 22:
In this lesson students will apply exercise adherence strategies.
> Activities: Turnstile
>   1,2,3 is 20

SUBSTANCE ABUSE PREVENTION

Lesson 23:
In this lesson students will further validate the importance of healthy peer relationships in substance abuse prevention as well as exploring the concept of natural highs.
> Activities: 2–3 Person Trust Leans
>   Levitation

Lesson 24:
In this lesson students will discover the impact of substance abuse on family systems and strength of assertiveness in response to the pressure to use substances.
> Activities: Instigator
>   Triangle Tag

Lesson 25:
In this lesson students will further explore the influence of different drugs.
> Activity: Essence of Health

Lesson 26:
In this lesson students will differentiate between substance use, misuse, and abuse and experience the challenges of maintaining a strong peer connection.
> Activities: Pi Chart Use, Misuse and Abuse
>   Welded Ankles

Lesson 27:
In this lesson students will identify sources of peer and community support for substance abuse prevention.
> Activity: Wall of Support

Creating Community

LESSON 1

In this lesson students begin to establish a healthy learning community by learning one another's names and practicing behaviors that promote belonging and respect.

ACTIVITY	LEARNING OBJECTIVE	TIME	PROPS	HEALTH SKILLS
Name Time	At the conclusion of this activity, students will be able to: • State the names of people in the class. • Apply communication skills. • Apply fast-paced problem solving skills.	15 minutes	• Stopwatch	• Interpersonal communication • Self-management
Pairs Sequence Three Things In Common	• Begin fostering healthy relationships. • Apply effective communication skills with peers.	10 minutes	• None	• Accessing information • Interpersonal communication
Last Detail	• Apply observation skills. • Relate the importance of noticing details in preventing unintentional and intentional injury.	10 minutes	• None	• Self-management • Accessing information
FVC Anticipation	• Describe behaviors that promote a healthy learning environment. • Identify behaviors that promote cooperation. • Apply communicating healthy and cooperative behaviors.	15 minutes	• None	• Self-management • Interpersonal communication • Analyze influences

TEACHER'S NOTES:

FRAMING	SET-UP PROCEDURE	REFLECTION

Name Time

Set Up:

1. Create a large open space in your classroom.

Framing:

"Relationships that are established at home, in the school or community help us to that feel we are part of a group. Being part of a group helps us to feel secure and supported. The first step in building relationships is learning one another's names."

Procedure:

1. Ask students to form a circle inside the open space so you can explain the task.

2. Have the class go around the circle and say their first names.

3. Ask the students to look at the person on their right and left and remember who they are. They need to remember the people on both sides of them as the class will eventually have to recreate the circle exactly as it is.

4. Tell the class that the objective is to solve the challenges you are about to give them in the shortest possible time. Each attempt will be timed and the class wants to achieve its best (shortest) time.

5. The first task is to reform the circle in alphabetical order according to their first names. The clock will not stop until the circle is formed and all the names in the group have been said out loud, in alphabetical order.

6. Once the group has completed its initial solution, tell them the time. This will serve as a benchmark.

7. The second task is to reform the circle as it was originally. Again the clock doesn't stop until the circle is formed and all the names have been said in sequential order.

8. Once the class has finished, tell them the time, and ask if anyone has any strategies for improving on that time.

9. Allow the class another round to decrease the times if appropriate.

10. The final task is to complete both of the line-ups one after the other with no break or stop between the two.

11. First the group lines up alphabetically and says all of the names out loud; then the group quickly reforms in the original line up and repeats the names again in sequential order.

12. Announce the time and allow time to discuss strategies for improvement.

Reflection:

Questions for Discussion:

1. "Can you identify ways in which you communicated that helped you complete the challenges quickly?"

2. "Can you identify which behaviors were helpful and which were not helpful?"

3. "Does anyone believe they can recite everyone's name? If so, let's hear it." (You can do this a couple of times.)

 Additional Thoughts

• *Some groups assume that they have to line up first and then say the names. The rules as written allow the group to say the names at any time as long as they are said in order. Another out of the box solution would be to allow the group to say the names simultaneously. Decide if you want to allow for this option and adjust the language of the rules to allow for this flexibility.*

. . . .

Three Things In Common

Set Up:

1. Create an open space in your classroom.

Framing:

"During this class we will have many opportunities to learn what we have in common with one another and where we differ. This is important to understanding one another's perspective as we continue to build our classroom community."

Procedure:

1. Ask students to find a partner and introduce themselves to that person if they do not know them very well.

2. Tell the students that their challenge will be to find three things they have in common with their partners.

3. A fair commonality is something that partners didn't know about each other before and things that they can't tell by looking at each other. For example, "we are both in seventh grade" or "we both have brown hair" would be a violation of the rules.

4. Give the students about five to eight minutes to complete the conversation.

5. Go around the class and have partners share at least one thing they had in common.

Reflection:

Questions for Discussion:

1. "Can you identify one thing most of your classmates have in common?"

2. "Can you identify one thing most of your classmates didn't have in common?"

3. "Why do you think it is important to know what people have in common and where they differ?"

. . . .

The Last Detail

Set Up:

1. Be sure there is enough space in your classroom for pairs of students to stand about three feet apart from one another.

Framing:

"Doesn't it feel good when someone notices you or tells you something that will help you manage a situation? Noticing small changes in one another or the little things in our environment makes a big difference in maintaining our safety as well as the safety of others. It's all about the details!"

Procedure:

1. Have students partner up and stand in one of the spaces. Join in if the numbers are not even.

2. Begin with partners standing face to face with about three feet between them.

3. Tell the partners they will have one minute to carefully study each other noticing as many details or little things as possible.

4. Ask students to turn their backs toward each other. They can remain about three feet apart from each other.

5. Explain that they then each have 90 seconds to alter five things about their appearance. (i.e., roll up sleeve, take off glasses, etc).

6. When both partners are ready, they may turn back to face each other and try to identify as many of the changes as possible.

7. Tell students that once the guessing is over, any undiscovered changes may be revealed.

8. Tell students that the changes they make must be visible (no fair changing your state of mind or putting your loose change in another pocket).

Reflection:

Questions for Discussion:

1. "What skills did you use to identify changes?"

2. "Can you identify different situations where it is helpful to notice the little changes, both those that are positive and those that are troubling?"

3. "How can you apply the skills you have identified to keep yourself and others safe?"

. . . .

Full Value Anticipation

Set Up:

1. Create an open space in your classroom big enough for your class to form a circle.

Framing:

"We have talked about the importance of knowing each other's names, what we have in common and how we can notice details to keep each other safe. Now we are going to focus on some behavioral guidelines to keep our learning community healthy and growing."

Procedure:

1. Ask students to find a partner and then form a circle standing next to their partner.

2. The group will identify expressions that represent four behaviors (trying hard, being safe, playing fair and having fun) while in the circle and then students will work with their partners for the second half of the activity.

3. Introduce the basic concepts of the Full Value Contract. (These are: be safe, be here, be honest, commit to goals, care for self and others and let go and move on.)

4. Ask students to define and to create a gesture that represents what it looks like when someone is giving their best effort. Mirror a few of the responses, then pick one expressive gesture and have the class practice it.

5. Ask for a definition and demonstration of what it looks like when someone is being safe both physically and emotionally. Mirror a few of the responses and

then pick an expressive gesture for this behavior. Have the group repeat both gestures.

6. Repeat this process to create gestures for playing fair and having fun. You should periodically repeat/reinforce the previously established gestures.

7. Explain to the class that they are going to have the opportunity to practice their ability to communicate with each other without talking by anticipating what their partner will do.

8. Have students stand with their backs to their partners and at the count of three turn around and show one another one of the behavioral expressions. Explain that their goal is to match their partner without talking or planning!

9. The teacher counts to three for the first couple of attempts and then has the partners do a few rounds on their own count.

10. Switch partners a couple of times and let them complete a few rounds.

Reflection:

Reflection Activity:

1. Have the students circle up and check in on what it was like to try to connect with their partner without the use of verbal communication. Ask students to identify times in the class when someone's behavior may be perceived as in conflict with others. For example, even though someone is giving their best effort it still feels unsafe to someone else. (What is true versus what seems true and how do you talk to each other in a valuing way about the difference?)

Knowledge Review:

2. Underpin the notion that good intentions are important in conflict resolution and prevention.

 Additional Thoughts

• *Do not count number of successes and failures!*

• *Matching perfectly is less important than trying to match, reinforcing a cooperative versus competitive environment.*

7.2

CREATING
COMMUNITY

LESSON 2

In this lesson students will apply skills that reinforce and expand the healthy classroom community.

ACTIVITY	LEARNING OBJECTIVE	TIME	PROPS	HEALTH SKILLS
Name Roulette	**At the conclusion of this activity, students will be able to:** • Correctly use names of other students to continue building a healthy learning community and sense of belonging. • Recognize one another's strengths.	20 minutes	• 2 Hula Hoops™	• Interpersonal communication
Transformer Tag	• Identify three approaches to problem solving. • Describe examples of when to use each approach.	10 minutes	• 4 cones	• Core content • Interpersonal communication • Self-management
Circle The Circle	• Apply sharing information about problem-solving strategies. • Apply caring for self and others—physically.	15 minutes	• 2 Hula-Hoops™ • Index cards • Pens or pencils	• Self-management • Advocacy • Interpersonal communication

TEACHER'S NOTES:

FRAMING	SET-UP PROCEDURE	REFLECTION

Name Roulette

Set Up:
NONE

Framing:

"Each of us has special abilities and traits. These go well beyond what we look like. These strengths make us individual and unique. It is important that we identify and use our strengths as we learn and grow. This helps us to experience enjoyment and a feeling of self-confidence."

Procedure:

1. Divide the class into two groups and ask each group to make a circle with everyone facing the center.

2. Put the two circles together so that it looks like the number eight.

3. Place a Hula-Hoop where the two circles meet, flat on the floor so that one person from each circle is standing in it.

4. Tell students that when you say, "GO," the two circles will begin to rotate in opposite directions, either clockwise or counterclockwise. Decide on the direction before you say, "GO."

5. Say that when you say, "STOP," two people (one in each circle) will be standing back to back in the hoop and that when you say, "LOOK," those two people spin around and the first of the pair to name the other person wins that person for their circle.

6. After several rounds, tell the class you are going to change the challenge a bit. This time when you say, "STOP," each group needs to describe the other group's part of the pair (person with their back to your group) without using any physical characteristics. For example, if Katie and Lisa are back to back, then Katie's circle will describe Lisa to Katie without using any physical attributes until Katie says the name Lisa or vice versa. You can't say blonde hair, but you could say good listener.

7. The first person in the pair to say the other person's name wins that person for their circle.

Reflection:

Questions for Discussion:

1. "Can someone volunteer to name everyone in the class?"

2. "Tell me what it was like to try to describe each other without using physical characteristics."

3. "How do you think our strengths will help us to continue to establish a safe learning community?"

Reflection Activity/Knowledge Review:

4. Have someone note the responses to the above on flip chart paper and post them in the classroom.

. . . .

Transformer Tag

Set Up:

1. Clear a large, open space in your classroom.
2. Set out four cones to mark boundaries for tag game.

Framing:

"You know when you are trying to decide what DVD to rent and one of your friends has to look at all of the DVDs while another friend is already at the rental counter? Well, that's because there are three main approaches to problem solving. Some of us are thinkers and like to have a plan. Some of us are wingers and like to get in there and try everything out. Some of us get a feeling about something and go with our gut. It is important to recognize that each of these styles has a place in our group and that one style will be more helpful than the others at certain times. Most of us use all three but each of us has a preference."

Procedure:

1. Ask students to form a circle inside the cones.
2. Tell students that they are going to play a tag game where everyone can tag and no one will be out, but that they will have to start by representing one of three problem-solving styles.
3. Explain that there are some people who are thinkers. They are always thinking before they act, have everything planned out and are very organized. They are represented by having their hand on their head.
4. Next say that there are others who just jump right in and get involved in whatever is happening. They are wingers and are represented by putting their hand on their hip.
5. Finally, there are the people who use their instincts or feelings and act on things when they get a sense of what is going on. They go with their gut and are represented by putting their hand on their stomach.

6. Ask the class, on the count of three, to represent their favorite problem solving style by putting their hand on their head, hip or stomach.

7. Say to the students: "In this tag game, you can switch other people over to your style. For example, if my hand is on my head and I tag someone who has their hand on their hip, they have to change to their head." Demonstrate this with someone in the group.

8. Tell the class that you are going to practice fast walking in the cones and the tagging will begin when you hear the word _____ (whatever word you'd like). "Remember, when you hear the word 'Freeze', everybody stops where they are."

9. Stop the game when everyone is the same sign…really, it happens!

Reflection:

Questions for Discussion

1. "What did you observe?"

2. "Does something similar happen when you are trying to make decisions with your friends?"

3. "Did you think there were times when someone was thinking too much (being too emotional or too quick to decide)? How did you feel when that happened?" (For example: Were they frustrated, understanding, patient, etc.)

4. "Can you identify situations which would require the use of one of the three approaches to effectively manage health and wellness behaviors?"

· ·

Circle the Circle

Set Up:
NONE

Framing:

"We have spent the first few classes getting to know one another and establishing behavioral goals for our classroom. Things can begin to move quickly as the semester progresses. It is important to remember to care for ourselves and others as we get busier throughout the coming year."

Procedure:

1. Ask the students to hold hands with the person next to them and to form a big circle.

2. Place one large hoop between two people (resting on their grasped hands).

3. Explain to the students that they are to try to get the hoop around the circle as quickly as possible without letting go of hands.

4. Next, increase the challenge by adding the second hoop. The hoops will move in opposite directions around the circle (over the people), eventually crossing over each other and returning to the starting point.

Reflection:

Reflection Activity:

1. Give each person a 5 x 7 inch index card. Have them rank from one to five (five is excellent and one is poor) first how well the group helped solve the problem of getting the hoop(s) around the circle and secondly how well the group cared for themselves and one another, physically, while passing the hoop. They can spread out to do this. Give them a few minutes.

2. Come together as a large group and ask individuals to explain what criteria they used to determine their ranking.

3. Finally ask each student to complete a sentence on their card. The sentence is: Today I learned (<u>students should fill in this blank</u>) about safe and healthy relationships.

4. Collect the cards and let the students know you are going to save them for the next lesson.

 Additional Thoughts

• *Be sure that the hoops are large enough for everyone to successfully pass through.*

• *For an added challenge, you can time this activity.*

LESSON 3

In this lesson students will develop positive peer relationships by recognizing physical and emotional safety parameters.

ACTIVITY	LEARNING OBJECTIVE	TIME	PROPS	HEALTH SKILLS
Don't Touch Me	**At the conclusion of this activity, students will be able to:** • Discover how to manage personal space/needs in a large group setting. • Create a system in which everyone's needs are met as efficiently as possible. • Identify situations at home and in school where students need to accommodate others.	30 minutes	• Poly spot for each person • Hula-Hoop™ • Stopwatch	• Core content • Self-management • Analyze influences
Mergers	• Apply creative thinking and problem-solving strategies. • Apply awareness of and respect for each other's personal and community spaces.	20 minutes	• Various lengths of rope that can be tied into loops. One for each student • Index cards from previous lesson	• Self-management • Interpersonal communication • Advocacy

TEACHER'S NOTES:

FRAMING	SET-UP PROCEDURE	REFLECTION

Don't Touch Me!

Set Up:
NONE

Framing:
"We all have personal needs concerning health and wellness. Fulfillment of those needs can be a challenge when living in a community and family setting."

Procedure:

1. Ask each student to take a Poly Spot and form a large circle, standing on their spots.
2. Place the hoop in the center of that circle.
3. Tell the group that the goal for this activity is to have everyone get their individual needs met, simultaneously, signified by passing through the hoop in the center.
4. Explain the rules:
- Everyone must begin and end movement at the same time.
- Only ONE person can pass through the hoop in the center at a time.
- You cannot end up on your original spot.
- Only two people can be in the center hoop at one time.
5. Each attempt will be timed. If there are any collisions, or anyone stops early, the group will start again.
6. Once a system is created, the class will have the opportunity to improve on the system's efficiency through more attempts.

Reflection:
Questions for Discussion:

1. "Can someone tell me what it felt like to "accommodate" everyone in the class?"
2. "What needed to happen for everyone to be able to get their needs met?"
3. "What is it like at home (school, etc.) when other people's needs are in conflict with yours?"

Mergers

Set Up:

Create a large open space in your classroom and invite students to stand in a circle. Place ropes in a pile in the center of the circle.

Framing:

"One of the things we learned in the last lesson is that healthy friendships and relationships flourish in an environment that is safe and valuing. How do you think changes in personal space and access to resources impact how we treat one another?"

Procedure

1. Ask the students to each take a rope and tie it in a loop.
2. Have them lay the loop anywhere in the open space and then stand inside it. No portion of their feet may extend over or beyond the loop.
3. Explain that people are safe only when they have both feet inside a loop and that the loops cannot be moved or re-tied into larger loops
4. Before any movement takes place do a quick whip around the class, with each student taking a moment to identify one of the things they remembered about healthy relationships from the last lesson.
5. Tell students that when they hear the words "Challenge yourself," they must move to a new loop. Remind them that to be safe they must have both of their feet within the perimeter of the loop.
6. Explain to students they can take as much time as needed to find a new space and they can walk on the floor spaces between loops to get to a new place.
7. After two or three changes, acknowledge safe behaviors and increase the challenge by removing one of the loops. This will force someone to share his/her loop. Repeat this several times until many students are sharing loops with one another.
8. The final goal is to include everyone inside one loop.

Reflection:

Questions for Discussion:
1. "How did you come up with your solution?"
2. "How did your behavior change from being in your own loop to being in a loop where you were surrounded by others?"
3. "What is it like at home (school, etc.) when other people's needs are in conflict with your own?"

4. Pass out the index cards from the previous lesson. "Can you share an example of when the behavior written on the card happened or did not happen during the activity?"

5. "Tell me what we can do to keep building and reinforcing safe and healthy relationships in challenging situations."

 Additional Thoughts

• *You will need loops of different sizes with one loop that can fit all of the participants' feet.*

• *Don't make it too easy as people can fit into a smaller loop than they think.*

• *One solution is for students to sit on the floor with their feet within the rope.*

LESSON 4

In this lesson students will develop positive peer relationships by recognizing physical and emotional safety parameters.

ACTIVITY	LEARNING OBJECTIVE	TIME	PROPS	HEALTH SKILLS
House of Health	**At the conclusion of this activity, students will be able to:** • Formalize guidelines/rules for working together in the health classroom. • Recognize the difference between put downs and positive messages. • Demonstrate communication skills that convey respect and support.	40 minutes	• Large paper (at least 4 feet by 4 feet) • Markers • Construction paper • Scissors • Tape • Extra index cards • Index cards from previous lesson	• Interpersonal communication • Goal setting • Decision making • Advocacy • Self-management

TEACHER'S NOTES:

FRAMING	SET-UP PROCEDURE	REFLECTION

House of Health

Set Up:
NONE

Framing:
"During the last class we identified behaviors that would help us feel safe and challenge us in our health class. Some of these behaviors are on the cards from the last class. Let's strengthen our commitment to those behaviors by creating a House of Health."

Procedure:

1. Gather all of the students around the paper with the index cards from the previous class placed in the middle.
2. Have extra index cards, markers and tape readily available.
3. Ask students to read the behaviors on the index cards and decide what helpful behaviors and attitudes they would like to add to those.
4. Have students write those words on the extra index cards.
5. Have students go around and say what they meant by the words they chose. Even if the words are the same, meanings may be different for different people.
6. Tell them that their challenge is to create a three-dimensional structure, or a House of Health, that supports all of the behaviors they identified.
7. Students may use all of the resources available.

Reflection:
Questions for Discussion:

1. "What do you notice about the behaviors that are on your House of Health?"
2. "Explain why these attitudes and qualities are important to healthy relationships and taking care of yourself and others?"
3. "Can we agree to give our best effort in practicing these behaviors in our health class? If so, give me a 'thumbs up'!"

 Additional Thoughts

- *Keep this structure visible and use it as a reference point for acknowledging behaviors in the class, check-ins and debriefs.*
- *The House of Health will serve as your Full Value Contract.*

Goal Setting

LESSON 5

In this lesson students will experience the principles of goal setting and peer support.

ACTIVITY	LEARNING OBJECTIVE	TIME	PROPS	HEALTH SKILLS
Left/Right Pairs Tag	**At the conclusion of this activity, students will be able to:** • Explain the concept of goal-setting. • Apply interpersonal communication skills with partners. • Analyze influences/information.	15 minutes	• 4 cones	• Goal setting • Decision making • Self-management • Interpersonal communication
Help Me	• Apply the principles of goal setting. • Describe ways to overcome barriers to achieving goals.	20 minutes	• 3 rubber rings per group • 1 Hula-Hoop™ segment per group • Masking tape	• Goal setting • Decision making • Self-management

TEACHER'S NOTES:

FRAMING	SET-UP PROCEDURE	REFLECTION

Left / Right Pairs Tag

Set Up:

1. Clear a large, open space in your classroom.
2. Set out four cones to mark the boundaries.

Framing:

"We all need goals to give direction and meaning to our lives. Awareness and understanding of personal goals help young people make decisions and judgments —take action—in a way that is consistent with what they feel is important. This activity will help you experience achieving a goal and what influenced your ability to do that."

Procedure:

1. Ask students to find a partner and stand side by side.
2. Tell the students that they are going to play a fun tag game with their partners.
3. Ask the people standing on the left-hand side of the partnership to raise their hands. These people can only move straight forward or to the left with a 90 degree angle turn. Model this motion.
4. Ask the people standing on the right-hand side of the partnership to raise their right hand. Explain that these people can only move straight forward or to the right with a 90 degree angle turn. Model this motion.
5. Explain that the turns need to be square, right angles, not arcs. Model what not to do with the arcs and then reaffirm acceptable 90 degree turns.
6. Ask the partners to decide who will be the "tagger" first. Explain that the person who is "tagger" will chase only their partner. When they tag their partner, they stop and say "I reached my goal!" Their partner will also stop, count to ten and then try to tag the "tagger."
7. Explain that their partner should use the counting time to get as far away as possible!

Reflection:

Questions for Discussion:

1. "What is it like to try to reach your goal of tagging your partner when you have limited mobility?"
2. "How did the limited movement in this activity affect your ability to make good decisions?"
3. "What did you do to track your partner and reach your goal amidst all of the other influences/information (other students playing the game)?"
4. "Where can you go to access good information to reach your goals?"

Help Me

Set Up:

1. Use masking tape to create two parallel lines about five to six feet apart.

Framing:

"Group memberships and friendships are particularly important during this time of life. As you become more independent you rely on your peers to share experiences and help reach your goals. This activity gives you an opportunity to experience the importance of peer support in goal achievement."

Procedure:

1. Divide your class into groups of five.
2. Give each group a Hula-Hoop™ segment and three rubber rings.
3. Ask one person from each small group to hold the Hula-Hoop segment in an upright position on the ground on the line you've made with masking tape. The rest of the people in the groups are gathered on the opposite line.
4. Tell students that each person will have an opportunity to toss the three rings to see how many of them they can get on the Hula-Hoop segment held up by their group member.
5. Explain that the holder may not move the Hula-Hoop segment to help position the ring.
6. Tell students that they will have a practice round and then a round where the score is kept. The score is kept by adding up the total number of rings that landed on the Hula-Hoop segment for each small group.
7. Be sure to help the students ensure that everyone gets a try tossing the rings and holding the Hula-Hoop segment.
8. Explain that for the next round, everything stays the same except that the person holding the Hula-Hoop segment may move it once the ring has been tossed. This should allow for more rings to land on the Hula-Hoop segment.
9. Once again be sure to help the students rotate positions so everyone gets a chance to be the tosser and the holder.
10. Add up the number of rings that landed on the Hula-Hoop segment. Allow time for a practice round and then keep score.
11. Compare the scores from the first scoring round when they couldn't move the Hula-Hoop segment and the second scoring round when they could move the Hula-Hoop segment.

Reflection:

Questions for Discussion:

1. "How was it different getting the ring on the hoop segment when it was being held still as compared to when it was being moved?"

2. "What made it easier when the hoop segment was being moved?"

Reflection Activity:

3. Have students brainstorm ways that they can help each other acheive their goals in health and in life.

LESSON 6

In this lesson students will affirm their understanding of the importance support and feedback have in overcoming barriers to goal achievement.

ACTIVITY	LEARNING OBJECTIVE	TIME	PROPS	HEALTH SKILLS
In The Basket	**At the conclusion of this activity, students will be able to:** • Apply goal setting. • Identify influences on achieving goals. • Describe ways to overcome barriers to goals.	30 minutes	• 3 containers • Tossables • Boundary rope	• Goal setting • Decision making • Interpersonal communication

TEACHER'S NOTES:

FRAMING	SET-UP PROCEDURE	REFLECTION

In The Basket

Set Up:

1. Clear a large open space in your classroom.

2. Place the boundary rope at one end of the open space leaving about three feet behind where students can stand.

3. Place all the balls for easy access on the outside of the boundary—in the three feett or so are where students will stand.

4. Have all the participants stand on the outside of boundary rope.

5. Place the containers at three different distances from the rope—on the other side of the rope than the students and the balls. The distance from the rope to the first container (10 pts) should prevent any member of the class from leaning in and dropping the balls into the container. The next one should be halfway out (20 pts) and the third (30 pts), out farther still.

Framing

"Practicing healthy behaviors as an adolescent can be very challenging. Personal standards of behavior or goals for behavior are often challenged when they are in conflict with peers. It is important to understand how the process of overcoming barriers to goal achievement can be accomplished by individual behaviors, group support and quality feedback."

Procedure:

1. Explain to the class that their task is to set a group goal based on a 90 second round. Points are achieved by tossing balls into the various buckets.

2. At no time may anyone touch the ground inside the boundary marker.

3. Any balls that do not make it into the container must be left there until the time stops for the first two rounds.

4. Record the number of points and compare this to the group goal.

5. Explain that when trying to achieve goals it is important to have support. For the next two rounds you will be able to have support—up to nine people acting as "backboards" at each bucket. Backboards can use their bodies to get balls in a bucket, but cannot use their hands to catch or retrieve them.

6. Ask the class to set a new goal now that they have support. Play two more 90 second rounds.

7. Finally, explain that, in addition to support, feedback is helpful in achieving goals. For the next two rounds you will be able to have feedback in the form of up to four people who will be able to retrieve balls and return them to the

other side of the boundary where they may be tossed again until the round is up.

8. Ask the class to set a new goal now that they have support and feedback. Play two more 90-second rounds.

Reflection:

Questions for Discussion:

1. "What strategies did you use to reach your goals?"

2. "How did the addition of support and feedback change your strategy?"

3. "How did the addition of support and feedback influence your ability to achieve your goals?"

4. "What are some of the barriers that hurt your chances of reaching your goals?" (i.e., drugs, gangs, sexual activity or other self destructive behavior)

5. "How can an effective strategy with support and feedback help you to overcome those barriers?"

Healthy Relationships

LESSON 7

In this lesson students will explore the concept of positive peer role models and begin to understand how effective communication skills influence peer interactions.

ACTIVITY	LEARNING OBJECTIVE	TIME	PROPS	HEALTH SKILLS
Have You Ever?	At the conclusion of this activity, students will be able to: • Identify and celebrate positive health and wellness behaviors. • Acknowledge positive peer role models. • Recognize and identify similar healthy experiences that promote friendship.	10–15 minutes	• None	• Analyze influences • Interpersonal communication • Goal setting • Decision making • Self-management
Back Talk	• Practice effective listening and speaking skills. • Begin to conceptualize the relationship between clear communication and prevention of conflict.	20–30 minutes	• Play dough • Colored straws • Popsicle sticks • Pipe cleaners • Etc. • Enough sculpting materials to make certain that each partnership has identical materials.	• Interpersonal communication • Accessing information

TEACHER'S NOTES:

FRAMING	SET-UP PROCEDURE	REFLECTION

Have You Ever?

Set Up:
NONE

Framing:

"Health and wellness incorporates many of our actions, behaviors and thoughts. It is important to recognize and celebrate the healthy actions, behaviors and thoughts that we do or have currently. Be sure to notice if there is someone who has accomplished something that you have always wanted to do and to notice those who have accomplished the same things you have already done."

Procedure:

1. Ask the class to form a circle.
2. Demonstrate the celebration sequence.
3. Celebration Sequence:
   - Two claps on thighs, two claps with hands, two clicks/snaps of the fingers, finished off with fingers pointed at each other and a big "Yeah!!"
4. Explain that you are going to discover some of the experiences that people in the class have participated in by asking questions.
5. One student will go to the center of the circle and ask something like "Have you ever been swimming in the ocean?" Challenge the person who is asking the question to form a question about an experience that they have had, so that they also answer "Yes" to the "Have you ever?"
6. Anyone who has been swimming in the ocean comes to the center of the circle and does the celebration sequence, led by the person who asked the question.
7. The remaining class members, on the outside of the circle, applaud the people in the middle with a quiet clap—clapping only two fingers from each hand.
8. Class members continue to ask questions to find out more about each other.

Reflection:

Question for Discussion:

1. "What are some of the common and unique experiences people have had that you identified in this activity?"

Additional Thoughts

• *This experience makes self-disclosure interesting. Many of the students may not recognize the merit in what they have done. The discussion section can follow one person admitting to having done an activity that no one else can believe or that the group is interested in hearing more about. The stories should not be used to romance crime or drug use but should provide a way for the student to talk about something he or she has done. Many of the "Have you ever" questions may be thrill-seeking activities that are risky or dangerous while others involve having fun without harming self or others. The teacher should direct the reflection about this activity to a discussion about substance use, thrill-seeking behavior that does lead to bad outcomes or identifying activities that promote a similar thrill but have a healthy outcome.*

Back Talk

Set Up:
NONE

Framing:
"Have you ever explained something to someone and felt certain that they understood exactly what you meant only to discover later that they completely misunderstood your original intention? Good communication involves the accurate transfer of thoughts and feelings, but sometimes that is difficult to achieve. Let's see how we do…"

Procedure:

1. Ask the students to each find a partner.

2. Divide the materials into identical groups for each pair.

3. Each partner receives identical materials. Have partners sit back to back.

4. Instruct the partnerships to create a sculpture that represents either a healthy student or an unhealthy student.

5. Be very clear that each person in the partnership is creating the sculpture simultaneously, coming up with an image of what a healthy or unhealthy student "looks like."

6. Partners must verbally describe their co-creations during the process but may not turn around or show one another what they are doing.

7. The goal is for each partnership to create identical sculptures without looking at each other's creations until both agree that the task is complete.

8. After both agree, partners should turn around and show their sculptures to one another.

Reflection:

Questions for Discussion:

1. "Remember that the object was for each partner to create an identical structure while sitting back to back. What surprised you the most when you turned around?"

2. "How did you and your partner decide what to create? Where was the leadership?"

3. "How did you describe/communicate with each other?"

4. "What types of conflict occurred during this process?"

5. "How do you think your perceptions or interpretations of what you heard impacted how you felt?"

6. "How did you prevent conflict from occurring or manage conflict when it did occur?"

LESSON 8

In this lesson students will solidify and support a positive sense of self-esteem by participating in activities designed to encourage healthy risk taking.

ACTIVITY	LEARNING OBJECTIVE	TIME	PROPS	HEALTH SKILLS
Measured Breath with Visualization	At the conclusion of this activity, students will be able to: • Relax and refresh the body in one breath. • Identify a positive experience to visualize while practicing stress reduction.	10 minutes	• None	• Self-management • Core content
Human Camera	• Apply the concept of positive peer interaction. • Apply responsible decision making and its benefits in maintaining trust with peers.	15 minutes	• None	• Self-management • Core content • Interpersonal communication
Go For It!	• Encourage healthy risk taking behavior. • Apply assertiveness and refusal communication skills.	30 minutes	• None	• Goal setting • Decision making • Interpersonal communication

TEACHER'S NOTES:

FRAMING	SET-UP PROCEDURE	REFLECTION

Measured Breath with Visualization

Set Up:
NONE

Framing

"Creating positive images and self-talk statements is a great way to improve self-esteem. Sometimes when under stress, the mental pictures we have of ourselves and the things we say to ourselves become very negative. In those times it is important to take a deep breath and redirect our minds and voices to the positive."

Procedure:

1. Ask students to stand or lie in a comfortable position and recall an experience they had when they felt really good about themselves. It could be doing well in school, in sports, helping someone out, etc.
2. Tell the class that you are going to ask them to practice taking deep breaths.
3. Tell them that you are going to ask them to inhale to a count of six, hold that breath for a count of seven and then exhale to a count of seven.
4. Practice this a couple of times.
5. Explain that, for this round, when they are holding for the count of seven, they should try to recall the image of the experience when they felt really good about themselves and let it fill their minds and bodies.
6. Tell them to try to take a few breaths themselves, at their own count: inhaling for six, holding for seven and exhaling for seven, with their image in mind.

Reflection:

Question for Discussion:
1. "Can someone tell me what this experience was like for you?"

Knowledge Review:
2. Explain that they can use this tool anywhere at any time.
3. Also explain that it works better the more they practice.

Question for Discussion:
4. "Can you identify some times that you might put measured breathing into practice?"

Human Camera

Set Up:

NONE

Framing
"Healthy relationships have certain characteristics—trust and empathy being two of them. Trust means being able to rely upon someone, believing that the person will act in your best interest, or is dependable. Empathy means sharing another's emotions, thoughts or feelings—"walking in another's shoes." This activity is a good place to understand how to practice trust and empathy as we continue to build healthy relationships in our classroom."

Procedure:

1. Divide the class into pairs.

2. Clarify the safety boundaries for this activity.

3. Explain that one person will be a camera and one person the photographer. The photographer will be using his or her partner as a camera.

4. Tell the students that the camera is very fragile and relies on the photographer to take good care of it.

5. The partner who is the photographer then chooses an image that represents positive peer interaction or what a good friend might look like. This should be in the classroom or within other safe parameters you define. The photographer must take note of the subjects they intend to photograph.

6. The partner who is the camera has three options (Challenge by Choice – defined in the introduction).

   a. Move to the image with eyes open, stop and then close eyes just for the photo.

   b. Move to the image with eyes closed, with physical and verbal guidance from the photographer.

   c. Move to the image with eyes closed and verbal guidance only from the photographer. It is always up to the camera to decide how they want to be guided!!

7. The photographer gently tilts his/her partner's head (the camera) in such a way that his/her eyes are directly in front of the chosen subject.

8. Then, gently tapping on the shoulder, he/she activates the shutter. With the cue of the shoulder tap, the "camera" opens and closes his/her eyelids (shutter) very quickly in order to record the scene.

9. The pairs should switch roles and check-in with the following debriefing questions.

Reflection:

Questions for Discussion:

1. "How did your picture reflect positive peer interactions or what good friends look like?"

2. "In what ways were you practicing trust and empathy during this activity?"

3. "Tell me your thoughts about how people see different details. What is the value of different perspectives? What are the potential pitfalls?"

Knowledge Review:

4. "From today forward we are going to focus more mindfully on practicing positive peer interactions: trust, empathy, and, in addition, support, good communication and respect."

 Additional Thoughts

• *Blindfolds can feel threatening. Make them available for those who would like help keeping their eyes closed or would like an extra challenge versus passing them out and saying "You don't have to use them if you don't want to." By doing so, you can remain true to Challenge by Choice. Peeking helps some students maintain balance and orientation and is not 'cheating.'*

. . . .

Go For It!

Set Up:

1. Create a large open space in your classroom.

Framing:

"We often face internal or external pressure to do things that we may not be completely comfortable with. Assertive behavior involves standing up for oneself. Assertive people will say what they think and act on their beliefs without hurting themselves or others."

Procedure:

1. Ask the class to line up around the perimeter of the open space.

2. Explain to students, "The challenge for the next activity is for individuals to learn how to take healthy risks and how to support each other in doing so.

Each of you will have the opportunity to move through the open space in whatever pattern you choose. The challenge is that you will do this with your eyes closed. The rest of us will be here to support you by keeping our hands up and, giving you a gentle High Five when you come too close to the edges, saying, 'Stop!' Our challenge is to not talk otherwise!"

3. Students determine the speed (fast walk at most) and the direction of their crossing; for example, moving diagonally across, around the perimeter and so on depending on the level of risk/challenge they identify as healthy for themselves.

4. Students must announce their path and speed to the class before closing their eyes and beginning the challenge. Spotters must acknowledge their understanding and support by saying simultaneously, "Go for it!"

5. Reinforce that the role of the spotters (the people on the outside) is to keep the person who is crossing safe and to support the decision that they have made regarding how fast and how far they want to go. Spotters hold their hands up in front of their chests. If the person crossing is coming toward them, the spotters lift their hands to meet the hands of the walker, thereby telling the walker to stop.

6. Repeat with as many rounds as necessary to allow everyone to have a chance to participate.

Reflection:

Reflection Activity

1. Bring the class together in a circle. Ask each person to imagine that they just videotaped this activity.

2. Have them play through the video in their head and to freeze frame on one point in the activity where they had a strong feeling or emotion. The feeling can be associated with being a spotter or a risk taker.

3. Once everyone has had time to think, go around the group hearing responses. Follow up with the questions:
   • "How do you feel in risky situations as compared with safe situations?"
   • "Tell me about a situation where someone was encouraging you to do something that you knew was wrong or that you did not want to do."
   • "How did you handle this? What else could you have done?"
   • "How do you maintain the respect of your peers when you don't do something they want you to do?"

Additional Thoughts

• *Treat this activity seriously and make certain the group is ready to be responsible for each other's physical and emotional safety. If they cannot commit to keeping each other safe or are having trouble spotting, do not try this activity.*

This activity may be best played in a large space—outdoors or a gymnasium. Be sure that the space is somewhat contained and familiar if you do choose to move the students to a different location.

Stress Management

LESSON 9

In this lesson students will define the concept of stress and recognize the importance of stress management in lifelong heath.

ACTIVITY	LEARNING OBJECTIVE	TIME	PROPS	HEALTH SKILLS
Pi Chart Stress	**At the conclusion of this activity, students will be able to:** • Define stress.	15 minutes	• Flip chart paper • Markers	• Core content • Accessing information • Analyze influences
Stress Reduction Stations	• Describe the physical and mental response to stress and implications for health and wellness. • Explore effective stress management reduction techniques.	40 minutes	• Yoga video/disc • Progressive relaxation script • Guided imagery script (scripts found on page __) • Different types of music (heavy metal, rap, classical, new age) • Paper and pencils for each student	• Self-management • Interpersonal communication • Core content

TEACHER'S NOTES:

FRAMING	SET-UP PROCEDURE	REFLECTION

Pi Chart Stress

Set Up:

1. You'll be giving your class, in groups of three, a piece of paper with the word Stress on the top and the words Looks Like, Sounds Like, Feels Like in three columns beneath. Have enough to give each small group one sheet beforehand.

Stress

Looks Like	Sounds Like	Feels Like

Framing:

"This is an excellent opportunity to clarify and expand on the definition and implications of stress."

Procedure:

1. Ask the class to organize themselves into triads.
2. Tell the class that they are going to spend some time defining the term stress by filling out the columns.
3. Give the class an example: Stress may look like someone biting their nails, it may sound like talking fast and it may feel like the whole body is rigid.
4. Explain that the columns may be filled in with written words, phrases or pictures.

Reflection:

Reflection Activity:
Ask the small groups to present their definitions to the entire group and have a general discussion, highlighting common themes as well as unique aspects.
Use the charts to lead into the next activity.

 Additional Thoughts

- *If groups of three are not possible, keep the small groups to no more than five students to ensure that everyone has a chance to contribute.*

- *If you have a large class you can post the charts and have students participate in a collective "gallery tour" versus individual small group presentations. Then ask for common themes as well as unique aspects.*

Stress Reduction Stations

Set Up:

1. Set up the four different stations throughout the classroom. It is helpful to have simple instruction guidelines posted at each station. One station will be listening to music; the second will be viewing and doing the poses from a yoga DVD; and the third and fourth will be following the scripts found on page 346.

2. Leave enough room for students to move easily from station to station and actively participate at each station.

Framing:

"Stress is a part of life. Some people respond to stress with mental symptoms, while others experience physical symptoms. Some people experience both. Managing stress well is one of the most powerful tools you will have for disease prevention and lifelong health. It may help to know how you experience stress so you can choose coping strategies that are most effective."

Procedure:

1. Divide the class into four small groups, gathered at each of the stations.
2. Give each student a piece of paper and pencil.
3. Review the concepts of stress, stress response and its relationship to lifelong health and wellness.
4. Introduce or review methods for tracking the heart rate.
5. Quickly review the instructions for each station.
6. Explain to students that they will have the opportunity to experience four different coping strategies for managing stress as represented at each station. They will have seven to ten minutes to try out the coping strategy and will rotate to the next station to the right when they hear the word "switch."
7. Tell students that you would like them to notice and record changes in their bodies and in their thought processes as they experience the different stations on the paper you've given them.

Reflection:

Questions for Discussion:

1. "When you think about your experiences at the different stations, is there one or a couple of strategies you think could help you reduce stress?"

2. "Tell me about some ways that you can incorporate some of the strategies we used today into your daily life."

 Additional Thoughts

• *Recommendations for yoga DVDs and scripts for progressive muscle relaxation and imagery scripts are provided in the appendix.*

LESSON 10

In this lesson students will experience the difference between healthy and unhealthy stress and identify how to access appropriate sources of support.

ACTIVITY	LEARNING OBJECTIVE	TIME	PROPS	HEALTH SKILLS
Balloon Frantic	**At the conclusion of this activity, students will be able to:** • Identify some warning signs of unhealthy stress. • Describe healthy ways to deal with stress and depression. • Analyze when situations call for simple acts of caring and when they require getting the help of a caring adult.	15 minutes	• Balloon or small beach ball for each student • 10 Extra balloons or small beach balls	• Self-management • Interpersonal communication • Analyze influences
What Did You Do That For?	• Identify strategies that can be used to avoid confrontation or resolve conflicts peacefully in stressful situations. • Apply healthy anger management strategies in stressful situations.	15 minutes	• 1 small beach ball per 2 students	• Interpersonal communication • Self-management • Goal setting • Decision making
FVC Closure			• Full Value Contract (Lesson Four)	

TEACHER'S NOTES:

FRAMING	SET-UP PROCEDURE	REFLECTION

Balloon Frantic

Set Up:

1. Clear a large open space in your classroom.

Framing:

"Stress occurs when the pressures on us exceed our ability to cope. Many different emotions arise when we are presented with stressors. Stress is commonly thought of as negative; however, some degree of stress is necessary to challenge and motivate us. Therefore the goal is not to eliminate stress but to manage its negative aspects."

Procedure:

1. Pass out one balloon or small beach ball to each person.
2. Ask students to blow up the balloons and tie them off.
3. Tell the students that the balloons represent their emotions and that they are going to have the opportunity to manage their emotions by tapping the balloon, with their hands only, to keep it in the air.
4. Explain to the class that their challenge is to keep their emotions positive by keeping the balloons in the air as long as possible.
5. If any balloon touches the floor, students must alert each other by yelling "I'm stressed." At this point, a student bends down and lifts the balloon into the air again.
6. After 30 seconds, stop the action and have people hold their balloon. Reflect on what it was like to manage their individual emotions.
7. Explain to the class that not only are they responsible for keeping their own emotions up, but they are now responsible for keeping the whole class's emotions up! That means anyone can hit anyone else's balloon in an effort to keep it in the air.
8. Remind students to alert the rest of the class when they see a balloon fall to the ground by saying, "I'm stressed."
9. Adding a third challenge, on the count of three everyone launches their balloon into the air toward the center of the circle—away from where they stand —and the activity continues as before.
10. Stop the action after about two minutes.

Reflection:

Questions for Discussion:

1. "Can someone describe what happened when you tried to manage everyone's emotions versus just their own?"

2. "What happened to your focus when balloons started touching the ground?"

3. "How do you think this kind of juggling or failure to juggle relates to depression? Eustress? Distress?"

4. "Tell us about some coping strategies that were effective in keeping the balloons/emotions up amidst the chaos of all the emotions."

5. "What are some examples of situations in your life when you would need help from caring adults in managing stress and depression?"

 Additional Thoughts

• You may want to have two groups to start if class is larger than 15 and you have the space.

• You can add balloons in the second round to make it more challenging.

• You can substitute small beach balls for balloons.

What Did You Do That For?

Set Up:
NONE

Framing:
"Some reactions to stress are helpful because they manage the stressful feeling in a positive way. For example, if someone says an unkind word to me I can take a deep breath and think of one of my strengths. Some reactions to stress are harmful because they create additional stress. For example, if someone says an unkind word to me I can be nasty or hit them. Violence and conflict can be harmful and unhealthy. The goal is to respond to stressful situations in the healthiest manner possible."

Procedure:

1. Give each student an inflated beach ball.

2. Divide students into pairs or triads.

3. Tell the class that the next activity is going to involve a high level of challenge and that they must be as respectful as possible within the rules of the activity.

4. Explain to each partnership that they will start the activity standing back to

back, about one foot apart and, at an agreed-upon signal, each person will take two steps back (away from their partner) and then turn and face him or her.

5. Once they turn, partners must "launch" their ball in the direction of their partner. A launch is accomplished by tapping the beach ball toward their partner—not spiking or slamming or throwing, but tapping! The ball should travel three to six feet with this type of propulsion.

6. Partners may move their bodies to avoid being touched by the balloon; however, students' feet are "glued" to the floor once the turn has been made.

7. Play several rounds and have students keep track of how many total touches they had within their partnerships.

Reflection:

Questions for Discussion:

1. "Can you tell us what it felt like when you were being 'attacked by' your classmates?"

2. "Can you tell us what it felt like to be 'glued' to the floor while being 'attacked?"

3. "Are there some times in your life when you have felt under attack and unable to get away (how they may have felt in this activity)? How do you think a feeling of being trapped relates to anger and violence?"

4. "What are some strategies that you can use to avoid confrontation or resolve conflicts peacefully?"

Conflict Resolution

LESSON 11

In this lesson students will apply conflict resolution and problem-solving strategies while working together in small groups.

ACTIVITY	LEARNING OBJECTIVE	TIME	PROPS	HEALTH SKILLS
Make the Right Choice	**At the conclusion of this activity, students will be able to:** • Identify situations that may produce conflict.	20 minutes	• None	• Interpersonal communication • Self-management
Cooperative Carpet Ride	• Identify cooperative problem-solving behaviors. • Apply the three Cs - communication, compromise, cooperation to solve problems.	30 minutes	• 1 piece of flip chart paper per three students • Rope, cones, masking tape or the like to mark a start and finish line	• Goal setting • Decision making • Advocacy

TEACHER'S NOTES:

FRAMING	SET-UP PROCEDURE	REFLECTION

Make the Right Choice

Set Up:

1. Clear a large, open space in your classroom.

Framing:

"Whenever people spend time with one another, conflict naturally arises. Conflicts may occur between two or more people—family members, friends or acquaintances. Conflicts can be resolved in positive or negative ways."

Procedure:

1. Ask the group to stand in a circle. Ask for a student to volunteer to stand in the middle.

2. Explain that the game is played just like Rock, Paper, Scissors except that everyone in the circle is playing against the person in the middle.

3. Review motions for each, and what "beats" what. (Please see sixth grade, Lesson Thirteen, page ___ if you need to review.) Have everyone on the perimeter of the circle face away from the center of the circle. At the count of three, everyone turns and shows one of the three signs—rock, paper or scissors.

4. The person in the middle also chooses one of the three motions. Everyone in the circle checks to see how they did against the person in the middle. Play a few rounds just to get the feel of the game. Each round or two, invite a new student to the middle, replacing the other student.

5. For the second part of the activity, change the rules slightly. If you are beaten by the person in the middle, you have to sit down or step out of the circle. If you have the same hand motion or beat him/her, nothing happens. Play a few rounds until most people are sitting. Continue to change the person in the middle after each round or two and eventually let everyone back in the game.

6. Repeat with one more change. This time have the person in the middle announce what hand motion they are going to use before you start counting.

Reflection:

Questions for Discussion:

1. "How well did you do against the person in the middle?"

2. "Did you use the same hand signal for each round? Why (or why not?)"

3. "Which person in the game was it the best to be, middle or circle? Why?"

4. "How hard was the game when you knew what the person in the middle was going to do?"

5. "When you are being pressured to use drugs, how do different situations require different responses?"

6. "What would happen if you used the same response in all situations?"

7. "How would you say 'No' to your best friend? Your close friend? Someone you sort of know? A stranger?"

8. "Would the situation you are in determine how you say 'No'? For example, if you knew in advance what the situation might be and planned ahead would it be easier to say, 'No'?"

 Additional Thoughts

• *You will probably only have to do the last part of the activity once to get the message across that if you know what the person is going to do, your own choice will be easy.*

Cooperative Carpet Ride

Set Up:

1. Clear a space about 20 feet long. Mark one end as a start. There should be enough for your groups of three to line up side by side, while standing on their flip chart paper. Mark the other end as the finish line.

Framing:

"Communication, compromise and cooperation, better known as the Three Cs are helpful problem-solving tools. Our ability to use them effectively is influenced by the level of challenge of the problem, the resources available and the people we are working with."

Procedure:

1. Divide the class into teams of three and give each group a piece of flip chart paper.

2. The paper should be placed on the ground lengthwise with one end facing the start line and one end facing the finish line. (Carpeted or tile floors work best.)

3. Students can opt to take shoes off (works better this way).

4. Explain that the object of the activity is for each group of three to cross the space in front of them using the flip chart paper as their magic carpet. Students need to take care of their resource as each time it tears or someone steps off, the small group has to stop and think about how they can work more efficiently (key learning) before they can move forward.

5. Students will have three minutes to plan a strategy for moving the paper before they start. They may not touch the paper while planning.

6. Have all teams begin at the same time. All members must be standing on the paper once the activity starts.

7. Activity is not over until all teams have crossed the finish line or the magic carpet is destroyed.

8. Keep the magic carpets and debrief in small groups.

Reflection:

Reflection Activity:

1. Keep students in their small groups.

2. Ask each small group to identify an example of how their group used each of the Three Cs.

3. Ask each small group to identify an example of when the Three Cs would be helpful to solve problems in school or at home.

 Additional Thoughts

• *The easiest way to move the paper is for the three people to stand close together at the end of the flip chart paper that is closest to finish line. Someone reaches down and carefully bunches up the flip chart paper behind them, leaving a little flap to stand on. The group moves onto the flap, the paper is flattened out again, now in front of the three people. They then step to the edge closest to the finish line and repeat the process.*

LESSON 12

In this lesson students will explore the impact of verbal and nonverbal responses in the prevention, promotion or resolution of conflict.

ACTIVITY	LEARNING OBJECTIVE	TIME	PROPS	HEALTH SKILLS
Quick Line Up	At the conclusion of this activity, students will be able to: • Apply communication skills while responding quickly to visual cues.	8 minutes	• None	• Goal setting • Decision making • Interpersonal communication • Accessing information
Negotiation Square	• Apply problem solving/negotiation skills. • Develop skills to de-escalate intimidation. • Identify influences that promote peace and discourage violence. • Demonstrate strategies that can be used to avoid confrontation or resolve conflicts.	20–30 minutes	• None	• Goal setting • Decision making • Interpersonal communication • Accessing information

TEACHER'S NOTES:

FRAMING	SET-UP PROCEDURE	REFLECTION

Quick Line-Up

Set-Up:

1. Clear a large, open space in your classroom.

Framing

"When people react to feelings or respond to cues, they may be passive, assertive or aggressive. Both nonverbal and verbal messages accompany each style. Our reactions impact our ability to manage conflict effectively."

Procedure:

1. Ask students to form a square—four equal sides or as equal as possible—around you.

2. Step to one side to explain the directions so that everyone can see you.

3. Say to the students: "I am going to move around the room and your goal is to get into the same formation as you are in now as quickly as possible. The same formation means that the line that is in front of me will always be in front of me, back in back, etc. The square is always formed around me. Your line is trying to be the most efficient at reading the situation, or where I am going, and efficiently organizing yourselves into position. When you feel your line is in the right spot, raise your hands and shout, 'We're here!' Any questions?"

4. After explaining the directions, move back into the center of the square. Start the activity by slowly turning 180 degrees and stopping. The class should respond accordingly by reorienting the square to its original position.

5. Start walking and turning before you stop again. Continue raising the challenge by speed and direction.

6. Explain to the group that they may not move until you are done moving and have said, "GO."

Reflections:

Questions for Discussion (students should stay standing in their game positions)

1. "What was it like to get your line organized amidst the chaos?"

2. "What was it like to orient yourself or align yourself with the person who was in the middle when they changed their mind (by changing their direction)?"

3. "How can these observations help us when approaching conflict management?"

Next Step:

4. After reflecting, have the students stay in their square formation for Negotiation Square which is the next activity.

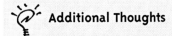

Additional Thoughts

• *Do not have students hold hands while they are moving.*

Negotiation Square

Set Up:

1. Use the formation from previous activity.

Framing:

"Expressing ideas is the level at which people begin sharing personal information. An individual takes the risk of disclosing thoughts and carefully monitors the response of the listener. Whenever people spend time with one another, conflict naturally arises. Everyone has conflict. Conflict isn't a bad thing. Common reasons for conflicts with peers include violating trust, disloyal behavior, being unavailable and poor communication. Learning how to resolve conflicts helps families and friendships run more smoothly. Resolving conflicts strengthens the relationships that are important in our lives."

Procedure:

1. Have each line form a small group and position themselves in the room so that the other small groups are unable to see or hear what they are doing.

2. Tell the small groups that their task is to create a collective sound and motion for their side. For example, the wave with a "whoo-hoo" sound. Remind students to keep their sounds and motions to themselves for the time being.

3. Ask small groups to return to the square, lining up on their original side when they are ready.

4. At the count of three, have each side present their motions and sounds simultaneously. Then have each side show their motions and sounds individually.

5. Explain that the goal is to eventually have each side display the same motions and sounds without discussing it with the other groups. Ask them to return to their spots and decide which of the sounds and motions they would like to show, again, keeping quiet until they come back to the square.

6. On the count of three have everyone show their chosen motions and sounds.

7. Keep going for a few rounds to see if having the same motions and sounds on all four sides can be accomplished!

Reflection:

Reflection Activity:

1. Have one person from each side come together to form new groups. (Do the best you can if it doesn't work out evenly). For example: if you had sixteen students, each new group would have one student from each of the old sides.

2. Ask the new groups to discuss how their original group came up with their motion and sound.

3. Ask groups to discuss what influenced their decisions to change or stay with their motion and sound in their original groups.

4. Ask groups to discuss how the activity would have been different if they were able to talk with one another across lines.

5. Finally, have students identify influences that promote peace and discourage violence and strategies that can be used to avoid confrontation or resolve conflicts.

 Additional Thoughts

• *Be aware of how you present the initial challenge. If you say that everyone needs to be doing one of the four motions and sounds (that went together when presented) for success, that limits the possibility of creating win-win solutions in which a combination of the different sides may be presented. Some groups will get this right away. Some may never get to that solution. If students limited their choices to one of the four, be sure to bring it up in the debrief.*

LESSON 13

In this lesson students will identify the impact of culture on conflict management and teach students to be effective allies.

ACTIVITY	LEARNING OBJECTIVE	TIME	PROPS	HEALTH SKILLS
Sea of Diversity	**At the conclusion of this activity, students will be able to:** • Identify things that prevent people from different backgrounds from understanding or interacting with one another. • Identify qualities and values which would promote cross-cultural understanding. • Apply problem solving/negotiation skills.	40–50 minutes	• Stepping stones • Tossables • Masking tape • Markers • Cones or 2 ropes for boundary markers • Feelings Marketplace Cards	• Decision making • Self-management • Analyze influences
Everybody Up!	• Explore how to be an effective ally. • Connect personal responsibility with being a good friend or peer.	10 minutes	• None	• Interpersonal communication • Advocacy • Self-management • Analyze influences

TEACHER'S NOTES:

FRAMING	SET-UP PROCEDURE	REFLECTION

Sea of Diversity

Set Up:

1. Clear a large open space in the classroom.

2. Set up two border areas to delineate a space on the floor that is as long as 12 large strides (or as many students as you have in the group, plus three) apart.

3. Place half the pile of stepping stones and half the bag of tossables, along with colored markers and self-stick cards or masking tape at each end of the space.

Framing:

"During our process of coming together as a class we've begun to understand that our differences can be accessed as strengths but can also become points of conflict. In this activity we are going to identify the things that prevent us from appreciating our differences, and think about the positive influence that our differences bring to this learning community."

Procedure:

1. Divide the class into two groups, one at each end of the boundaries.

2. Ask students to identify obstacles that prevent people from different backgrounds from interacting with and appreciating one another. Have students write these on tape and put them on the tossables. (If you do not have many props you can also use index cards.)

3. Ask the students to fill the space between the two border areas with the identified barriers (tossables).

4. Ask the students to write on tape (to be put on the stepping stones) the qualities or resources that would help people appreciate one another. One statement per stone.

5. Using only the stepping stones as tools, each group needs to move their whole team across the marked space without anyone touching the ground with any part of their body or without touching any of the barriers.

Reflection:

Reflection Activity:

1. Ask students to form a circle. Spread the Feelings Marketplace Cards in the center of the circle. Ask students to take as many cards as they can find that represent how they felt from beginning to end of this activity. Have each student share their feelings and ask for specific examples of when they felt different emotions.

2. Ask students to search through the cards and pick any that would reflect an acknowledgement for anyone in the group. For example: "I want to give Maddie 'supportive' because she helped me stay out of the 'sea."

3. Have each student share their cards—publicly acknowledging each other when appropriate.

4. Ask students to reflect on different times when friends have been positive toward people who were different from them and then negative toward people who were different from them. "What did it feel like in both situations? Would you do anything differently now?"

5. Go around the circle one last time asking for a key learning from this activity.

 Additional Thoughts

• This activity can be made as difficult as required to challenge the class and yet allow them to have a successful experience. Ways to make it more difficult include:

   a. Use a rule stating that if ANYONE touches the ground the entire group must start over.

   b. Decrease the time allowed.

   c. Lengthen the distance required to cross the river.

   d. Limit the number of blocks and/or state that if the blocks lose human contact at any time, they will be physically removed.

• There will be lots of chatter, which is good. Try to pick up cues/themes for the reflection.

• This activity leads nicely into the next one.

Everybody Up!

Set Up:
NONE

Framing
"Being an effective ally or responsible friend involves supporting but not overpowering another person."

Procedure:

1. Have everyone find a partner. It is helpful if people team up with someone close to their size.
2. Ask two people to sit on the floor facing one another. Their toes should be touching, their knees bent, and their bottoms on the floor.
3. Explain that the goal of the activity is for each pair to simultaneously pull themselves up to a standing position.
4. Once the pairs are successful, ask the pair to team with another pair and attempt the same process with four people.
5. Continue to join with other pairs until eventually the whole group is making the attempt together.

Reflection:
Questions for Discussion:

1. "How were you able to stand together with one other person (two other people, and so on)?"
2. "How are these skills and strategies related to being an effective ally?"
3. "Can you share some examples of times when you might be able to stand together with someone when they are being discriminated against?"

LESSON 14

In this lesson students will learn how to identify and apply strategies to access quality health information and analyze influences on health behaviors.

ACTIVITY	LEARNING OBJECTIVE	TIME	PROPS	HEALTH SKILLS
Trash Relay	**At the conclusion of this activity, students will be able to:** • Explain how stress and information overload impacts effective decision-making. • Explain how advertising influences health behaviors. • Distinguish between reliable and unreliable sources of information regarding healthy behaviors and disease prevention.	20 minutes	• 2 of each type of tossable object • Cones for boundary markers	• Analyze influences • Accessing information • Self-management • Core content
It's Knot My Problem	• Help one another access and apply quality information to manage a stressful situation.	30 minutes	• 40–60 feet of rope tied together at the ends	• Self-management • Advocacy • Interpersonal communication

TEACHER'S NOTES:

FRAMING	SET-UP PROCEDURE	REFLECTION

Trash Relay

Set Up:

1. Place the cones in a large rectangle. Make two identical piles of objects at the small end of one side of the rectangle.

Framing:

"OK, it is Saturday morning cartoon hour, or better yet, prime time evening television hour and the commercial mania is about to begin. You are going to be bombarded with all sorts of information about different products, diets, sales, fitness equipment, music, clothing, more sales, etc. Some of this information is accurate but much of it is designed to get you to BUY something. Your job is to filter out the "trash" from the quality information. Ready…"

Procedure:

1. Divide the class into two groups. Have each half make a line from the pile of objects to the cone at the opposite end of the rectangle.

2. Explain to each side that their goal is to get all of the objects from the starting end to the other as quickly as possible. In fact, they want to do it faster than the other side.

3. Everyone must touch all of the objects in their line. Objects can only be passed one at a time. The side is finished when all of the objects are behind the far cone. No throwing, just passing!

4. Play one round. Ask the students what worked well, what they would do differently.

5. Next tell the class that the objects have now become pieces of information regarding healthy behaviors and disease prevention and that the rubber chicken and green fleece ball (for example) are the only sources of valid reliable information and must be passed all the way down the line and back. Objects must be randomly passed without separating out the quality information from the "false advertising."

6. Explain that the rest of the rules are the same. The game ends when all the unreliable information is on the other side of the cones and the reliable information is back at the start.

7. Play another round.

8. Add one more round but this time not only are two objects previously identified as quality information, but during the course of the activity the person at the beginning of the line randomly identifies two more objects that represent quality info and thus need to go all the way down the line and back.

Reflection:

Reflection Activity:

1. Have students pair up with a member from the opposite team. Ask them to discuss how each of their groups managed moving the information (props).

2. Ask them to identify what happened specifically to their side's ability to communicate effectively with one another during the activity.

3. Ask them to discuss how they identified the reliable information in the activity and how they identify reliable information in life.

Next Step:

4. Have the class come back together and share observations.

Question for Discussion:

5. "Can you tell some strategies that would help you better identify reliable information when you are being bombarded with advertisements?"

. . . .

It's Knot My Problem!

Set Up:

1. Clear a large, open space in your classroom.

2. Loosely coil the rope so that the loops of the coils are slightly separated from one another.

Framing:

"Have you ever felt like you were in a jam? A situation where you were faced with a particular problem or decision and were unclear about what to do? Sometimes the media overwhelms us with information about how to be healthy, fit, how to look, what is "cool" and what is not. So much information can make us feel stuck and unsure of what to do next.

Procedure:

1. Instruct students to stand in a circle and place the rope in the center of the circle

2. Have the students reach down and place one hand on the rope.

3. Next ask students to stand up and back slightly. The rope will be in a giant "knot."

4. Tell students that the goal of the activity is to untangle the knot without tak-

ing their hand off of the rope. They will be finished when the rope is in one big circle.

Reflection:

Reflection Activity:

1. Ask students to draw two lines on a sheet of paper to form four squares. In the upper left square write a problem or decision you were faced with recently. In the upper right square write or draw a picture that epitomizes your personal motto for managing stress. In the lower left square write or draw a picture that represents something at which you are the BEST. In the lower right square write or draw something that captures how you dealt with the problem you recently faced. Allow students to keep this as a badge of honor for their ability to positively solve problems. If you have the financial resources, have the group do this on individual bandanas using permanent markers so that they can keep and wear them.

Or

Questions for Discussion:

2. "How did you collectively handle the challenges you were presented?"

3. "Did you find it easy to have your ideas heard? Why or Why not?"

4. "What do you do when you get 'stuck' or can't find a 'way out?'"

5. "How is it possible to solve a problem from deep inside the situation?"

6. "What happens to you when you have thoughts about wanting to give up? What do you want to do when that happens?"

7. "What do we want to remember about this activity to help us cope with peer pressure and stress?"

 Additional Thoughts

• *Stress safety when stepping over one another, turning wrists and shoulders.*

• *If the class is unsuccessful after a long period of time, 10-15 minutes, allow them to break and then re-grip one connection that the group mutually agrees upon, and then resume their attempt to untangle. A successful attempt will result in one large circle.*

• *This activity may also be done in two small groups of 12-15 with two different ropes.*

Nutrition

LESSON 15

In this lesson students will access nutritional information and identify principles of healthy eating habits while working under pressure.

ACTIVITY	LEARNING OBJECTIVE	TIME	PROPS	HEALTH SKILLS
Name 5	**At the conclusion of this activity, students will be able to:** • Identify healthy eating habits and nutritional practices. • Quickly recognize and choose healthy options. • Explain the impact of stress, relationships and food on health.	15–20 minutes	• Ball or toss-able • Markers • Flip chart paper	• Core content • Self-management • Accessing information
Nutrition Golf	• Identify the differences between sound nutritional practices and fad diets. • Identify misleading information about nutrition.	30 minutes	• Fact cards • Recording sheets • Myth cards (sample myths found on page __) • Nutrition question cards (sample questions found on page __) • Rubber rings • Hula-Hoops™	• Core content • Goal setting • Decision making • Interpersonal communication

TEACHER'S NOTES:

FRAMING	SET-UP PROCEDURE	REFLECTION

Name Five

Set Up:

1. Create a large, open space in your classroom.

Framing:

"Did you know that only one out of five youths eat the recommended five servings of fruits and vegetables per day? Did you also know that the benefits of healthful eating include better growth and development, better performance in the classroom and prevention of diseases and adolescent problems such as obesity, eating disorders and cavities? What stops us from eating well?"

Procedure:

1. Ask the students to form a circle. When the activity begins, someone will be standing in the middle of the circle with the object.

2. Play starts when the person in the middle presents the ball to a person on the outside of the circle and asks that person to name five of some type of category related to nutrition. For example name five categories in the Food Pyramid or five types of leafy green vegetables.

3. The person on the outside has the opportunity to "accept" the challenge or to "deny" the challenge. If the person accepts, they need to name five items in the category before the ball gets passed around the outside of the circle. If they decline, the person in the middle has to name five. Either way the ball is passed around the circle as quickly as possible.

4. If the ball makes it around before the five things are named, the person doing the naming is in the middle. So, a student who doesn't complete the challenge is in the middle.

Reflection:

Questions for Discussion:

1. "What are some of the ways that you can maintain a healthy diet?"
2. "How does being under stress impact your ability to make healthy food choices?"

Reflection Activity:

3. Ask students to create a "T" chart on appropriate and inappropriate ways to manage stress with reference to establishing healthy nutritional habits.

Appropriate	Inappropriate

Nutrition Golf

Set Up:

1. Write either nutritional questions or myths (to be answered true or false) on index cards. Samples of these are in the appendix.

2. Place the cards at nutritional information stations around your classroom. Each station will represent a hole on the Nutrition Golf Course. Have one question and one myth card per group, per hole. (These could be color coded so each group will know theirs. For example, Tommy's group answers the questions written with red marker.) Set up as many "holes" as you have time and space for.

Framing

"A healthful diet should have all the nutrients your body needs to maintain health and fitness. However, there are many representations, myths and marketing strategies which falsely define healthful diets – for example, that carbohydrates are bad for you or that drinking orange juice is just as good as eating an orange. This activity will help us differentiate fact from fiction."

Procedure:

1. Divide the class into groups of three to five students. Give each small group a rubber ring and recording sheet.

2. Explain to students that they are going to be playing a version of mini golf called Nutrition Golf. The object is to get around the course with the lowest score in tosses and the highest score in correct nutrition information.

3. Students move from "hole" to "hole" by tossing the rubber ring to one of their group members. The group member must catch the rubber ring by forming a point with their entire hand for the ring to settle on—not by grasping it. Groups must keep track of the number of tosses it takes to reach each hole.

4. Tell students that once they are at the hole they must answer the nutrition questions or myths as quickly and accurately as possible before they can move on to the next station.

5. The activity finishes when everyone has completed the course.

Reflection:

Knowledge Review:

1. Review correct answers as a large group.

2. Identify reasons for and impact of false information in the marketplace.

Reflection Activity:

3. Celebrate most coordinated group (least number of tosses) and most nutritionally knowledgeable group.

 Additional Thoughts

• *Examples of nutrition questions and myths are in the appendix on page(>>>).*
• *This activity may be best played in a large space, outdoors or a gymnasium.*

LESSON 16

In this lesson students will work together to access healthy food choices and consider the effect media has on nutrition and body image.

ACTIVITY	LEARNING OBJECTIVE	TIME	PROPS	HEALTH SKILLS
Eyes, Body, Mouth	At the conclusion of this activity, students will be able to: • Explore the connection or sometimes disconnection between the eyes, body, and mouth with regard to healthy food choices. • Explain the impact of stress, relationships, and food on health.	20 minutes	• Objects representing healthy food choices • Blindfolds optional	• Self-management • Goal setting • Decision making • Interpersonal communication • Core content
Media Messages	• Define looking good—what is a healthy appearance. • Describe the relationship between body image and well being. • Explain how advertising influences health choices.	20–30 minutes	• Several popular magazines, newspapers, etc. • Questions (found on page ___) • Flip chart paper • Markers	• Core content • Accessing information • Analyze influences

TEACHER'S NOTES:

FRAMING	SET-UP PROCEDURE	REFLECTION

Eyes, Body, Mouth

Set Up:

1. Flip chart and post the guidelines for the roles of eyes, body and mouth. (These are found in the procedure that follows.)

Framing:

"Have you ever heard the expressions 'My eyes were bigger than my stomach' or 'I am so hungry but I am not eating because I look fat.' Eating a balanced diet, appropriate to your size and activity level is one of the most important things you can do to be healthy. Sometimes, however what we tell ourselves, how we feel about our looks or hunger and what we see in the mirror do not always encourage healthy nutritional habits."

Procedure:

1. Ask the students to organize themselves into groups of three.
2. Each team of three has an object (representing a healthy food) that they need to retrieve.
3. Two of the team players either have their eyes closed or are wearing blindfolds. With this said only one team player (the eyes) can see where the object is. The "eyes" unfortunately aren't allowed to speak. However, the "eyes" are working closely with one of the blindfolded people (the mouth).
4. While the mouth can't see, he/she can be touched by the "eyes." This gives the team the ability to non-verbally relay what the "eyes" see to the "mouth" who tells the last blindfolded team member (the body) what to do.
5. The "body" is the only team member who can actually pick up the object. To make communication easier the eye/mouth team can follow along behind the body to offer proper guidance.
6. Other than verbal instructions from the mouth, the body is on his/her own. No physical guidance is allowed. However, the body and mouth are free to talk with each other so that questions can be answered.
7. After explaining the activity itself, have the group plan their signals and communication strategy. Remind them to create a "stop" command. At this point, the idea of the hands or "bumpers up" during blindfold activities should be familiar. "Bumpers up" is an important safety element of this activity.
8. After one round with a pretty straight-forward placement, try a second round with people in different roles and with the object in a more challenging location i.e., off the ground, under some sweat shirts.

Reflection:

Questions for Discussion:

1. "What was it like to coordinate the eyes, mouth and body in retrieving the healthy food?

2. "Tell us about some times when you feel as though your eyes, mouth and body are working against one another. In concert with one another."

3. "What are some strategies you'd like to put into place to help maintain your nutritional goals?"

. . . .

Media Messages

Set Up:

NONE

Framing:

"Food choices are influenced by many factors – age, gender, friends, family, cultural background and locality. To capture the interest of the consumer, food producers spend billions of dollars each year on advertising and packaging foods and images related to the foods we eat and how they make us look."

Procedure:

1. Divide students into groups of three to five. Have participants sit in a circle with a couple of magazines in the middle.

2. Pass out question sheets to each person. Questions are in the appendix.

3. Pass out flip chart paper and markers to each small group.

4. Ask the students to look through the magazines and write down responses to questions on flip chart paper.

5. Have students also consider observations from "prime time" television shows as well as the morning news channel.

6. Then ask the groups to create a second chart by writing down how they would describe themselves.

Reflection:

There are often wonderful conversations that occur naturally within the course of this activity…listen well!

Questions for Discussion (after the charts are complete):

1. "How do you feel about the differences between the images you see in the

media and how you see yourself? How do you think the media effects your behavior?"

2. "What would be helpful in making this group a safe place to be 'who you really are' versus who you are 'supposed to be?"

Reflection Activity:

3. Have students define "looking good" and list elements that contribute to a healthy appearance.

7.17

NUTRITION

LESSON 17

In this lesson students will create and support representations of healthy "bodies" on different diets.

ACTIVITY	LEARNING OBJECTIVE	TIME	PROPS	HEALTH SKILLS
Model Citizens of Nutrition and Fitness	**At the conclusion of this activity, students will be able to:** • Demonstrate ability to select a balanced diet using the food guide pyramid. • Design an appropriate diet for weight gain or loss, low in salt and saturated fats.	40 minutes	• Game Frame • Alphabet Soup Kit	• Core content • Interpersonal communication • Accessing information

TEACHER'S NOTES:

FRAMING	SET-UP PROCEDURE	REFLECTION

Model Citizens of Nutrition and Fitness

Set Up:

1. Set up Game Frame in an open space in the classroom.
2. Divide the foam alphabet letter blocks in half and evenly distribute on both sides of the Game Frame.

Framing:

"The food and exercise pyramids are great guidelines for proper nutrition and fitness. The key is to know how to adjust them for different body types, dietary restrictions and age groups."

Procedure:

1. Divide the class into two small groups and ask each group to stand on either side of the web.
2. Explain to the class that they are going to create "model citizens for nutrition and fitness" with the foam letters.
3. The model citizen will be created with the foam letters. He/she (model citizen) must be passed back and forth through the game frame to have letters added on to him/her.
4. The first pass involves only one letter; at the end, the last pass will include all the letters linked together as one healthy, nutritionally sound body. Whenever a letter passes through to the other side, it must be attached to another letter piece before being passed again
5. Only two letters at a time may be added to the "body" as it moves back and forth through the web.
6. After each letter is added, the puzzle must be passed to the other side before other letters can be attached.
7. Once an opening has been used, it can only be used one more time before it is closed. (Two times total)
8. During the activity, no person or letter may touch the web or frame. The consequence of a touch is that half of the letters in the "body" have to start over from the beginning. But three or four holes would re-open as a result.
9. As the letters are assembled and linked together, the "body" may never break apart. If even one letter becomes separated, the group has to start the entire activity over from the beginning.
10. Once the last letter has been attached, the entire "body" must be passed back to the other side without disrupting the letters in any way and placing it safely on the ground.

11. Say: "The first model citizen for nutrition and fitness will be a middle school soccer player. You must create the letter body in the "shape" of a healthy middle school soccer player and identify the components of a healthy diet for this person as you are developing his physique. Try to identify a component or aspect from the food pyramid for beginning with each letter you attach."

12. The second model citizen can be a teenage male trying to lose 20 pounds.

Reflection:

Questions for Discussion:

1. "How did you determine what the different bodies needed to be healthy?"

2. "How did each of you contribute to creating model citizens?"

3. "How would you change the model for a young child? A sedentary adult male with diabetes? A woman with high blood pressure?"

LESSON 18

In this lesson students will reinforce the previous lesson by identifying a healthy body image for themselves.

ACTIVITY	LEARNING OBJECTIVE	TIME	PROPS	HEALTH SKILLS
Passport to the Future	**At the conclusion of this activity, students will be able to:** • Define "looking good" and list elements that contribute to a healthy appearance. • Explain importance of healthy body image in developing positive self-esteem.	40–50 minutes	• Game Frame • Color paint chips (see Additional Thoughts for this activity for how to make) • Pens	• Core content • Self-management • Goal setting • Decision making • Advocacy • Interpersonal communication

TEACHER'S NOTES:

FRAMING	SET-UP PROCEDURE	REFLECTION

Passport to the Future

Set Up:

1. Set up the Game Frame in an open space.

Framing

"Having a healthy body image is very important for adolescents. There are many advertisements, pictures, ideas of what we are "supposed to look like" to be acceptable. We have identified the reasons why these images are presented and the reality of looking like models, etc. What you see before you is your future. You decide what a healthy body image is for you and choose a path to the future that recognizes the challenge of maintaining that healthy body image with determination and the support of your peers."

Procedure:

1. Have everyone gather on one side of the Game Frame.
2. Review spotting and safe lifting.
3. Ask students to think about a negative belief or attitude about themselves that they want to "let go of" particularly around their body image.
4. Ask students to picture and reinforce a healthy image of themselves – one in which their bodies are strong, balanced and appropriate for their body type and culture.
5. Explain that the game frame/web represents the future and that each student will have the opportunity to choose their own path to the future by passing through a hole in the web.
6. Further explain that the goal is to choose a hole that represents the challenges that adolescents face in maintaining a healthy body image. "Remember while being healthy is challenging, you can do it. By identifying our challenges, we can know where we need extra self-determination/ability to keep our goals as the focus and support from peers, family and community."
7. Students then help one another through the different holes. (Please read the Additional Thoughts section that follows for detailed safety procedures BEFORE beginning this activity.)
8. Tell students that if anyone touches the Game Frame/Web while being passed through, the person returns to the starting side of the game frame/web at which point the group stops and reflects on better ways to support that person in maintaining their healthy body image while moving into the future.
9. Remind the class that it's not just the person who is passing through who is responsible for not touching—everyone is responsible for helping each other.

Reflection:

Reflection Activity:

1. Spread the color chips on the floor. Ask each person to select a color that expresses the feelings and thoughts they had as they went through the Web.

2. Have them write those feelings and thoughts on this chip.

3. Have students share with the class why they chose that color.

4. Give students the color chip to remind them of the feelings and thoughts they had that support maintaining a healthy body image.

 Additional Thoughts

• *Treat this activity seriously and make certain the group is ready to keep each other physically and emotionally safe. If they cannot commit to keeping each other safe or are having trouble spotting do not try this activity. Properly trained teachers are needed for this activity.*

Rules to Highlight:

    a. People may not go over the top or under the Web.

    b. The group can only use each other for support.

    c. No outside resources or holding the posts are allowed (if you are using the portable Web, you may want to have someone brace it).

    d. A successful pass through the Web is defined as the person being passed through a hole while not touching any portion of the Web. The people who are spotting cannot touch any portion of the Web either. If a touch occurs, that person needs to return to the starting point and try again.

    e. The teacher must spot, NOT CARRY, the first two people as they go through the Game Frame/Web.

    f. Safety and spotting are critical. No diving or tossing through the Web. Head, neck and shoulders should be protected at all times. The teacher must pay vigilant attention to safety during this activity.

• *Color chips are made by collecting paint sample strips and cutting the different shades into smaller "chips."*

Physical Fitness

7.19

PHYSICAL
FITNESS

LESSON 19

In this lesson students will identify anatomically correct muscle groups and rein-force principles of cardiovascular fitness.

ACTIVITY	LEARNING OBJECTIVE	TIME	PROPS	HEALTH SKILLS
Macro/Micro Stretch with Muscle Identification	**At the conclusion of this activity, students will be able to:** • Identify different body parts. • Actively stretch before doing aerobic activity. • Explain the importance of stretching.	15 minutes	• None	• Core content • Self-management
Striker	• Apply heart rate tracking during an activity. • Explain concepts of cardio fitness.	20 minutes	• 2 or 3 large, inflated beach balls • Cones	• Core content • Self-management • Goal setting • Decision making

TEACHER'S NOTES:

FRAMING	SET-UP PROCEDURE	REFLECTION

Macro/Micro Stretch with Muscle Identification

Set Up:

1. Clear a large, open space in your classroom.
2. Post human anatomy chart where the class can see it.

Framing

"Flexibility is one of the most important, yet most overlooked, components of fitness. Let's see how well we remember our anatomy by identifying what muscles we are stretching."

Procedure:

1. Ask the class to stand in a circle.
2. Explain that we are going to practice active stretching and review of muscle/body parts by passing a stretch around the circle.
3. Explain that the first person will start with a large muscle group, for example, hamstrings. Identify the muscle group and execute the stretch, passing to the right. (Like "the wave" the crowd performs during sporting events.)
4. The class holds the stretch for a count of 20 seconds. The person to the right of the starter then executes a small muscle group stretch, i.e., triceps, identifying it and stretching with proper alignment, etc.
5. Continue alternating from macro to micro until each person gets a chance. Allow students to help one another identify names and proper stretches, if needed, unless reviewing for a test!

Reflection:

Knowledge Review:

1. Review proper stretching techniques.

Question for Discussion:

2. "How do stretching and flexibility fit into an overall fitness score?"

 Additional Thoughts

• *Be sure to do a dynamic warm-up before moving into a light stretch, holding for a maximum of 20 seconds.*

Striker

Set Up:

1. This activity is intended for a large open space like the outdoors or a gymnasium.

2. A goal line for each of two teams should be marked off using cones or other markers. The size of the goals and the distance between them is up to you, taking into consideration the group's size and ability.

Framing:

"Exercising your heart is very important. Who remembers how to track their heart rate? Who remembers what it means to be cardiovascularly fit?"

Procedure:

1. Separate the class into two even teams.

2. The object is for each team to try to score goals against the other.

3. The game is started by having a member from each team jump for the ball at center court, like a basketball jump-ball.

4. The ball is passed down the field/gym by the team members, each team heading towards the other team's goal line.

5. No intentional body contact is allowed and you can strike the ball only with a flat palm.

6. Points are earned each time one team gets the ball through the other team's goal.

7. After a goal has been scored, the team that has just scored gets the ball and starts off at their goal.

Reflection:

Reflection Activity:

1. Have students monitor their heart rate before, during and after this activity and reflect on findings.

Knowledge Review:

2. Revisit how changing one's heart rate relates to cardiovascular fitness.

 Additional Thoughts

• *This is a very active game that gets the heart rate up.*

• *Watch for fatigue.*

• *You can add another ball if you have more than 20 people.*

LESSON 20

In this lesson students will practice aspects of four components of physical fitness and identify different activities that promote each of those four components.

ACTIVITY	LEARNING OBJECTIVE	TIME	PROPS	HEALTH SKILLS
Fitness Baseball	**At the conclusion of this activity, students will be able to:** • Identify four types of exercise. • Describe benefits of four types of exercise (aerobic, flexibility, strength, endurance). • Discuss how each activity should be performed to be effective and the amount of time necessary to receive benefits.	40 minutes	• Rubber chicken or tossable object	• Core content • Interpersonal communication • Decision making

TEACHER'S NOTES:

FRAMING	SET-UP PROCEDURE	REFLECTION

Fitness Baseball

Set Up:

1. Create a large, open space.

Framing

"There are many ways to be fit. Most of us focus on only one or two of the fitness components instead of all four."

Procedure:

1. Divide the class into two teams.
2. One team starts with the rubber chicken (or tossable object).
3. Explain to the class that this game is like baseball in that each team will have an "at bat" and the possibility to score runs.
4. Explain that the "at bat" team will toss the chicken anywhere and the outfield team has to run to the chicken, line up and pass it over and under each other as quickly as possible. When it gets to the last person say, "STOP!"
5. Meanwhile, the "at bat" team has clumped together and is scoring runs by having one person run around their team until they hear "STOP!"
6. The outfield team then tosses the chicken and the game continues with the other team running to it and passing it over and under each other as quickly as possible, etc.
7. You can keep track of the runs but it usually doesn't matter!
8. Emphasize that only one person may be scoring runs at a time.

Reflection:

Questions for Discussion:
1. "What were some of the ways you accessed the components of fitness during this activity?"
2. "What changes did you notice in your heart rate?"
3. "What strategies did you use to make this more challenging for each throw?"
4. "How can you relate being supported and being challenged to keeping yourself fit?"

Reflection Activity:
5. Divide the class into four groups, one for each type of exercise. Have students brainstorm examples of activities and benefits that would fit into one of four types of exercise.
6. Pass the sheets around and have each group add to original lists.
7. Review and post charts in class.

LESSON 21

In this lesson students will expand their understanding of cardiovascular fitness by focusing on the concept of intensity.

ACTIVITY	LEARNING OBJECTIVE	TIME	PROPS	HEALTH SKILLS
Heartbeat Stations	**At the conclusion of this activity, students will be able to:** • Explain how changing the intensity of physical activity affects heart rate and perceived exertion.	30–40 minutes	• Heart rate monitors if available • Paper and pencils • Stopwatch	• Core content • Interpersonal communication • Self-management

TEACHER'S NOTES:

FRAMING	SET-UP PROCEDURE	REFLECTION

Heartbeat Stations

Set Up:

1. Set up an aerobic endurance circuit with five activities that vary in intensity: walking through cones, jumping rope, jogging around the gym, dribbling a soccer ball, running the agility ladder, (or another activity that suits your group).

Framing

"Exercising our heart and lungs is very important in establishing and maintaining a healthy lifestyle. One way to understand how to do that effectively is to track our heart rate while participating in activities of varying levels of intensity."

Procedure:

1. Divide the class into five small groups.
2. Give each student a sheet of paper and pencil.
3. Define intensity and ask students to predict which of the five activities they feel have greater intensity and why.
4. Review method for tracking heart rate and have students record their resting heart rate.
5. Ask each small group to go to one of the five stations and explain that their goal is to participate in that station's activity for 30 seconds and then measure their heart rates.
6. Groups will then rotate to the left, following the same procedure at each station.

Reflection:

Questions for Discussion:

1. "Were any of your predictions of intensity correct or incorrect? Why do you think you made the wrong or the right prediction? What assumptions did you have prior to doing this activity that made you predict correctly or incorrectly?"
2. "At which station did your heart beat the fastest? At which station did your heart beat the slowest? What do you think caused the changes in your heart rate?"
3. "Can you tell me how you would modify any of the activities to increase or decrease the intensity?"

 Additional Thoughts

• *It is helpful if you manage the time for the entire class as they move through the stations and calculate heart rates.*

• *This activity may be best played in a large open space, outdoors or a gymnasium.*

LESSON 22

In this lesson students will apply exercise adherence strategies.

ACTIVITY	LEARNING OBJECTIVE	TIME	PROPS	HEALTH SKILLS
Turnstile	**At the conclusion of this activity, students will be able to:** • Apply problem solving skills. • Apply effective communication and support in achieving a group goal.	10 minutes	• 1 long rope (20-25 feet)	• Interpersonal communication • Advocacy • Self-management
1, 2, 3 is 20	• Identify barriers to exercise adherence. • Recognize consequences of physical inactivity. • Identify strategies to maintain exercise programs.	40 minutes	• 1 long rope (20-25 feet)	• Self-management • Goal setting • Decision making • Interpersonal communication • Advocacy

TEACHER'S NOTES:

FRAMING	SET-UP PROCEDURE	REFLECTION

Turnstile

Set-Up:

1. Lay a jump rope on the floor in an open space.

Framing:

"We all have different preferences for how we like to exercise. Some of us like to go it alone, some of us like to work with one or two other people and still others like to work out in groups. The important thing is that we all keep moving."

Procedure:

1. The group lines up on one side of the jump rope.
2. Ask for a volunteer to help turn the rope.
3. Tell the group the goal is to get everyone from one side of the rope to the other side of the rope *without missing a turn of the rope.*
4. Explain that the rope becomes active as soon as the first person passes through it. That is, as soon as one group member passes through, the remaining must follow without missing a turn of the rope.
5. Students may jump or run through the rope while it is turning.
6. If the rope swings empty for a turn or gets caught on someone then the whole group returns to the original side to start again.

Reflection:

Turnstile serves as a warm-up for *1, 2, 3 is 20.*
Question for Discussion:

1. "Can you identify some of the strategies you used to keep everyone moving?"

. . . .

1, 2, 3 is 20

Set-Up:
NONE

Framing:

"Now that we all know what we are supposed to do to be physically fit let's see how we do with creating and implementing a fitness plan. While it may seem easy to follow through with a fitness plan, it is often difficult. Being able to maintain a fitness program requires looking to our own and our class mates' strengths and abilities and organize our plan in a way that keeps us moving!"

Procedure:

1. The group lines up on one side of the jump rope and is given the riddle: 1, 2, 3 is 20.

2. Tell the group that you have a riddle to solve. The solution to the riddle unlocks the means to maintaining a fitness plan and must be solved by moving through the rope.

3. The group has to move through the rope without missing a turn of the rope while demonstrating the solution of the riddle to the teacher.

4. The only feedback that the teacher will give is in dropping the rope when the solution is wrong. The teacher will also count out loud.

5. Tell the group that they may begin whenever they are ready and can have as many attempts as they would like in solving the riddle.

Reflection:

Questions for Discussion:

1. "Can someone tell me how you solved the riddle?"

2. "Now that we know a little bit about each others strengths and interests, how can we support one another in getting and staying fit?"

3. "What other kinds of feedback and support would have been helpful in solving this riddle? In becoming fit or maintaining fitness?"

4. "What are the barriers to being physically fit?"

5. "What are the consequences of not being physically fit?'

 Additional Thoughts

Riddle Solution:

• *Participants must proceed through the rope in groups of 1, 2 then 3, back to 1, 2 and 3 until it equals 20 passes through.*

Substance Abuse Prevention

7.23

SUBSTANCE
ABUSE
PREVENTION

LESSON 23

In this lesson students will reaffirm the importance of healthy peer relationships in substance abuse prevention as well as reinforcing the concept of natural highs.

ACTIVITY	LEARNING OBJECTIVE	TIME	PROPS	HEALTH SKILLS
2–3 Person Trust Leans	**At the conclusion of this activity, students will be able to:** • Describe behaviors in friendships that promote health. • Identify differences between healthy and harmful behaviors in relationships.	30 minutes	• None	• Interpersonal communication • Self-management • Advocacy
Levitation	• Identify legal and fun activities that are alternatives to drug use. • Apply refusal skills in peer pressure situations.	30 minutes	• Flip chart paper • Markers	• Interpersonal communication • Self-management • Advocacy

TEACHER'S NOTES:

FRAMING	SET-UP PROCEDURE	REFLECTION

2-3 Person Trust Leans

Set Up:

1. Clear a large, open space in the classroom.

Framing:

"Earning someone's trust takes time and is a major responsibility once it has been achieved. Likewise, trusting someone else can be a challenge and a risk. There is great power in a friendship where there is mutual trust. Adolescents have many challenges to maintaining healthy friendships and trust."

Procedure:

1. Have everyone find a partner and stand next to that partner in a circle.
2. The teacher should demonstrate proper spotting – hands up at chest height, palms open facing away from the body, legs bent at the knees for flexibility, one foot in front of the other in a stable stance.
3. Explain to the class that they are going to revisit healthy relationships and trust. The way they will do that is by having one person be the leaner; the other, the spotter in their partnership.
4. The leaner stands with his/her back to the spotter, arms folded across the chest. The leaner should be reminded to secure his/her arms across the chest to ensure not throwing out arms and elbows. The person leaning should also keep knees and body straight, stiff as a board, falling directly backwards.
5. Spotters stand behind the leaners, in the trained spotting position. Spotters should start with their hands directly on the leaners' shoulder blades for the first lean. They can slowly move back as they continue working with each other.
6. When both leaners and spotters are ready, a series of calls are initiated by the leaners.

   Leaners: "Spotter are you ready?"
   Spotters: "Spotter ready."
   Leaners: "I'm ready to lean."
   Spotters: "Lean away."

7. Several leans can be completed by the leaners. These leans should always be at a distance from the hands of the spotter that is comfortable for both leaner and spotter, modeling healthy risk taking and relationship support.
8. If there is a fall—STOP! Use it as a "teachable moment" to show that if a mistake is made things do not have to continue down that path—stop, evaluate and try again. Move through this evaluation process with the pair.

9. Switch roles in the partnership and then move out to the larger group so that people have a chance to work with everyone if they decide to.

Reflection:

Questions for Discussion:

1. "How did it feel to be the leaner?"
2. "How did it feel to be the spotter?"
3. "What are some behaviors in friendships that promote health?"
4. "What are some of the differences between healthy and harmful behaviors in relationships?"
5. "What are some things you did in this activity to promote health and encourage a healthy relationship with your partner?"

 Additional Thoughts

• *Treat this activity seriously and make certain the group is ready to ensure their own and others' physical and emotional safety. Things to look for: are students falling down, are they piking, are students stepping back. These are indications that the partners need to stop, reconnect and try again. The spotter can ask the leaner, "What would help you feel safer?" As the teacher, you may have to model this.*

Levitation

Set Up:

1. Clear a large, open space in your classroom.
2. Have flip chart paper and markers ready for each student in your class.

Framing

"People take drugs for many different reasons. Some are: to feel better, to feel different, to help them cope and to socialize. One of the goals of drug education is to get students "hooked" on "life highs" as opposed to drug highs. Here's one way to get high—but not on drugs—with a little help from your friends."

Procedure:

1. Ask students to stand in a circle while you explain the instructions.

2. Tell them: "This levitation activity will give you an opportunity to rely on the full support of the group."

3. The student to be lifted should lie on his/her back on the floor/ground with hands by their sides.

4. Lifters kneel around the student to be lifted. One student is assigned to be responsible for the head and neck. **Training is required to know how to do this properly.** Cradle the head with one hand and the neck with the other hand.

5. Demonstrate proper lifting positions (i.e., use legs, not back) and explain that each group member will have the opportunity to be lifted from the ground to waist level and then gently lowered back to the ground.

6. On a signal from the head person, the student is lifted a couple of feet up, to about waist level and then moved laterally back and forth as if in a swing. Slowly the procedure is reversed until the student is gently returned to the prone position. From lift-off to landing takes about 30-40 seconds.

7. Gently lower the head to the ground upon landing.

8. Repeat for all students who wish to be lifted.

Reflection:

Questions for Discussion:

1. "Your peers group can have positive and negative influences on your behavior. How did this activity help you have a positive experience with other people in the class?"

2. "What did it feel like to be lifted by your peers?"

Reflection Activity:

3. Have each student create a poster depicting an activity that is an appropriate alternative to using drugs.

 Additional Thoughts

• *Treat this activity seriously and make certain the group is ready to ensure their own and others' physical and emotional safety. This activity should be done only after two-to-three-person spotting has been completed successfully. Specific directions to activities requiring spotting should be referenced Project Adventure's* Guide for Challenge Course Operations *and be used only in conjunction with proper training. Model the first few lifts.*

7.24

LESSON 24

In this lesson students will begin to appreciate the impact of substance abuse on family systems and the power of assertiveness in resisting the pressure to use substances.

ACTIVITY	LEARNING OBJECTIVE	TIME	PROPS	HEALTH SKILLS
Instigator	At the conclusion of this activity, students will be able to: • Identify the subtle and not so subtle effects a person with an addiction or their own "agenda," can have on the people around them. • Define and describe the dysfunctional family.	20 minutes	• 4 cones for boundary markers	• Self-management • Advocacy • Accessing information • Interpersonal communication
Triangle Tag	• Identify techniques for handling conflict in the family. • Describe different types of peer pressure. • Recognize various influences to use or not use drugs. • Demonstrate assertiveness when saying no to simulated drug offers.	20 minutes	• None	• Self-management • Interpersonal communication • Advocacy

TEACHER'S NOTES:

FRAMING	SET-UP PROCEDURE	REFLECTION

Instigator

Set Up:

1. Set up cones or other boundary markers delineating a clear space in which your class will be able to comfortably walk around.

Framing

"At least seven million American teens have alcoholic parents. Alcoholism runs in families, and children of alcoholics are four times more likely than other children to become alcoholic. Adolescents also have parents who are using other types of drugs. Often children whose parents are addicted act as though "everything is fine" in an effort to maintain the appearance of having healthy parents and home."

Procedure:

1. Ask the class to gather inside the cones.
2. You will need two volunteers to be the detectives.
3. Explain that the class will be moving in different ways in the marked off area and that the type of movement will be determined by a selected "leader" or "instigator" from the group of remaining students.
4. Tell the "detectives" that they will go out of the room until someone says, "Ready." When they return, their goal is to work together to identify who the instigator is by watching changes in the class's movement, etc.
5. Detectives stand on the perimeter of the group (but may move around) for the first few rounds.
6. The detectives have to come to consensus on three choices. If they do not guess correctly, the instigator is revealed and another round is started.
7. Go through a few rounds with different instigators and detectives.
8. Switch to have detectives in middle of group.

Reflection:

Questions for Discussion:
1. "How did the person who was the instigator change the group's behavior?"
2. "How easy was it to respond/not respond to the behavior change?"
3. "What were the differences in detecting the instigator from the outside of the circle as compared with the inside?"
4. "Describe ways that young people who are living with parents with addiction try to appear "normal"?
5. "Identify three sources of support or intervention for managing dysfunctional family conflicts."

Triangle Tag

Set Up:

NONE

Framing:

"We all face the challenge of trying to make healthy choices. For example what to eat, whether or not to exercise, whether or not to do drugs, are all choices that we make. In this activity the person who is the tagger will act as a negative influence and try to tag a selected member of the group in an attempt to "get them to do something unhealthy," e.g., take drugs. The other two people in the group will try to provide healthy peer support by keeping the bad influence away from their friend."

Procedure:

1. Have the class split into groups of four.
2. Select a student to be "it" (the negative influence) and another student to be tagged (friend who needs help).
3. The person who is the "friend who needs help" should link hands with the two other people in the group. The person acting as the "negative influence" is on the outside of this circle. The "negative influence" will be trying to tag the selected person while the "friends" try to keep the "negative influence" from succeeding.
4. The circle can move in any direction, but the group must remain connected. The person acting as the negative influence cannot dive through the group to try to tag the person and must remain on the outside of the circle. The person who is being helped must say "No!" or "Stay Away!" or "You can't get me!" to the negative influence.
5. Have students switch roles several times so that everyone who wants to can try each role.

Reflection:

Reflection Activity:

1. Ask students to form a large circle and respond to the following questions with a "fist to five" approach.
   - "How challenging was it to negatively influence or tag someone?"
   - "How challenging was it to protect someone from being influenced?"
   - "How challenging was it to be protected?"
2. Ask students to identify various influences to use or not use drugs.
3. Finally have students describe different types of peer pressure and how positive peer pressure can help them make healthier choices.

LESSON 25

In this lesson students will create a group sculpture that represents being under the influence of different drugs.

ACTIVITY	LEARNING OBJECTIVE	TIME	PROPS	HEALTH SKILLS
Essence of Health	**At the conclusion of this activity, students will be able to:** • Recognize the harmful physical effects of alcohol and other drugs. • Relate negative effects on relationships, goal achievement and ability to communicate effectively.	45 minutes	• Bags of tossables • Stepping stones • Spot marker • Variety of props • 1 long boundary rope (60 feet) • 1 medium length boundary rope (10–15 feet)	• Core content • Accessing information • Analyze influences

TEACHER'S NOTES:

FRAMING	SET-UP PROCEDURE	REFLECTION

Essence of Health

Set Up:

1. Place the props in a pile in the middle of a circle created by the medium length boundary rope. The circle should be six to eight feet in diameter.

2. Place the second boundary rope in a large circle around the medium length boundary rope. They should form a target with the props in the middle. The distance between the two ropes should be at least 20 feet.

Framing:

"Drugs are powerful and, at times, unpredictable. Some drugs slow people down and some speed people up. The effects of any drug depend on a person's age, weight, gender, medical history and the setting where the drug is used. This activity will help you to understand the detrimental effects certain drugs have on your ability to perform a task."

Procedure:

1. Divide the students into four groups representing different drugs: nicotine, marijuana, alcohol, and hallucinogens.

2. Tell the students that they are going to create a sculpture that represents the "Essence of Health" with the items in the middle circle. Tell them, "First, we are going to look at some unhealthy behaviors."

3. Have each group identify short-and long-term effects of the drug they have been assigned. Have each group "act out" the effects to the other groups. For example, the alcohol group could portray its effects on fine motor control by acting as if they are fumbling with their keys.

4. Explain to your students that they will now create the "Essence of Health" sculpture.

5. To do this, they stand in the outside circle. The inside circle—with the props—is the sculpture space.

6. Each group needs to remember and use the drug-induced disability they portrayed.

7. The challenge is that each group will have to cross into and work in the sculpture area portraying the effect they chose earlier and when someone stops portraying the chosen effect, the whole group starts over. For example, the nicotine group might hold their breath while in the sculpture space and as soon as one of the people in their group takes a breath, the ENTIRE group must return to start again.

8. The sculptures need to use ALL the props in the circle.

Reflection:

Questions for Discussion:

1. "What was it like to try to accomplish the goal of the activity while pretending to be under the influence of the various drugs?"

2. "How did your communication and feelings toward one another change as the activity progressed?"

3. "Did your definition of the "Essence of Health" change as it became more difficult to create your original sculpture?"

4. "How would the process be different if you were not impaired by the substances?"

5. "What have you learned about the effects of substances on your ability to perform?"

 Additional Thoughts

• As a teacher, be aware that this will be virtually impossible—to build a sculpture while acting under the influence—and isn't that the point!

• Note that the intention is not to glamorize or "joke" about the effects of the various substances but this may occur as a way of managing the challenge of completing the task under the given guidelines. Be sure to stop and redirect the class if necessary.

7.26

LESSON 26

In this lesson students will differentiate between substance use, misuse, and abuse and experience the challenges of maintaining a strong peer connection in supporting drug free lifestyles.

ACTIVITY	LEARNING OBJECTIVE	TIME	PROPS	HEALTH SKILLS
Pi Chart Use, Misuse and Abuse	At the conclusion of this activity, students will be able to: • Define the words use, misuse and abuse. • Begin to create a common understanding of the issues relevant to alcohol, tobacco and other drugs. • Differentiate between legal and illegal drug use within the context of who uses drugs and why.	25 minutes	• Flip chart paper • Markers	• Core content • Accessing information • Analyze influences
Welded Ankles	• Identify how to stay connected to peers while choosing to abstain from using drugs. • Learn how to support others who want to abstain, quit and counter the negative influences of substance abuse.	25 minutes	• Feelings Marketplace Cards	• Decision making • Self-management • Interpersonal communication • Advocacy

TEACHER'S NOTES:

FRAMING	SET-UP PROCEDURE	REFLECTION

Pi Charting Use, Misuse and Abuse

Set Up:

NONE

Framing:

"There was a time when people would say that legal drugs were good, illegal drugs were bad, and prescription drugs were helpful. However, drugs may be helpful or harmful depending on how they are used. There are three main categories of drug use—use, misuse or abuse."

Procedure:

1. Ask the class to organize themselves into three groups.
2. Give each small group a piece of paper with either the words *substance use, substance misuse* or *substance abuse* on the top and the words *looks like, sounds like, feels like* beneath (refer to previous Pi Charting activity on page…) and markers.
3. Tell the class that they are going to spend some time defining the words use, misuse and abuse with regard to substances.
4. Ask students to begin to fill out the charts in their small groups. Give the class an example: Substance Use looks like smoking a cigarette, sounds like heavy breathing and feels like relaxation.
5. Rotate sheets to each group reminding students that they cannot alter what someone else has written—just add to the definition.
6. Definitions may be written words, phrases or pictures.
7. Ask the groups to present their definitions to the entire group and have a general discussion.

Reflection:

Knowledge Review:

1. Review each chart and take this excellent opportunity to dispel myths about substance use, misuse and abuse.

 Additional Thoughts

• Keep the small groups to no more than five students to ensure that everyone has a chance to contribute.

• If you have a large class you can post the charts and have students participate in a collective "gallery tour" versus individual small group presentations. Then clarify myths and so on.

Welded Ankles

Set Up:

1. Clear a large, open space in your classroom.

Framing

"Tobacco is considered to be a 'gateway drug' or drug that leads to the use of other drugs including alcohol. According to the National Institute on Drug Abuse, 12-17 year olds who smoke cigarettes are 14 times more likely to abuse alcohol, 100 times more likely to smoke marijuana, and 32 times more likely to use cocaine than are their non-smoking peers. We know that staying committed and connected to peers is the best way to avoid ever getting started, but this is a challenge."

Procedure:

1. Ask the class to line up on one side of the room, standing side by side with their feet shoulder-width apart and ankles "welded" together.
2. Typically, a group of 10 students "welded" together should be your maximum, but fewer than eight is not challenging enough. So, split your students into small groups using these guidelines.
3. Explain to the class that their task is to walk across the room to the other side, turn around and walk back while maintaining their ankle connections.
4. Be sure to tell the class that if they lose connection they need to start again.

Reflection:

Reflection Activity:

1. Scatter the Feelings Marketplace Cards on the floor and have students sit in a circle around them.
2. Ask the students to select several cards that represent the different feelings that arose during this activity.
3. Have the class go around and share their feelings.
4. Discuss how these feelings relate what it feels like to abstain or quit using a substance or stopping an addiction.
5. Have students identify feelings and strategies that were helpful in moving across the space.
6. Discuss how these feelings and strategies may be accessed in supporting one another in abstaining, quitting and countering negative influences of substance abuse.

💡 **Additional Thoughts**

• *Do not allow students to tie their shoe laces together!!*

• *Be sure there is enough maneuvering space for more than one group!*

7.27

SUBSTANCE
ABUSE
PREVENTION

LESSON 27

In this lesson students will identify sources of peer and community support for substance abuse prevention.

ACTIVITY	LEARNING OBJECTIVE	TIME	PROPS	HEALTH SKILLS
Wall of Support	**At the conclusion of this activity, students will be able to:** • Identify sources of support available to meet the challenges of substance abuse prevention. • Identify community resources to help manage interventions and treatment for substance abuse. • Identify family, school and community resources available to help maintain a healthy lifestyle.	40–50 minutes	• Several pieces of colored paper cut the size of index cards or multicolored index cards • Pens or pencils or markers • Masking or scotch tape	• Core content • Accessing information • Analyze influences • Advocacy

TEACHER'S NOTES:

FRAMING	SET-UP PROCEDURE	REFLECTION

Wall of Support

Set Up:

1. Clear space on a classroom wall to create the Wall of Support.

Framing

"We have spent a lot of time exploring the different challenges of being a healthy adolescent, most recently with respect to substance abuse prevention. Sometimes being healthy can seem overwhelming and lonely. Let's build a wall of support to combat those feelings and reinforce our commitment to being healthy young people!"

Procedure:

1. Pass out index cards and/or papers and writing instruments to students.
2. Ask each student to identify as many sources of individual, family, school, and community support as possible.
3. Have students write each one on a separate slip of paper.
4. Ask students to begin to build a "Wall of Support" by taping rows of their resources onto a wall.
5. Students should do this individually, i.e., I would tape all six of my identified resources, then Joe would do his, Barbara hers, etc. Students will be overwhelmed with the amount of support that is available to them.

Reflection:

Questions for Discussion:

1. "Take a moment to reflect on your Wall of Support. Do you see any categories or commonalities in the resources identified?"
2. "Are there any surprises?"
3. "What is it like to know that all that support is available to you as you choose to maintain a healthy lifestyle?"
4. "What's missing?"

Grade 8

INJURY PREVENTION / MENTAL EMOTIONAL HEALTH

CREATING COMMUNITY

Lesson 1:

In this lesson students will begin to understand concepts of health and wellness as well as Adventure-based learning.

  Activities: Paradigm Shift
        Elevator Air
        Name Card Exchange
        Silent Line-Up

Lesson 2:

In this lesson students will strengthen and expand their understanding of concepts of health and wellness—identification of the different domains of wellness and specific behaviors related to healthy self-concept and self-esteem.

  Activities: Name Gesture
        Everybody's It X 2
        Be Like Me Tag

Lesson 3:

In this lesson students will begin to understand the concepts of different learning styles and identify behaviors that support effective learning.

  Activities: Cross the Line
        Tower of Power (FVC)

GOAL SETTING

Lesson 4:

In this lesson students will apply supportive behaviors through active cooperation and competition as well as identify goals for the semester.

  Activities: Pass the Power
        Expectations/Concerns

Lesson 5:

In this lesson students will identify individual health behavior goals for the semester.

  Activities: Name Toss with Goal
        Popcorn

STRESS MANAGEMENT

Lesson 6:

In this lesson students will practice distraction control, refusal skills and assertive communication.

  Activities: Hi, Lo, Yo and No!
        Measure Breath w/Visualization

Lesson 7:

In this lesson students will recognize different effects of stress, begin to understand individual stress responses and the impact stress has on effective decision-making.

  Activities: Up Chuck
        I Hear You But I Can't See You

STRESS AND CONFLICT

Lesson 8:

In this lesson students will experience the relationship between stress and conflict as well as the challenge of maintaining healthy family and peer relationships in order to better understand.

  Activities: Balloon Bash
        Balloon Trolleys

Lesson 9:

In this lesson students will apply the concept of caring for self and others.

  Activities: Circle the Circle
        Helium Hoop

Lesson 10:

In this lesson students will explore their ability to act cooperatively in a chaotic, competitive setting.

  Activities: Conflict Connection

CULTURAL AWARENESS/RELATIONSHIPS

Lesson 11:

In this lesson students will be introduced to the concepts of changes in perception and communication with regard to diversity.

  Activities: Snowflake
        See Ya!

Lesson 12:

In this lesson students will better understand concepts related to diversity, culture, discrimination, prejudice and stereotypes.

Activities: Defining Ourselves
Pi Charting

Lesson 13:

In this lesson students will further explore culture – their own and others'.

Activities: Change Up
Culture Jam

Lesson 14:

In this lesson students will share cultural heritage and traditions as well as explore feelings associated with different social groups.

Activities: History of My Name
Mind, Body, Soul

Lesson 15:

In this lesson students will reinforce concepts of peer support and healthy relationships and create a peer support network that will sustain major put downs.

Activity: Great American Egg Drop

NUTRITION

Lesson 16:

In this lesson students will review the components of a healthy diet.

Activities: Food Pyramid Tag
Food Pyramid Juggle

Lesson 17:

In this lesson students will find there nutrient match and learn how to select a nutritious meal.

Activities: I Need Someone Who
Fast Food Frenzy

Lesson 18:

In this lesson students will explore the concepts of fad dieting and body image.

Activities: Nutrition Have You Ever?
Oh, The Shape I'm In

Lesson 19:

In this lesson students will create a visual representation of their body image timeline and identify contributing influences to nutrition and weight management patterns.

Activity: Pictures of Me

PHYSICAL FITNESS

Lesson 20:

In this lesson students will identify multiple opportunities for fitness and recognize the benefits of cardiovascular fitness.

Activities: Fitness Whomp 'Em
Fast Back

Lesson 21:

In this lesson students will further explore the consequences of a lack of physical fitness and establish proper exercise, nutrition and sleep patterns.

Activities: Hospital Tag
Healthy Lifestyle Relay

Lesson 22

In this lesson students will support one another in staying active and review principles of physical fitness.

Activities: Team Tag
Let's Get Together For Fitness

Lesson 23:

In this lesson students will learn how to manage consequences of making unhealthy choices while implementing a plan to promote health and fitness.

Activity: Pathways To Health and Fitness

SUBSTANCE ABUSE PREVENTION

Lesson 24:

In this lesson students will revisit the concepts of positive peer pressure and come to consensus on how to help each other stay safe and substance free.

Activities: Leader/Follower
Spaghetti Junction

Lesson 25:

In this lesson students will practice the buddy check-in system for social situations as well as begin to understand how to access community resources and take personal responsibility for staying substance free.

Activities: I'm OK, You OK? Tag
It Takes a Village

Lesson 26:

In this lesson students will further apply decision making and problem solving skills.

Activities: Needle and Thread Tag
ATOD 12 Bits

Lesson 27:

In this lesson students will explore the relationship between risk factors and the support needed to move safely through social situations, while recognizing the appeal of thrill seeking.

Activity: Pipeline

Creating Community

8.1

COMMUNITY
BUILDING

LESSON 1

In this lesson students will begin to understand concepts of health and wellness as well as Adventure-based learning.

ACTIVITY	LEARNING OBJECTIVE	TIME	PROPS	HEALTH SKILLS
Paradigm Shift	At the conclusion of this activity, students will be able to: • Examine health and wellness from a variety of perspectives. • Review the principles of Adventure-based learning.	5–8 minutes	• None	• All
Elevator Air	• Recognize components of an open, healthy learning community. • Differentiate between healthy and unhealthy learning communities.	8–10 minutes	• None	• Interpersonal communication • Self-management • Advocacy
Name Card Exchange	• Recall the names of people in the group. • List three personal preferences and accomplishments that correlate with self esteem. • Apply the process of accessing accurate information from peers.	15 minutes	• Index cards • Markers	• Interpersonal communication • Accessing information • Analyze influences • Core content
Silent Line-Up	• Practice non-verbal communication skills. • Reinforce their recollection of the names of people in their class.	5–8 minutes	• None	• Interpersonal communication • Goal setting Decision making

TEACHER'S NOTES:

FRAMING	SET-UP PROCEDURE	REFLECTION

Paradigm Shift

Set Up:

NONE

Framing:

"The way we look at things greatly impacts our ability to make good decisions and solve problems successfully. It also defines how we think about ourselves and others. Being able to understand our own perspective and to consider other points of view is essential to creating and maintaining a healthy lifestyle."

Procedure:

1. Ask the students to stand in a circle.
2. Ask them to imagine that there is an analog clock on the ceiling, facing downward.
3. Have students point their index fingers toward their imaginary clock, fully extending their arms upward and begin to circle their arms clockwise (they will be standing still—moving just one arm).
4. They should keep moving their arms clockwise pointing to where they see 12, then to 3, 6, 9 and back to 12.
5. Tell students to continually watch the tip of their finger and continue circling throughout the exercise.
6. Ask students to slowly lower their finger by bending their elbow. Note that the finger remains pointing upward toward the clock and continues to circle.
7. Continue bending the elbow until their fingers are below their chins, then have them look down at their circling finger.
8. Ask students to observe in what direction the finger is now circling.
9. Have students repeat process a couple of times on their own.

Reflection:

Question for discussion:

1. Most students will be a bit surprised to find that their finger is now going counterclockwise. Ask them, "How did this happen?"

Knowledge Review:

2. Most students will say that it is from looking at things from a different point of view. Use this as a starting point to explain the comprehensive concept of health and wellness and the Adventure-based learning approach in this class. Remind students of the concepts and approaches covered in grades six and seven if appropriate.

Additional Thoughts

• *Some students will turn their hand as they bring the finger downward, resulting in no change of direction. That's OK! Ask them to try again. And then explain that if you automatically adjust, by turning your hand, the direction of the circle won't change. You can choose to highlight this as an example of our natural tendency to keep things "status quo" and the challenge of changing perspectives, or not!*

Elevator Air

Set Up:

1. Clear an open space in the classroom.

Framing

"What happens when people get on an elevator? (Pause for answers.) There is a certain feeling of awkwardness. People are not talking. They are looking at the numbers that indicate what floor you are on and giving each other lots of space. Let's call that Elevator Air. Elevator Air happens in groups and classes, especially when we are talking about health and wellness. We want to change Elevator Air and create a learning community that is open and responsive. Let's practice creating that learning community."

Procedure:

1. Have students stand in a circle within the open space.
2. Introduce the activity and tell students that "it is important to recognize Elevator Air. Elevator Air suffocates our learning community. To help us recognize it, we are going to practice crossing the circle with 'thick' Elevator Air".
3. Ask students to cross over to the other side of the circle, at the count of three, in a way that represents thick Elevator Air; (i.e., no talking, no eye-contact, no touching).
4. You can invite students to put their hands up in front of their torso to act as bumpers in the event of physical contact.
5. Ask students to reflect for a moment on what that felt like and what it would be like to try to learn in that type of environment.

6. Ask students if they have ever experienced the very common head nod or smile greetings. People are not really going all out and saying hello, but unlike Elevator Air, they are acknowledging each other's presences.

7. Ask the students to cross again at the count of three still not touching each other, but acknowledging a few people with a nod or a smile.

8. Ask students to reflect for a moment on what that felt like and what it would be like to try to learn in that type of environment.

9. Finally, ask students to cross for the last time at the count of three, greeting at least three people in a way that feels comfortable. Say to the students, "You can give each other a high five, a hand shake, a low five, or a hug—whatever works for you and the person you are greeting." This round will really get rid of the Elevator Air!

10. Ask students to reflect for a moment on what that felt like and what it would be like to try to learn in that type of environment.

Reflection:

Question for Discussion:

1. "How did you feel the three crossings differed from each other?"

Knowledge Review:

2. Ask students to identify some things that may be important in developing an open learning environment. For example, saying hello to one another.

3. Remind students that all three greeting styles they experienced are common when working in groups and that it is up to the class to create and reinforce the type of learning community they would like to be.

 Additional Thoughts

• *It is a good idea to check in after each crossing by asking each student what it was like to cross within the different parameters. The responses you get will be more focused than if you discuss all three at once.*

Name Card Exchange

Set Up:
NONE

Framing

"Accessing reliable information is one of the most important things you can do to help make good decisions about your health. Sometimes, however, by the time we hear 'the news' the information has been changed considerably. Do you remember the game Telephone? This activity is a bit like Telephone in that we are going to be exchanging information about ourselves with the class. We will do our best to listen and remember what we learned about our classmates and see what happens to information even with the best intentions!"

Procedure:

1. Have the students form a circle.

2. Pass out index cards and markers to students.

3. Have three questions prepared for the class.
   Sample Questions:
   a. Favorite/Least Favorite Food?
   b. Favorite Movie?
   c. Favorite Song?
   d. Favorite Recreation?
   e. Greatest Adventure?

4. Ask students to write their name or nickname on the front of the index card.

5. Collect markers.

6. Ask students to think of the response to the three questions you have chosen.

7. Have students introduce themselves to one other person and talk about their response to the three questions. Someone might say, "Hi, my name is Pete and Chinese pot stickers are my favorite food. I loved the Lord of the Rings movies and my favorite song is Clocks by Coldplay."

8. Explain that when the introductions are done, students are to exchange cards, and therefore exchange identities! For example, if Alison and Katie exchanged information, Katie would then introduce herself to someone else, while holding the name card that says Alison, and while sharing the three pieces of information about Alison.

9. Ask students to exchange identities at least three times and then step to the outside of the circle so that people will know when someone is finished.

10. Once the group is finished, have students introduce the person whose card they are holding and the responses to the three questions.

11. It is important to remind students at this point that, "This is not a test. This is about what happens to information as it gets passed along, so do the best you can to remember. In the spirit of creating that open learning community…if you are stuck…ask for help! Also, if you choose to make something up, be respectful and safe."

12. Explain to students that one person will go, give the name card back to the person they introduced, then that person will introduce him/herself and so on until everyone has been introduced.

Reflection:

Questions for Discussion:

1. Ask students to state the range of responses to each question. For example, "What were some of the favorite foods we heard about?"

2. "How helpful is it to know what similarities and differences you have with your classmates?"

3. "Did anything surprise you about the responses?"

4. "What happened to the information as it was passed along from person to person?"

Knowledge Review:

5. Finally have students identify some skills and strategies to obtain accurate information about their peers and health and wellness.

6. Review names.

 Additional Thoughts

• *Remind students that you are creating a safe learning environment and that it is not appropriate to make up stories about their peers when speaking about them. Be sure to emphasize that the goal is to do the best they can when representing other students in the class and to ask for help if they can't remember the responses to the questions. Address any inappropriate comments by stopping the process. Have the student being referenced share his or her own responses to the questions.*

Silent Line-Up

Set Up:

1. Clear an open space in your classroom.

Framing:

"This activity presents a little different kind of challenge because it involves completing a task without using speech, sign language or written communication. It is also a great way to remember each other's names."

Procedure:

1. Have students stand in a circle inside the space.

2. Tell the class that the goal of this activity is to line up in a circle, alphabetically by the first letter of their first name, as quickly and accurately as possible without talking or using any other kind of communication such as showing ID cards and so on.

3. Identify the beginning (A) of the circle, and the end of the circle (Z)

4. Tell them that they should raise their hands in a victory sign (demonstrate) when they think that they have lined-up in order, letting you know that they are definitely finished.

5. Go!

6. Before you debrief or have people share names for accuracy, introduce the thumbometer concept.

7. Tell the class that "the thumbometer is referred to as the confidence meter. If your thumb is straight up in the air, you are 100% confident that the class is lined up accurately. If your thumb is pointing straight down toward the floor, you are 100% confident that the group is not lined up accurately. If your thumb is pointing sideways and moving up and down a bit then you are confident that some people are in the right spot, but not everyone." Demonstrate each thumbometer position as you explain it.

8. Ask the group to show their confidence meter reading on the count of three and acknowledge the response.

9. Tell the class that if any adjustments need to be made, they should make them now while remaining silent.

10. Repeat confidence meter showing.

11. Repeat the activity until everyone is confident or you run out of time.

Reflection:

Questions for Discussion:

1. "Can you please go round from the start point to the end point and say your names out loud?"

2. "Did you line up in the right order?"

3. "What skills did you use to be able to line up without talking?"

4. "Where else might these skills come in handy for you during the coming semester?"

8.2

CREATING
COMMUNITY

LESSON 2

In this lesson students will reinforce and expand on their understanding of the concepts of health and wellness. They will identify the different domains of wellness and specific behaviors related to healthy self-concept and self-esteem.

ACTIVITY	LEARNING OBJECTIVE	TIME	PROPS	HEALTH SKILLS
Name Gesture	**At the conclusion of this activity, students will be able to:** • Name students in class. • Identify and reinforce behaviors related to healthy self-concept and self-esteem.	10 minutes	• None	• Self-management • Interpersonal communication
Everybody's It X 2	• Apply cooperation skills in competitive setting. • Apply effective decision making skills in highly active environment.	10 minutes	• 4 cones for boundary markers	• Self-management • Goal setting • Decision making • Interpersonal communication
Be Like Me Tag	• Identify specific health behaviors in the different domains of wellness. • List relevance of identified health behaviors to self-esteem and self-concept.	20–25 minutes	• 4 cones for boundary markers	• Self-management • Interpersonal communication • Core content

TEACHER'S NOTES:

FRAMING	SET-UP PROCEDURE	REFLECTION

Name Gesture

Set Up:

NONE

Framing

"As we continue to build our learning community it is important that we create an image or picture for ourselves of what healthy eighth grade students might look like or sound like. It is also important that we reinforce these images to keep them present in our minds."

Procedure:

1. Ask the class to stand in a circle.
2. Ask the students to think of a full body gesture that represents what they believe healthy Middle School students look like and sound like.
3. Tell students to say their names and perform their gestures, one by one.
4. Tell students that after each person performs, the group will mirror back what they have heard and seen that person do.
5. Say "For example, my name is Michelle, and I am taking a deep, cleansing breath. You will all follow by saying, 'Michelle' and take a deep, cleansing breath."
6. Ask for a volunteer to start and decide to go to the left or right of that person until everyone has had a chance to express themselves individually.

Reflection:

Reflection Activity:

1. Make some observations on the gestures that were displayed to represent healthy middle school students.
2. If the students seem ready, you can ask them what they observed.
3. Remember this is a fairly quick check-in, unless something major developed during the activity or from the discussion

---

 Additional Thoughts

• *Give students the option to pass if they are not quite ready with their gesture. Be sure to come back to them after you have gone around the circle once.*

Everybody's It X 2

Set Up:

1. Clear an open space in your classroom.

2. Create a boundary area with your cones that is suitable for the number of players. For ten people a 20' x 20' area should suffice. Increase the size accordingly for additional players.

Framing:

"Trying to stay healthy requires some vigilance. You have to watch what you eat, exercise and avoid the temptation of unhealthy behaviors such as drugs and alcohol. You also have to know how to find help when you get stuck. This is a fun activity that will test your ability to be vigilant and avoid the temptation of bad influences and behaviors as symbolized by getting tagged. Avoid being tagged and help others become unstuck and you will be crowned 'most healthy'."

Procedure:

1. Have students form a circle inside the boundaries.

2. Explain, "We are going to play a game of tag, with a twist! Guess who is it? Everybody is it! You might remember this from another grade."

3. Tell the class, "This is a good time to discuss safety guidelines. An appropriate tag is a gentle touch on the back of the shoulder area." Demonstrate an appropriate tag. "We are going to move at a fast walk, not a run, a fast walk like this." Demonstrate a fast walk.

4. Tell the class that on the Start command everyone will be trying to tag everyone while at the same time everyone will be trying to get away from everyone. As soon as a person is tagged, they immediately freeze with their hands open, facing outward and up in a high five position. Demonstrate this position. The last person moving will be, as described in the Framing section, the healthiest person in the group.

5. Ask the class to identify a favorite fruit and pick one, for example, strawberries. Tell the students, "When you hear me say, "Strawberries" the tagging will begin. Until then, we will practice fast walking in the boundaries."

6. Say a couple of different fruits and then say "Strawberries" to begin the tagging. The tagging continues until there are two people left unfrozen.

7. Play another round and then have the class form a circle to explain the second version of Everybody's It.

8. Explain to the class that "the game is fundamentally the same, except that when you are frozen, one of your classmates can unfreeze you by giving you a 'high ten.' A high ten is like a high five but with both hands."

9. Ask for a favorite vegetable as the start command for this round and then start the class in the same sequence as the first version.

10. The tagging will continue until you call an end to the game as students will continuously be frozen and unfrozen.

Reflection:

Questions for Discussion:

1. "How vigilant did you have to be to successfully avoid unhealthy influences in the first version?"

2. "How vigilant did you have to be to successfully avoid unhealthy influences in the second version?"

3. "How does working at being healthy in the game, with and without support, relate to your life?"

4. "What are some skills that you have learned that could help you avoid things that may not be healthy for you and access things that are healthy for you?

 Additional Thoughts

• *Some rules:*

    a. No running; fast walking only.
    b. Tags should be made only with hands; no kicking.

• *The second version will most likely continue until you stop it so watch for fatigue and end the game while people are still pretty active.*

Be Like Me Tag

Set Up:

1. Clear an open area in your classroom.

2. Create a boundary area with your cones that is suitable for the number of players. For ten people a 20'x 20' area should suffice. Increase the size accordingly for additional players.

Framing:

"There are many ways to be healthy beyond eating well and exercising. In this activity we are going to reinforce and expand our ideas of what healthy behaviors are by identifying examples from the different domains of wellness. Participating in behaviors from the different domains directly affects the way we describe and feel about ourselves."

Procedure:

1. Ask students to form a circle inside the boundaries.
2. Revisit the wellness domains (physical, social, spiritual, environmental, emotional, and mental) with your class. Explain the importance of a balanced approach to being healthy.
3. Similar to Name Gesture, have students create a unique gesture using only one hand that represents a healthy behavior from any of the wellness domains. Some examples are the motion of brushing your teeth or a hand to the ear for active listening.
4. Be sure that each student has a different sign/motion and that the gesture requires only one hand.
5. Go around the circle and have students show their healthy behavior and have them explain how it relates to a wellness domain.
6. Next explain to the class that they are going to participate in a tag game. The objective of the tag game is to try to get your classmates to "be like you" and participate in a variety of healthy behaviors.
7. The activity begins with everyone performing their healthy behavior while moving (you can choose the speed, but a fast walk works well for the average number of students in the average classroom) within the boundaries. At your signal, students may start tagging one another. Once again they are all taggers. Once tagged, the person changes his or her healthy behavior to that of the person who tagged them.
8. Say to the students "For example, "if I have my hand on my ear for active listening and I tag Sean who is brushing his teeth, he stops brushing his teeth and puts his hand on his ear for active listening. Both of us continue trying to tag others to switch them to active listening."
9. The group can continue tagging until you tell them to stop.
10. Do another round or two.

Reflection:

Reflection Activity:

1. Have students find a partner and discuss what kinds of healthy behaviors they each were able to experience.
2. Ask the partners to each identify three ways that these healthy behaviors influence how they describe themselves (self concept) and how they feel about themselves (self-esteem).

Additional Thoughts

- *You may get a lot of questions during the explanation stage of this activity. Be patient and give a variety of examples.*

- *Remind students to keep tagging and not to freeze when tagged.*

- *Stop the game when everyone is performing the same one or two motions.*

- *Divide the class into two smaller groups if it is larger than 20 students and have them play in two separate spaces.*

LESSON 3

In this lesson students will begin to understand the concepts of different learning styles and identify behaviors that support effective learning.

ACTIVITY	LEARNING OBJECTIVE	TIME	PROPS	HEALTH SKILLS
Cross the Line	**At the conclusion of this activity, students will be able to:** • Recognize that there are different learning styles. • Apply strategies for maintaining positive interpersonal relationships in their classroom.	20 minutes	• 2 15-foot ropes or 4 cones	• Decision making • Analyze influences
Tower of Power (Full Value Contract)	• Establish behavioral guidelines for the class. • Associate the importance of bonding, communication and responsibility in enhancing self-esteem. • Connect positive thinking with well-being.	30 minutes	• 50-100 9-12 inch balloons • Masking tape • Markers	• Core content • Interpersonal communication

TEACHER'S NOTES:

FRAMING	SET-UP PROCEDURE	REFLECTION

Cross the Line

Set Up:

1. Clear an open space in your classroom.

2. Place one piece of rope on the ground in a straight line at one end of the open space leaving enough room for the class to gather behind that line.

3. Place the second piece of rope on the ground, in a straight line, about 30 feet away also with room for students behind it. Cones can be used instead of rope. They would be placed at the four corners of a large rectangle.

Framing:

"Each of us has a preferred learning style or way we like to learn. It is important that we understand not only how we as individuals like to learn but how our classmates like to learn so we can support and encourage one another this semester."

Procedure:

1. Ask students to "clump together" behind one of the lines or behind two cones at one of the small ends of the rectangle.

2. Ask students to identify some ways that people like to learn. Say, "For example, by reading, by touching, by talking with others, by taking their time and reflecting." Be sure to dramatize the types of learning you are citing as you describe them to the class. For example, a dramatization of reading might be looking at a pretend book whose pages are flipped with one hand while being held by the other.

3. Explain to the class that the space between the lines or in the rectangle represents the classroom. They are going to have the opportunity to move through this classroom in a variety of ways.

4. The first crossing represents how students learn. Ask students to "Cross over the open space, individually, when you are ready, in a way that represents how you like to learn. It is fine if more than one person is crossing at a time, as long as people are individually expressing how they learn."

5. Notice what different people are doing. For example, "OK. We have readers; we have wanderers; we have people going backwards, etc".

6. Ask the class what types of learning styles they noticed.

7. Ask students to find a partner and with that partner, cross in a way that represents how they might help each other learn. Again, ask for ideas from the group first. Some examples of this are: pretending to have a discussion or pretending to take notes and share. (Note: If the group moves quickly to partners and is involved in getting ready to cross there is no need to get ideas).

8. Ask the partners to explain how they supported each other.

9. For the third crossing, have students organize themselves into two equal groups. Ask each group to cross in a way that represents how they like to have fun in the classroom.

10. Ask each group to identify the ways they like to have fun.

11. Finally, have the whole class work together in one large group and cross together in a way that represents their healthy learning community.

Reflection:

The debriefing for this activity occurs after each crossing during the activity.
Tell the group that they will need to remember what they represented for the next activity.

. . . .

Tower of Power

Set Up:

1. Clear a relatively large space in your classroom.

Framing:

"Healthy communities are founded upon strong friendships and respectful relationships. This activity explores what we need from others to build the kinds of connections that promote healthy communities."

Procedure:

1. Divide the class into three equal groups; one that represents support, one that represents fun and one that represents a healthy learning environment. Build upon the things students identified in the last activity.

2. Give each group several balloons and markers.

3. Have masking tape available.

4. Explain to the class that they are going to record the representations from the last activity on the balloons. The fun group's job is to remember the different ways the class represented having fun. The support group's task is to record the different ways students represented supporting one another. The healthy learning environment group's task is to record the different behaviors in a healthy learning environment.

5. Tell each group to blow up the balloons, tie them off and write only one representation per balloon. They have five minutes to complete this part of the activity.

6. Have the class come together and share what is written on the balloons. Ask if anything is missing and then add balloons if needed.

7. Explain to the class the next challenge is to take all of the balloons using only masking tape as an additional prop, and build the tallest, free standing tower possible.

8. Tell students that the finished structure represents the group's "Tower of Power" for building and maintaining positive relationships in their healthy learning community.

Reflection:

Questions for Discussion:

1. "Did you demonstrate some of the qualities/behaviors you wrote on your balloons as you built the Tower of Power?"

2. For each student: "Tell us about one thing you could do that will continue to improve your relationship with the people around you." and/or "Tell us about one thing you could do that will continue to support your healthy learning environment."

 Additional Thoughts

• *Limit one idea to each balloon but use as many balloons as there are ideas. For example, a group of 10 may use 25 balloons.*

• *You can keep the groups divided and have them each build a separate Tower of Power. Then bring the groups together to connect the three individual Towers into one for the entire class.*

• *Have the class denote the components of the Tower of Power on flip chart paper. This can serve as a Full Value Contract. Ask for a sign of commitment to try to uphold this FVC in your classroom. This can be posted on your classroom wall for ongoing use.*

Goal Setting

8.4

GOAL SETTING

LESSON 4

In this lesson students will practice supportive behaviors.

ACTIVITY	LEARNING OBJECTIVE	TIME	PROPS	HEALTH SKILLS
Pass The Power	**At the conclusion of this activity, students will be able to:** • Apply behavioral guidelines identified in the previous activity. • Integrate concepts of communication, responsibility and positive thinking.	20 minutes	• 4 cones for boundary markers • Rubber chicken	• Interpersonal communication • Advocacy • Self-management
Expectations and Concerns	• List expectations, as well as concerns about participating in the Adventure-based health class. • Discuss how to choose and work toward achieving goals. • Describe ways to overcome barriers to achieving goals.	30 minutes	• Flip chart paper • Markers	• Goal setting • Decision making • Advocacy • Self-management • Analyze influences

TEACHER'S NOTES:

FRAMING	SET-UP PROCEDURE	REFLECTION

Pass the Power

Set Up:

1. Clear a large, open space in your classroom.
2. Define this space with traffic cones or the like.

Framing:

"During the last class we created a Tower of Power which identified the ways that we can support one another in our classroom. This activity will give us the opportunity to practice those behaviors; however, our challenge will be to do that in a competitive setting."

Procedure:

1. Ask students to form a circle in the middle of the open space.
2. Have the rubber chicken with you as you explain the activity.
3. Tell the class that they are going to have the opportunity to challenge themselves and their ability to practice supportive behaviors while participating in a competitive tag game.
4. Ask for a volunteer to be "the tagger." The person who is "the tagger" represents the one person in the class who is willing to practice the behaviors on the Tower of Power. The goal of the person who is "the tagger" is to tag the people who are not "taggers" to get them to practice the supportive healthy behaviors.
5. The goal of those who are not "taggers" is to avoid being tagged. However, when a person is tagged, they become a member of the "tagger" or Tower of Power team.
6. Explain that a tag occurs when someone is touched with the rubber chicken below the knee on either leg. A touch anywhere else does not count.
7. Also let students know that when a member of the Tower of Power team is holding the rubber chicken, they can only take one pivot step in any direction. Other Tower of Power members can move about and position themselves to catch a pass/toss and tag a new "member."
8. Also tell the class that "things may get confusing and so at any time anyone can call, "Tower of Power." When this happens, everyone freezes and anyone on the Tower of Power team needs to stand tall and strong, flex their muscles and say, "We're here."
9. The game then resumes with everyone moving as "normal."
10. The game ends when everyone is on the "Tower of Power" team.

Reflection:

Questions for Discussion:

1. "Tell us what happened during this tag game."
2. "What strategies allowed one person to eventually get everyone else to become part of the Tower of Power team?"
3. "How does competition affect our desire to work together?"

Knowledge Review

4. Finish by going around the group and asking each student to identify one behavior from the Tower of Power that will help keep the class moving in a positive direction.

· ·

Expectations/Concerns

Set Up:

1. Prep six pages of flip chart paper—three with the word *Expectations* written on top and three with the word *Concerns* written on top.

Framing:

"I am interested to hear what your expectations and concerns are for this course. It is important that you express what you are thinking so that we set ourselves up for a successful semester. Expectations can be defined as what you are hoping to learn about, would like to achieve, etc. Concerns are anything that may get in the way of your ability to meet your expectations such as shyness, time management, etc."

Procedure:

1. Have students divide themselves into six equal groups of about three to five per group.
2. Give each group a piece of paper and some markers.
3. Explain to the class that each group will have one piece of flip chart paper with either *Expectations* or *Concerns* written on the top.
4. Tell the students that the goal of the activity is to get as many of their expectations and concerns recorded as possible. Each group will spend about 10-15 minutes on this, discussing their responses as they go.
5. After everyone is finished and ready to move on, have the three *Expectations* groups switch with the three *Concerns* groups.

6. Explain again that students will have 10–15 minutes to express themselves adding to what is already written on the paper they just received.

7. Be sure to explain to the students that they can star or check words that they are in agreement with, but they may not modify what anyone else has written.

Reflection:

1. This activity is best debriefed by walking through the information on the flip chart paper, starting with *Expectations* and then *Concerns*.

2. Always ask for clarification on items and encourage additions if needed.

 Additional Thoughts

• *This is an excellent tool for getting lots of information quickly, allowing students to have a voice.*

• *This may take longer than other activities, but is worth the investment as it sets parameters for doing activities during the rest of the semester and will provide you with great information.*

• *Be sure to clarify what the expectations are for the class and address concerns where possible as a teacher or class or both. For example, if a student says "I expect to be able to do 50 sit ups by the end of the semester," it is an opportunity to clarify what the class does and does not cover.*

8.5

GOAL
SETTING

LESSON 5

In this lesson students will practice supportive behaviors.

ACTIVITY	LEARNING OBJECTIVE	TIME	PROPS	HEALTH SKILLS
Name Toss with a Goal	At the conclusion of this activity, students will be able to: • State and commit to a personal goal for the health class. • Explore strategies for supporting one another in achieving their goals.	20 minutes	• Tossable Object	• Goal setting • Decision making • Advocacy • Self-management • Analyze influences
Popcorn	• Demonstrate the ability to set goals. • Describe steps for setting goals. • Identify influences on achieving goals.	30 minutes	• Popcorn bucket • Assorted bouncing balls and objects • Boundary markers as needed • Stopwatch	• Goal setting • Decision making • Self-management • Core content

TEACHER'S NOTES:

FRAMING	SET-UP PROCEDURE	REFLECTION

Name Toss with a Goal

Set Up:

1. Clear an open space in your classroom.

Framing:

"We have started to set goals and develop and clarify expectations for this class. In a moment I will ask you to set at least one goal for the semester. However, as we have all experienced, setting goals is useless unless we commit to them. I am wondering what 'commit to goals' means to you, and how we can support each other in achieving our health and wellness goals during this class."

Procedure:

1. Ask students to form a circle with you included in the perimeter.

2. Revisit the notion of setting goals and expectations from the previous lesson. Tell students that they will need to identify one individual goal related to health that they would like to achieve this semester. Once they have identified it, they should keep their goal to themselves until it is time to share it. They might need a few minutes to think about this. For example, "My goal is to drink at least six glasses of water a day this semester."

3. Hand the ball or tossable object to one student.

4. Beginning with the person who has the ball, have students verbalize their one goal, and then pass the ball to the person on their right who also says his/her name and goal. This continues around the circle until each student has verbalized one goal. You might say something like, "Try to remember each other's goal so you can better support one another."

5. Have the first person say his/her name and goal again, and toss the ball to someone else in the group. The second person says, "Thank you _____" (name of person who tossed the ball). _____'s goal is to _____. My name is _____ and my goal is _____."

Reflection:

Reflection Activity:

1. Have students take a few deep breaths and imagine they are working toward their goal.

Additional Thoughts

• *This can be a boring, lifeless attempt to get at goals unless you, the teacher, make it lively, and encourage group members to ask names and/or goals if they forget.*

• *Verbalizing goals and having them repeated by others makes them real and provides reinforcement for the individual.*

• *By making other group members aware of each individual's goal, the chance of the individual being reminded throughout the semester to fulfill the goal is increased.*

Popcorn

Set Up:

1. Create a large open space in your classroom.

2. Choose a playing area that allows for waffle-type balls to bounce, or change the rules to fit the playing area.

3. Set out a small "target" boundary marker around the bucket using rope. A small circle about three to five feet in diameter is usually sufficient. The distance from the boundary marker to the bucket can be varied according to the challenge desired for the group—if your students have difficulty aiming a thrown object, you may choose not to have a boundary/target with the bucket in the middle.

4. Fill the bucket so that the balls rise above the top, i.e., fill the bucket until the balls form a pile that rises above the sides of the bucket. This set up makes the activity more challenging since the last balls have to be "balanced" on top of the pile to complete the activity.

5. All balls start inside the bucket and students may position themselves anywhere around the bucket to start.

6. Have a stopwatch or other time-keeping device available.

Framing:

"We are going to move from individual to group goal setting. What are some of the practical guidelines or principles of goal setting? (Give time for them to respond.) The challenge for this activity is to apply those principles to achieve your best possible goal, using your whole class as a resource."

Procedure:

1. Explain to the class that the objective is for the students to return all of the balls into the bucket as quickly as possible.

2. Tell students that the game will begin when you start the stopwatch. They will toss all the balls into the air and then quickly replace the bucket inside the "target" boundary area.

3. Further explain that as students chase and recover the balls, they may not run or walk when they have a ball in their possession. A ball may only be moved toward the bucket by bouncing it or throwing it to another person. Anyone chasing and recovering balls is known as a "seeker."

4. Tell students that to put a ball back into the bucket, the ball should be bounced on the floor before landing in the bucket. A player may not bounce a ball, catch it and then toss it into the bucket on the fly. Anyone bouncing balls into the bucket is identified as a "bouncer."

5. Also, when bouncing a ball into the bucket, the bouncer should be standing outside the "target" boundary marker.

6. Balls may bounce on the floor inside the "target" boundary marker.

7. Once all the balls are back inside the bucket, stop the time and share the results with the class.

8. Allow a brief planning period for the class to assess its performance and to develop new strategies to improve its time. Have the class set a goal for the next round.

9. Play another round until the class has achieved its best performance.

Reflection:

Reflection Activity:

1. Ask students to work in groups of three and review the steps for setting goals.

Questions for Discussion:

2. "How were those steps applied during this activity?"

3. "What were the helpful and harmful influences they experienced or observed in setting and attempting to achieve goals during this activity?"

4. "How do those influences relate to 'real life?'"

 Additional Thoughts

• *When tossing, the balls should be thrown to achieve maximum disbursement. This way the balls are scattered over a wide area and the action is more exciting.*

Stress Management

LESSON 6

In this lesson students will practice distraction control, refusal skills and assertive communication.

ACTIVITY	LEARNING OBJECTIVE	TIME	PROPS	HEALTH SKILLS
Hi, Lo, Yo and No!	At the conclusion of this activity, students will be able to: • Identify strategies for staying focused when being distracted by others. • Apply stress-reducing strategies. • Apply refusal skills and assertive communication.	20 minutes	• Flip chart paper • Markers	• Self-management • Interpersonal communication • Analyze influences
Measured Breath with Visualization	• Relax and refresh the body in one breath. • Identify a positive experience to visualize while practicing stress reduction.	10 minutes	• None	• Self-management • Core content

TEACHER'S NOTES:

FRAMING	SET-UP PROCEDURE	REFLECTION

Hi, Lo, Yo and No!

Set Up:

1. Clear an open space in your classroom.

Framing:

"Have you ever tried to remember something when you are stressed or distracted? Some of us are very skilled at managing distractions while others need some help. This activity is a fun way to discover where our strengths and our challenges are in managing stress and distractions."

Procedure:

1. Have the students sit or stand in a circle.
2. Explain that this activity requires four basic moves, Hi, Lo, Yo and No, each with a corresponding hand gesture, and that the direction of the gesture dictates the direction of the activity.
3. The word "HI" is said by the beginner in the first move as the person makes a 'flat hand' motion with the hand above the head. The direction of the fingers (left or right) requires that the person sitting or standing at the designated side use a similar motion with the hands, but places their hand at their waist level and says "LO." Again the direction of the fingers points (left or right) to a group member who says 'YO" and points their arm and fingers at any person in the group. At this point, the sequence starts again.
4. To reiterate:

   First: HI = flat hand over player's head pointing to the left or right as HI is said.

   Second: LO comes from the HI player to right or left who pointed to the LO player and = flat hand at waist pointing either left or right as LO is said.

   Third: YO comes from the LO player to the left or right who pointed at the YO player and = fingers pointing at anyone in the group as YO is said.

   Fourth: sequence starts again…the person pointed at by the YO player is the new HI player.
5. Practice several rounds to allow people to get the rhythm of the sequence.
6. Add "NO." A player who was pointed at has the option, after YO only, to put both hands up in front of them as if to say stop, but say, "NO!" The message is then bounced back to the person who passed the YO, and he/she has to pick back up with HI.
7. Next, divide the group in half. Have one half of the group form a circle, and the second half of the group form another circle outside of the first half.

8. Explain to the groups that the inner circle will proceed with HI, LO, YO, NO while the outer circle will act as distracters.

9. Be sure to explain that distracters do not touch or block the vision of the inner circle. The distracters simply confuse other players by talking.

10. Switch inner and outer circles after a few rounds.

Reflection:

Knowledge Review:

1. Remind students that this was excellent practice for staying focused on making healthy choices when others are yelling and distracting you.

Questions for Discussion:

2. "When you were being distracted, what did you do to maintain your focus?"

3. "When you think about trying to be healthy right now, what are some of the distracters or sources of stress in your life?"

4. "How did it feel to know you have the option to say 'NO'? How is being able to say NO helpful in managing stress?"

Reflection Activity:

5. Divide the students into small groups. Keep the list posted during class.

. . . .

The Measured Breath with Visualizaton

Set Up:

1. Clear a space for the students to sit or stand or be comfortable in a circle in your classroom.

Framing:

"What is the first thing we forget to do when we get scared, excited or stressed? Breathe! Breathing is the least expensive but most powerful and most ignored skill we can use to help us manage just about any situation. In order to be able to use breathing effectively, we need to understand how to do it properly and to practice applying breathing in different situations."

Procedure:

1. Ask students to sit or lie in a comfortable position and recall an experience they had when they felt really good about themselves. It could be doing well in school, in sports, helping someone out and so on.

2. Tell the students that you are going to ask them to practice taking deep breaths.

3. Tell them that you are going to ask them to inhale to a count of six, hold that breath for a count of seven and then exhale to a count of seven.

4. Practice a couple of times.

5. Explain that this time when they are holding for the count of six, they should try to recall the image of the experience when they felt really good about themselves and let it fill their mind and body.

6. Tell them to try to take a few breaths themselves, at their own count of inhaling for six, holding for seven and exhaling for seven, with their images in mind.

Reflection:

Question for Discussion:

1. "What was Measured Breathing like for you?"

Knowledge Review

2. Explain that they can use this tool anywhere at any time…it is especially helpful when you feel yourself panicking.

3. Also explain that it works better the more they practice.

Question for Discussion:

4. "When might you use Measured Breathing? I use it (for example) when I am late and stuck in traffic."

 Additional Thoughts

• *You can combine this with Hi, Lo, Yo and No and have students apply breathing techniques to stress management/distraction management—when they are on the inside circle during the second phase of the activity.*

LESSON 7

In this lesson students will recognize some different effects of stress and begin to understand individual stress response and impact on effective decision-making.

ACTIVITY	LEARNING OBJECTIVE	TIME	PROPS	HEALTH SKILLS
Up Chuck	**At the conclusion of this activity, students will be able to:** • Identify some stressors that affect their daily lives. • Recognize that stress can have both positive and negative consequences. • Identify at least one mental, emotional and physical response to managing stressors.	10 minutes	• 1 fleece ball per student	• Self-management • Interpersonal communication
I Hear You But I Can't See You	• Begin to understand individual differences in response to stress. • Demonstrate the use of decision-making processes. • Begin to understand how effective stress management can affect well being.	30 minutes	• None	• Self-management • Interpersonal communication • Advocacy

TEACHER'S NOTES:

FRAMING	SET-UP PROCEDURE	REFLECTION

Up Chuck

Set Up:

1. Clear an open space in your classroom, large enough so that students can stand in a large circle.

Framing:

"Stress is the body's and mind's response to everyday demands. Demands or stressors can be people, objects, places, events or situations that cause you to react. Reactions to stress can be physical, mental and emotional and can be useful or harmful, energizing or exhausting. The key is to learn how to respond in a way that is healthy."

Procedure:

1. Have students stand in a circle or cluster.
2. Ask each student to identify a common stressor from their daily lives, making sure that each student's stressor is different; e.g., taking tests, doing homework or dealing with mean people.
3. Explain that the balls represent the identified stressors and that we are going to think about how stress affects our ability to respond.
4. Ask everyone to toss their balls aloft to a height of at least ten feet, and then attempt to catch one ball that they did not throw.
5. Count the number of balls that are not caught.
6. On the second round, ask students to catch as many balls as they can.
7. Count the number of balls that are not caught.
8. Repeat 6 and 7.

Reflection:

Questions for Discussion:

1. "Tell me about what happened."
2. "How did you react when you caught one ball?"
3. "Tell me one thought, feeling and/or physical response you had when you were trying to catch as many balls as possible. Do you think that thought, feeling and/or physical response helped or hurt your ability to catch balls?" Follow with "Why?"
4. "Tell me about some times in your daily lives when stress impacted your mental, emotional and physical responses in both helpful and harmful ways."

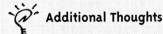
Additional Thoughts

• *Be sure that students are throwing the balls straight up in the air and being watchful of other students when trying to catch.*

• *This activity may be best played in a large space, outdoors or a gymnasium.*

I Hear You But I Can't See You

Set Up:

1. Clear an open space in your classroom.

Framing:

"How we view the world, other people, our place or sense of belonging in the world and our relationship to those things can strongly impact the kinds of stress we experience and, in turn, our level of mental, emotional and physical health."

Procedure:

1. Ask students to form a circle within the open space.

2. Explain to the group that the challenge for this activity is to line up from the lowest number to the highest number without speaking or the ability to see.

3. Explain that, in a minute, they will be asked to close their eyes. Say, "When your eyes are closed, I will go around and quietly tell each of you what your number is."

4. Ask what questions they have, and remind them about Challenge by Choice.

5. Make sure the students know to keep "bumpers up" and walk slowly when eyes are closed.

6. Ask the group to close their eyes while you go around and randomly number the class from "1" to however many students are in the class or each half of the class.

Reflection:

Reflection Activity:

Ask students to find a partner and reflect on the following:

1. "Compare and contrast how each person (in the pair, not among the group)

responded physically, mentally and/or emotionally during the course of the activity."

2. "Were your responses helpful or harmful in deciding how to line up?"

3. "How did not knowing where you belonged in the group and then finding your place in the group affect your stress response?"

4. "Name one positive physical, emotional and mental response to stressful situations."

 Additional Thoughts

• *It is a good idea to begin this activity by reinforcing the behaviors in the Full Value Contract. Be sure to offer blindfolds as an option and let students who are uncomfortable with moving with their eyes closed be spotters. Also, remind students that you will be actively spotting.*

• *Be aware of students' stress responses and encourage them to stop, breathe and then keep going if tensions begin to rise!*

• *Divide the class in half if there are more than twelve to fifteen students. Be sure that each group has a separate space.*

Stress and Conflict

LESSON 8

In this lesson students will experience the relationship between stress and conflict as well as explore the challenge of maintaining healthy family and peer relationships.

ACTIVITY	LEARNING OBJECTIVE	TIME	PROPS	HEALTH SKILLS
Balloon Bash	At the conclusion of this activity, students will be able to: • Begin to apply stress management skills during conflict. • Describe the relationship between stress, conflict and violence. • Describe behaviors and settings that threaten personal safety. • Describe ways to reduce teen violence.	25 minutes	• 1 12-inch round balloon per person (you should have some extras on hand) • Masking tape • 1 Marker per 5 students • Watch with second hand • Flip chart paper • Whistle (optional)	• Self-management • Interpersonal communication • Advocacy • Core content
Balloon Trolleys	• Begin to understand the importance of healthy relationships in managing stress. • Identify coping skills for maintaining healthy communication during stressful times.	20 minutes	• 1 12–14-inch balloon or small beach ball per student	• Core content • Interpersonal communication

TEACHER'S NOTES:

FRAMING	SET-UP PROCEDURE	REFLECTION

Balloon Bash

Set Up:

1. Create a large open space in your classroom.
2. Identify three separate areas within the open space and run a five-foot piece of masking tape on the floor from the outside edge of each area toward the center like a spoke on a wheel. (You could mark each area with cones or rope.)

Framing:

"Stress in the lives of young people seems to be on the rise. Recent studies have shown that violence as well as alcohol and drug use have been identified by students as coping strategies for stress. The use of violence and drugs or alcohol actually creates more stress in your lives. It is important that we understand how this process occurs and identify healthier stress management techniques.

Procedure:

1. Divide students into six groups of four to five people.
2. Have each small group line up on one side of a masking tape line. The small groups should stand about three feet back from the masking tape line.
3. Give the person in the middle of each line a balloon. Have them blow it up as large as they can and tie it off.
4. Explain that the object of the game is a lot like volleyball without the net. Each group scores a point when a balloon touches the ground on the opposing group's side of the masking tape.
5. There are no out-of bounds so the balloons may be hit over the team members' heads. The balloons may only be hit with hands. No kicking allowed.
6. Have each small group identify one thing that causes them negative stress represented by the balloon.
7. Explain that the play begins with the two people in the middle of each line hitting the balloon across the center line and that each round lasts for 20 seconds.
8. Each small group may score as many points during the 20 seconds as possible. When the balloon hits the floor, a point is scored by the opposing small group and the balloon is put back into play by whichever player is closest to the side where the balloon landed. Each small group keeps his or her own score.
9. Ask the group what questions they have. Reinforce proper hitting techniques. Begin.
10. Keep track of the time and stop groups when 20 seconds have passed. Check the scores from each of the small groups.

11. Have students rotate positions within their line so that they are across from a different person in each round.

12. Have each small team add another balloon, representing additional negative stressors. Now there will be four balloons in play instead of two.

13. Remind students of safety rules and then start a second round. When time runs out, check the scores.

14. Keep playing rounds and adding balloons representing negative stressors until there are ten balloons in play.

Reflection:

Reflection Activity:

1. Have students stand with their small group, facing the center of the room and forming a circle. Explain that the activity is going to be debriefed by performing a group sculpture. This means that you will ask the class a question. Each small group quickly gathers together and positions their bodies in a connected 'sculpture' that represents the response to the question.

2. Have students respond to the following questions:
   • "What was happening when there were only two negative stressors in play?"
   • "What was happening when there were four negative stressors in play?"
   • "What did you feel like doing when there were eight to ten negative stressors in play?"

3. Have each small group describe how their behaviors changed with the added stressors. For example, you noticed people hitting the balloons harder and speaking more intensely to one another. Relate this to conflict and violence.

4. Have each small group identify one healthy option for managing each of the negative stressors identified on their balloons and then share out with the class.

5. Record negative stressors and corresponding healthy management techniques on flipchart paper and keep them posted in the classroom.

 Additional Thoughts

• *This activity needs to be monitored very closely. Be sure to reinforce appropriate play guidelines such as not hitting balloons at people, staying at least three feet away from the center line on either side. Stop the action if you see any group getting out of control. You will most likely need your whistle as the noise level gets very high!*

Balloon Trolleys

Set Up:

1. Set up a curvy path throughout the desks in the classroom. Make the turns challenging but not too tight as students will have to pass through the path while connected to one another. You could outline this path with masking tape or have desks line its edge.

Framing:

"Healthy relationships are one of the most powerful sources of support for managing stressful situations. Unfortunately, we sometimes disconnect from our family and friends or communicate harshly when feeling overwhelmed and distressed. Let's see what it's like to stay connected as we move through different challenges."

Procedure:

1. Pass out one balloon to each student and ask them to blow it up and tie it off. Offer assistance if they are concerned with blowing up balloons.
2. Divide class into groups of 10–12
3. Ask students to form a line with their small group, standing front to back, like a trolley. Have them place their balloons between themselves and the person in front of them.
4. Explain that they can only use each other's pressure to support the balloons— no hands, arms or legs.
5. Explain that the challenge is moving the entire group through the path while staying connected to one another and not allowing any of the balloons to hit the floor.
6. Have students place their hands on the shoulders of the person in front of them.
7. The person at the head of the line will not have a balloon.
8. If a balloon hits the floor, the group in question should stop, retrieve the balloon, and the student who was in the front of the line moves to the end. The group can then carry on from where they lost the balloon.
9. Have the class form one large circle after each small group has finished the course.

Reflection:

Questions for Discussion:

1. "What was it like to try to stay connected as a group while moving through the path?"

2. "How did the emotions you and your classmates experienced during the activity impact verbal and nonverbal communication?"

3. "How does distress impact our relationships with our family and friends?"

4. "What are some coping skills to help us communicate with care when experiencing distress?"

 Additional Thoughts

• *Keep an eye out for emotional responses and comments regarding appropriate touch.*

• *Divide class into smaller groups if you are concerned with the students' ability to manage physical closeness of body positions. You can also place the balloons between the students as they stand side by side, if that is more manageable. Also, offer the option for students to be spotters if they are uncomfortable with the given body positions.*

LESSON 9

In this lesson students will practice the challenges of caring for self and others.

ACTIVITY	LEARNING OBJECTIVE	TIME	PROPS	HEALTH SKILLS
Circle the Circle	**At the conclusion of this activity, students will be able to:** • Demonstrate care for self and others. • Apply positive reinforcement.	10 minutes	• 2 Hula Hoops™	• Interpersonal communication • Self-management • Advocacy
Helium Hoop	• Explore the impact of individual behavior on the group process. • Begin to acquire management skills for frustration and decision making in a group setting. • Recognize the impact that others have on one's decision-making and behaviors.	30–40 minutes	• 1 Hula Hoop™ per 10 people	• Self-management • Analyze Influences • Interpersonal communication

TEACHER'S NOTES:

FRAMING	SET-UP PROCEDURE	REFLECTION

Circle the Circle

Set Up:

1. Create a large open space in your classroom.

Framing

"The ability to care for ourselves and others is an important skill. It is especially important when under the stress of trying to perform quickly. It is at times like these when we most need positive reinforcement. Let's give it a try."

Procedure:

1. Ask the class to hold hands with the person next to them forming a big circle.

2. Place one Hula Hoop™ between two people (resting on their grasped hands).

3. Explain to the students that the challenge is to try to get the Hula Hoop™ around the circle as quickly as possible without letting go of each others' hands.

4. Time a couple of rounds to see if the class can improve its efficiency.

5. Increase the challenge by adding a second Hula Hoop™. Place the two hoops over the clasped hands of two students, and have them travel in opposite directions around the circle eventually crossing over each other and going back to the originating point.

6. Designate one hoop as belonging to team A, and the other as belonging to team B. Do the activity again, with each team competing for the faster time.

Reflection:

Questions for Discussion:

1. "Did you act differently when the challenge went from a group effort with one hoop to a competition with two?"

2. "What happened to your positive reinforcement of and care for self and others when you began competing?"

Knowledge Review:

3. Ask students to silently reflect on what they could do differently in the next activity to better support one another and themselves.

 Additional Thoughts

• *Be sure that the Hula Hoops™ are large enough for everyone to be able to pass through successfully.*

Helium Hoop

Set Up:

1. Clear a large open space in your classroom.

Framing:

"Sometimes something seems that it should be easy and it is not and surprisingly we find ourselves in very difficult situations. We may feel stuck, overwhelmed, frustrated and want to blame someone else for what is happening. When we ground ourselves by managing our own thoughts, feelings and behaviors we can get through stressful situations and not be distracted by negative energy."

Procedure:

1. Divide the class into groups of 10 students and ask them to stand in a small circle with their index and middle fingers of one hand extended in front of them.

2. Explain to the class that their challenge is to lower the Hula Hoop™ as much as possible with everyone maintaining contact with the hoop at all times. No one may lose contact with the hoop.

3. Place a Hula Hoop™ in the center of the circle and ask students to rest the hoop on the front pads of their index and middle fingers only! Do this after you explain the challenge, because, as you know, as soon as you put it down, the 'helium' takes effect and they will not hear the rest of the briefing.

4. If anyone loses contact with the hoop, simply stop the process, return the hoop to waist height and try again.

5. Ask students to be aware of their communication and focus while participating in this activity.

Reflection:

Questions for Discussion:

1. "Was it as easy to do as you thought it would be when I gave you the directions?"

2. "How did you respond to the difficulty? Was it helpful or harmful to you in solving the challenge?"

3. "Were there any times during the activity when your group could have stopped and made different, healthier choices about how to proceed?"

4. "How does this experience make you think you'll handle 'real life' situations with possible healthier decision making?"

Additional Thoughts

• *Because this activity is more difficult than it sounds, it can elicit frustration very quickly. This is often evidenced by blame language. Redirect as needed.*

• *Groups will move with the hoop horizontally as well as vertically.*

• *The activity can also be finished very quickly. If so, have students switch spots in the circle and use their other hand and try again.*

LESSON 10

In this lesson students will explore their ability to act cooperatively in a chaotic, competitive setting.

ACTIVITY	LEARNING OBJECTIVE	TIME	PROPS	HEALTH SKILLS
Conflict Connection	**At the conclusion of this activity, students will be able to:** • Understand that cooperating rather than competing with peers is a more effective way to manage stressful situations. • Describe the importance of knowing and using conflict resolution skills. • Name four major categories of teen conflicts – those situations over which teens are most likely to argue or fight.	40 minutes	• 4 Large containers • 2 Boundary ropes • 12 Balls of one color (blue) • 12 Balls of a second color (red)	• Analyze influences • Interpersonal communication • Goal setting • Decision making

TEACHER'S NOTES:

FRAMING	SET-UP PROCEDURE	REFLECTION

Conflict Connection

Set Up:

1. Clear a large, rectangular space in your classroom.

2. Write and post the rules for different rounds on flip chart paper. (see Rules following Reflection)

3. Place a boundary rope across both of the shortest sides of the rectangle.

4. Label each container—front and back—with the color of one team's balls and each container's point value.

5. Place the containers between boundary markers (refer to diagram).

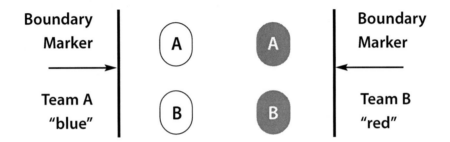

The distance from the boundary line to containers is usually four to six feet.

Framing:

"Cooperation and compromise are important aspects of healthy relationships. Conflicts often arise over territory, space, property and power, sometimes making it difficult to see the opportunity for cooperation or compromise."

Procedure:

1. Divide your students into two teams, blue—A or red—B. Then ask each team to divide into two equal groups. (There should not be more than 12 students in each of the four groups.)

2. Ask each of the groups to gather on the outside of one of the boundary markers. Each boundary marker has a group from the red team and a group from the blue team on it.

3. Explain to the students that despite the physical separation from their teammates, they will be working with them towards one goal—achieving the highest score by tossing the balls into the buckets.

4. Tell students that each of the four groups will have two target containers and 12 balls, all of the same color.

5. Although each sub-group is responsible for individual targets, the entire team attempts to achieve the highest score possible by getting all of its balls into its designated containers.

6. Explain the rules for round one and get started after answering any clarifying questions.

7. After round one is completed, introduce the rules for round two and proceed.

8. Repeat process for round three.

Reflection:

Reflection Activity:

Have students partner with someone from the opposite sub-group and respond to the following questions:

- "How did the element of competition influence the group's ability to cooperate?"
- "In what ways did the timing of each round influence people's willingness to cooperate?"
- "Name three major categories of teen conflict or situations when teens are most likely to argue or fight."
- "What are some ways that a win-win approach to this activity could have improved or did improve the overall performance of the class?"
- "How would these strategies be applied to the previously sited categories of conflict?"

Rules - Round 1

- The containers and boundary markers cannot be moved or adjusted.
- The students may briefly discuss strategy before the first round begins.
- The closest container is worth five points. The farther container is worth 10 points.
- The team will have three rounds to achieve their best score. Each round lasts 90 seconds (or until all balls are in the containers). If a group gets all the balls in containers before the time limit is reached, balls can be dumped out and thrown again. Groups need to remember how many balls were in a container when it was emptied to compile an accurate total score.
- All balls must be behind the boundary at the start of the round (Group A's balls must always start in Group A's area).
- Each sub-group may divide itself into Throwers and Retrievers. The roles are permanent for the round. The group decides how many people are in each role.
- Retrievers are only allowed to retrieve balls that are on the floor and send them back to the Throwers. Retrievers may not attempt to do anything to

assist a thrown ball into a container. Retrievers can roam anywhere in the area where the containers are.

- Throwers must remain behind the boundary marker at all times.

- To be counted as a successful score, a ball must bounce at least once on the floor before landing in a container. If a Retriever assists a ball into a container or a Thrower puts a ball into a container without bouncing it, the entire score for that container is nullified for that round (ouch!).

- The boundary markers and the containers may not be moved; they are permanently fixed.

Additional Rules - Round 2

The group may assign people to a third role – Backboards. Backboards may use their bodies to assist balls into a container. Backboards may not use their arms from shoulder to hands; they may only use their torso and legs. Throwers and Retrievers are needed as well.

Each role is permanent for the round.

Additional Rules - Round 3

For this round, all three roles are present and they are interchangeable at any time.

Additional Thoughts

• *In explaining this setup, your choice of language is critical. You want to state clearly that each sub-group is responsible for getting its balls into its containers. The implication is that each sub-group must throw its own balls; most students will assume that they have to throw their own colored balls. What you hope to establish is an opportunity for the sub-group to recognize a better solution, a "win-win" for themselves and the entire team. If group A gives its balls to group B to throw, group B is much closer to group A's high point-container and can easily produce a higher score. Likewise, if all the sub-groups can make the leap to this idea, the scores can be significantly higher and the task made much easier. Finding this solution requires trusting the other groups to support them and do their work. This new paradigm is not an easy one because they are physically separated and "responsible" for their own balls. They often focus only on their own objective and lose sight of the larger team goal.*

• *If questions are asked such as: "Can our group help the other group?" or "Does my group have to be the one to throw its colored balls into the container?", the recommended response is to repeat the general statement that each group is responsible for getting its own balls into the container, and that it is up to each group and its leaders to make that decision. The language is critical to avoid the sub-group's feeling that they were "set up" by the way in which the activity was presented. You need to set the stage and let them make their assumptions, yet allow them the flexibility to interpret the set up to create the win-win. The nuances are subtle but significant.*

• *Move into Round 1 as quickly as possible with a minimal amount of planning and discussion. Typically, groups will assume they are competing with the other groups to produce the highest score. Allowing too much time for discussion at the outset may allow the teams to identify and organize a collaborative strategy. If you hear such discussion, you may want to move into the action as quickly as possible. It's not that you want to prevent the groups from uniting behind a collaborative strategy, but the power of collaboration becomes even more evident and valuable if the first round evolves in a more chaotic, individualistic pattern.*

• *Between rounds, it is recommended that you record the scores for each sub-group and a total combined team score. For some people, recording the individual group scores pushes them to be more competitive. Be aware of this pattern and present the scoring in a manner that best matches the goals you are aiming for with this activity.*

Cultural Awareness/Relationships

LESSON 11

In this lesson students will be introduced to the concepts of changes in perception and communication and how they are influenced by diversity.

ACTIVITY	LEARNING OBJECTIVE	TIME	PROPS	HEALTH SKILLS
Snowflake	**At the conclusion of this activity, students will be able to:** • Practice effective listening skills. • Explain the importance of being able to ask clarifying questions (part of communicating well). • Discuss the value of individual perspectives in understanding and challenging assumptions.	15–20 minutes	• 1 Piece of paper per student	• Analyze influences • Interpersonal communication
See Ya!	• Generalize about feelings of inclusion and exclusion in peer groups. • Explore the impact of inclusive discussion versus differentiation in peer interactions.	20 minutes	• 1 5-foot piece of webbing or rope for every 3–4 students	• Analyze influences • Interpersonal communication

TEACHER'S NOTES:

FRAMING	SET-UP PROCEDURE	REFLECTION

Snowflake

Set Up:
NONE

Framing:

"How many of you have experienced a situation where someone gave directions and a totally unexpected reaction followed? Or how many of you have received instructions from someone, thought you understood what was said and then came to realize later that the two of you had totally different interpretations? Effective communication means being a good listener as well as a good speaker. However, our perspective greatly influences how we listen and speak."

Procedure:

1. Ask students to sit in a circle facing the center.

2. Give a sheet of paper to each student.

3. Explain to the students that in a moment you are going to give some directions that they should follow as carefully as possible.

4. Tell the students they are free to ask questions at any time during the activity.

5. Before giving any instructions, ask the students to close their eyes or use a blindfold if they feel they need it.

6. Tell the students they are going to fold the paper three times and tear the paper three times and that they should also listen carefully for any other instructions.

7. Ask the students to do the following sequentially:

   a. Fold the paper in half lengthwise (along the longest axis) and tear off a one inch square from the bottom right hand corner. Discard the piece you tore off.

   b. With the crease at the top of the page now, fold the paper in half again and tear off a one inch triangle from the upper right hand corner. Discard the piece you tore off.

   c. Finally, fold the paper in half again and tear a one inch semi-circle from the lower right hand corner. You might want to say, "Since the paper is thick, you may need to use your teeth to complete the tear. This is OK." Discard the piece you tore off.

8. When you have finished with all the commands, ask students to unfold the paper to its original shape and position. Remind them to keep their eyes closed until you tell them to open them.

9. Before having them open their eyes, ask them to vote thumbs up or down on whether or not each person feels he or she successfully followed the directions.

10. With their thumbs visible and holding the paper in front of them, ask people to open their eyes and look around at what was produced.

Reflection:

Questions for Discussion:

1. "What do you see when you look around at both the papers and the thumbs?"

2. "What caused the differences or similarities in your papers/snowflakes?"

3. "Did being able to ask questions help you make a snowflake?"

4. "Did not being able to see help you ask good questions?"

5. "How can different perspectives be seen as a strength or resource for people living or working together?"

6. "As peers, what lessons should we remember from this exercise in terms of how we want to communicate and value each other's perspectives?"

7. "What did you learn in this activity that will help you be more successful and understand each other better?"

. . . .

See Ya!

Set Up:

1. Develop five to six questions for discussion and five to six questions for determination (see the examples following the procedure).

2. Clear a large space in your classroom.

3. Tie pieces of webbing into a circle. They should be large enough so that three to four students can easily fit inside. You should adjust the number of circles according to your class size (i.e., for a class of 24 students, you'd have six to eight circles).

4. Scatter the circles around a large, open space in your classroom.

Framing:

"Friendships become more important to young people during the teen years. Friendships help us define who we are, offer us a sense of belonging and provide us with support. We want to fit in with and be like our friends. Often, when we try to fit in, we learn how different we are from one another. When we learn about differences, we can fall into stereotyping and prejudice. Pay attention to the changes in your thoughts, feelings and behaviors in response to the different questions during the next activity."

Procedure:

1. Have students divide themselves so that there are three to four players starting in every circle.

2. Begin by asking everyone to introduce themselves to their circle partners.

3. Explain that while the students in each circle might change, the number of people per circle will stay the same.

4. Tell students that no player may leave the circle until they hear the words, "See Ya!" and that the group will say, "See Ya!" after the teacher says, "Ready?"

5. Tell your students that people will leave and join their circle. When their circle is joined, they should have the same three or four in it that they started with. So, when one person leaves, your circle will want another person to join.

6. When someone leaves a circle the remaining students wave their arms and hands up in the air, and shout, "Over here, over here!" until a new student enters their circle—remember always the same number of people per circle. Practice the, "Over heres" for a few seconds—with feeling.

7. Explain that the game will begin with a discussion question, e.g., "Tell each other the last movie you saw and if you liked it or not." Give each small group about sixty seconds to discuss the question.

8. The discussion question will be followed by a determining question such as "Determine who is the tallest in your circle." Give each small group about 15 seconds to respond to the determining question.

9. At the end of the 15 seconds you will say, "Ready" and the "pre-determined" person (i.e., the tallest person) needs to leave the circle to the sounds of their group saying, "See Ya!" This person must quickly join another circle where the students are saying, "Over here! Over here!"

10. Repeat the process once everyone has a new group and they have introduced themselves.

11. Repeat eight through nine with new questions about five to six times.

Examples of Discussion Questions:

Tell Each Other:

- "If you have ever lived abroad or in a different state, where did you live and what was that like?"

- "Tell your circle about the last book you read and whether or not you liked it."

- "Tell your circle about the oldest person you ever met and what they were/are like."

- "What do you think about music that is usually listened to by cultural groups other than your own?"
- "Tell your circle if you have acted to protect the environment, if so, what you did and what you think about protecting the environment in general."
- "Tell your circle if you have ever spoken up about a comment or "joke" that was feeding stereotypes or prejudice? If you did, tell them what that was like."

Examples of Determining Questions:

Determine who:
- Is the tallest in your group
- Has the shortest hair
- Has the biggest feet
- Is the most flexible
- Has the most siblings
- Has the fewest pets

Reflection:

Questions for Discussion:
1. "What did you learn about each other?"
2. "How did it feel when you discussed a topic together as compared to when you had to separate someone from your circle?"
3. "How did it feel when you had to leave your circle?"
4. "How did your thoughts, feelings, behaviors change in response to the different questions?"
5. "What did you learn from this activity that will help you to communicate better with all different kinds of people?"

LESSON 12

In this lesson students will work together to create words representing concepts related to diversity, culture, discrimination, prejudice and stereotypes.

ACTIVITY	LEARNING OBJECTIVE	TIME	PROPS	HEALTH SKILLS
Defining Ourselves	**At the conclusion of this activity, students will be able to:** • Define and identify positive things about diversity. • Define and identify key elements of culture.	15 minutes	• Alphabet Soup Kit or a large set of Scrabble Babble letters	• Analyze influences • Interpersonal communication
Pi Charting	• Define stereotype, prejudice, and discrimination and give examples of each. • Describe how diversity, culture, stereotypes, prejudice and discrimination contribute to conflict or violence. • Identify strategies for preventing and dealing with prejudice-related conflict.	30 minutes	• 1 Piece of flip chart paper per small group • Markers	• Core content • Analyze influences

TEACHER'S NOTES:

FRAMING	SET-UP PROCEDURE	REFLECTION

Defining Ourselves

Set Up:

1. Clear a large open space in your classroom.
2. Spread the Alphabet Soup or Scrabble letters on the floor in the middle of the circle.

Framing:

"Diversity and culture are two major influences on our beliefs about and behaviors toward other people. Let's generate as many words as possible, both positive and negative, that relate to diversity and culture."

Procedure:

1. Divide the class into groups of eight to ten and have each group stand together in the open space. Your students should form a loose circle (or whatever shape) with the letters in the middle.
2. Ask each student to choose one consonant and one vowel. They should pick them up from the middle of the open space.
3. When they have their letters and have re-joined their group, tell students that they will have 10 minutes to come up with as many words as possible using the letters in their small group.
4. Explain that students may trade their letters at any time with the pile of extras in the middle, but may only have two letters in their possession at a time.
5. The words should be both positive (things that are good about) and challenging (things that make accomplishing hard) words related to diversity and multiculturalism.

Reflection:

The next activity, Pi Charting, will be your students' reflection activity.

Pi Charting

Set Up:

1. For as many small groups as you have, make a Pi Chart on one piece of flip chart paper with the word stereotypes, prejudice or discrimination on the top. (You'll be dividing the small groups from Defining Ourselves in half.) A sample Pi Chart is:

Sterotypes

Looks Like	Sounds Like	Feels Like

Framing:

"We have just created a variety of words to define culture and diversity. Now let's describe how multiculturalism and diversity affect how we look to one another, speak to one another and feel about one another."

Procedure:

1. Have the class divide their small groups from the previous activity in half.
2. Give each small group a piece of flip chart paper with a "pi chart" of stereotypes, prejudice or discrimination.
3. Tell the class that they are going to spend some time exploring the effects of multiculturalism and diversity.
4. Ask students to begin to fill out the charts in their small groups, giving them an example before they start.
5. Remind the students that definitions may be expressed as written words, phrases or pictures.

Reflection:

Knowledge Review:

1. Ask the groups to present their Pi Chart to the entire group and have a general discussion, highlighting common themes as well as how diversity, culture, stereotypes, prejudice and discrimination contribute to conflict or violence.
2. Identify strategies for preventing and dealing with prejudice-related conflict.

LESSON 13

In this lesson students will apply problem solving and communication skills as well as explore cultures.

ACTIVITY	LEARNING OBJECTIVE	TIME	PROPS	HEALTH SKILLS
Change Up	**At the conclusion of this activity, students will be able to:** • Utilize problem solving and planning skills. • Explore how physical stereotypes and common perceptions of categories influence how we interact with others. • Understand the importance of becoming aware of various styles when communicating across cultures.	20–30 minutes	• Cards displaying one number from 1-30	• Self-management • Goal setting • Decision making • Interpersonal communication
Culture Jam	• Apply effective communication skills across cultures. • Demonstrate respect for others regardless of personal and cultural differences.	30 minutes	• Spot markers	• Analyze influences • Decision making • Interpersonal communication

TEACHER'S NOTES:

FRAMING	SET-UP PROCEDURE	REFLECTION

Change Up

Set Up:

1. Clear a large open space in your classroom.

Framing:

"It is very easy to categorize people. In fact most of our legal documents have separated people by predetermined categories such as ethnicity, socioeconomic status or age in an effort to manage information more quickly. Sometimes, however, we forget that the categories represent actual people and that being quick is usually not an effective or appropriate way to value relationships."

Procedure:

1. Ask the class to stand in a circle and hand out a card to each person. It doesn't matter if the numbers selected are sequential, just as long as each person has a card. Be sure students do not look at the number on their cards.

2. Tell the students that for the first challenge they will need to line up as quickly as possible from the lowest number to the highest number.

3. You will give them a few (three to five) minutes to plan, but they cannot look at their numbers AT ALL while they plan. So, the goal is to develop and implement a solution without knowing what cards they are holding.

4. Tell the class that they will be timed on their execution and that they must signal you once they have finished the task so that the time is stopped.

5. Give the students their time.

6. Begin the next round by having them trade cards in a random fashion with at least three people—without looking at the numbers! (The idea is to have them swap enough that they won't know what number the person they swap with last has.)

7. Remind students that once they get a card to keep they must refrain from looking at it until they are ready to start the second round.

u. Ask students what they have learned from the first round that will help them in this round and give them a few minutes of planning time to refine their solution.

9. Repeat the challenge with the same guidelines as the first round. Report the time to the students.

10. Allow one or two more attempts. Swap the cards and ask students to identify what they have learned that will help them get better before each new attempt.

11. Increase the challenge with a new twist—students should line up alphabetically by the first letter of the number on the card they hold. Remind students to use the knowledge they have gained from the first few rounds and give them a few minutes to plan. Time this new attempt also.

12. Report the time to the group and invite them to try again if time and interest allow.

Reflection:

Questions for Discussion:

1. "What strategies did you use to line up quickly?"

2. "What happened when you switched numbers and then lined up alphabetically?"

3. "Was it different if the changes were "minor" (i.e., shuffling the cards, but the same numbers were always in use) or "major" (i.e., changing from lining up numerically to lining up alphabetically)?"

4. "Think for a moment about how we perceive numbers, how often do we actually spell them out? In this activity numbers are like people—if we base our interaction just on what we see or think we know, how can we get beyond our stereotypes/initial impressions to the "spelling out" of individuals?"

. . . .

Culture Jam

Set Up:

1. Have one spot marker with an arrow drawn or taped on it for each student.

2. Place the blank spot marker on the floor in the middle of an open space (represented by the top square in the diagram). Divide the remaining spot markers in half and place them in an arc on either side of the blank spot marker. Make sure they are an easy step away from each other. You should end up with one big semi-circle with half of the arrows pointing toward the center on one side and reversed on the other.

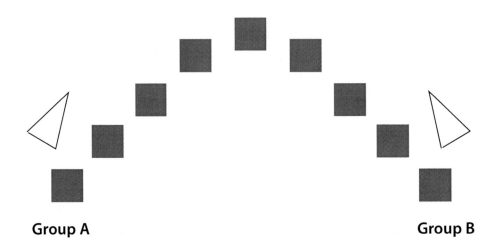

Group A   **Group B**

Framing:

"In this activity, we have two cultures who are addressing one issue. The two groups see things differently. The group on this side perceives this issue from their cultural perspective. The group on the opposite side perceives the issue from their own different cultural perspective. The challenge is for you to move to a place where you can see things from the other group's viewpoint. Of course, all societies have rules, so the challenge is also to follow the rules for navigating this cultural jam."

Procedure:

1. Divide the class in half.

2. Explain to the students that each small group is going to create a new mini culture with a new language or way of communicating. Tell them that they will need a greeting and some directions but cannot use any language or words that they currently use.

3. Have the two groups move to opposite ends of the room. Give each group eight to ten minutes to create their own language.

4. When both groups are ready, bring them over to the spots. Have one group stand on the places to the left of the middle spot, and the other group stand to the right. Both sides will be facing the middle unoccupied square.

5. Tell the students that the objective of this part of the activity is to have the culture on the left side end up in the places on the right side, and vice versa. The rules are as follows:

   Legal moves are:
   - a person may move into an empty space in front of them.
   - a person may move around a person who is facing them into an empty space.
   - the groups must use their new languages to try to negotiate the movements.

   Illegal moves are:
   - any move backwards
   - any move around someone facing the same direction as you are
   - any move that involves two persons moving at once

6. When any student performs an illegal move the whole group must start again at their beginning positions.

Reflection:

Questions for Discussion:

1. "What worked or didn't work in trying to solve this problem?"

2. "How did you feel if you had a suggestion that you couldn't communicate?"

3. "How did you feel if you had a suggestion that didn't work?"

4. "What happened to the languages each group created? Did you use them or some other way of communicating throughout the activity?"

5. "What different cultures or languages are represented in your homes/families?"

6. "What is it like at home or with your family when you are trying to express yourself and it feels like no one understands?"

Reflection Activity:

7. Post a sheet of paper with two columns. On one side have the group list some healthy ways to handle communicating with people from other "cultures." On the other side have them list unhealthy ways.

 Additional Thoughts

• *Have two spot marker set ups for classes of 20 to 30 students, adding an extra spot if you have an odd number of students.*

• *The only way for each group to switch sides is by alternating movements between each side. For example group A steps to the open spot and then group B moves around the person from Group A onto the open spot. This pattern continues until each group is on the opposite side.*

• *Be sure to have students go back to their original starting positions when they "get stuck"—perform an illegal move.*

LESSON 14

In this lesson students will share cultural heritage and traditions as well as explore feelings associated with different social groups.

ACTIVITY	LEARNING OBJECTIVE	TIME	PROPS	HEALTH SKILLS
History of My Name	**At the conclusion of this activity, students will be able to:** • Explain some of the stories behind peers' names. • Explain how our family relationships impact who we are as people. • Describe individual family traditions and activities. • Identify advantages and disadvantages of group membership.	15 per class for one week or one class period	• Students bring something to class that represents part of their family's heritage	• Interpersonal communication • Advocacy • Self-management • Accessing information
Give Me a Hand	• Use and identify some skills to challenge the assumptions we make about people who are different from ourselves. • Define at least one strategy that promotes inclusion and friendship.	30 minutes	• Paper • Markers • Scissors	• Analyze influences • Interpersonal communication

TEACHER'S NOTES:

FRAMING	SET-UP PROCEDURE	REFLECTION

History of My Name and Family Heritage Share Out

Set Up:

1. In preparation, have students bring an object from home that represents their family. Let them know that they should be prepared to explain the connection to everyone else in the class. Of course, it should be an appropriate positive object.

2. It is optional to have a display table set aside for students' objects to be viewed during the remainder of the class.

Framing:

"Instilling values and spiritual beliefs is an important function of the family. Families may be defined in many ways – for example: adopted families, step siblings. Perhaps you live with your grandmother, not your mother or father, etc. Passing on traditions and customs from one generation to the next keeps people's sense of heritage alive. Learning about our own and others' cultural backgrounds can enrich our lives making them more interesting."

Procedure:

1. Have students sit in a large circle with the person presenting the history of their name or family heritage object included.

2. Have several students during each class over the period of a week (or however long it takes to give everyone a turn) tell the history of their name and/or present their family heritage object.

3. Keep in mind that we are always practicing our Full Value Contract and being kind and respectful of one another. Be prepared to remind students if need be.

4. Encourage students to ask appropriate questions as their peers share information about their families.

Reflection:

Questions for Discussion:
1. "Tell us about some things people had in common."
2. "Were there ways in which you were different from everybody else?"
3. "Did any of the differences or commonalities surprise you?"
4. "How do you think your heritage impacts who you are today?"

Give Me A Hand

Set Up:

1. Identify a number of categories given to people with disabilities; for example, hearing impairment, visual impairment, physical disability, temporarily disabled, cerebral palsy, muscular dystrophy, and so on. Each student will trace and cut out one hand. You should try to have at least three or four hands in each of the categories. So, for a class size of 24, you'd have six categories. The number of categories you use will depend on the size of your group.

Framing:

"We are trying to encourage each other to share our feelings in a safe way and ask for help when we need it. Sometimes when we think something is bad, we don't talk about it, but often when we talk about something we think is bad, we find that there is more to it. Let's talk about people with disabilities—both what we perceive as positive and negative."

Procedure:

1. Ask everyone in the class to outline one of their hands on a piece of paper and then cut it out.
2. Divide the class into the decided number of categories and have each group write the name of their disability on the back of their hand cut-out.
3. Collect all of the hand cut-outs, mix them up and randomly redistribute throughout the class so that each student has a hand that is not his or her own.
4. Ask the students to find other people who belong to the same category and, once they've formed their groups, have them brainstorm a list of words, images, and stereotypes that they associate with the hand they've been given.
5. When the lists are done, ask the groups to talk among themselves and share how it felt doing this activity and to be associated with the "negative" and "positive" images.

Reflection:

Question for Discussion:

1. "Can you think of any ways that we consciously or unconsciously exclude people with disabilities because of some of the stereotypes we hold?"

Knowledge Review:

2. Go around the circle and have each student state a learning they gained from participating in this activity.

LESSON 15

In this lesson students will reinforce their understanding of peer support and healthy relationships.

ACTIVITY	LEARNING OBJECTIVE	TIME	PROPS	HEALTH SKILLS
Great American Egg Drop	**At the conclusion of this activity, students will be able to:** • Describe some parameters of healthy relationships. • Identify sources of support and how to access them.	45 minutes	• 20 straws per group • 36 inches of tape per group • 1 egg per group • Garbage bag, paper towels and a trash can for cleanup • Flip chart paper • Markers	• All

TEACHER'S NOTES:

FRAMING	SET-UP PROCEDURE	REFLECTION

Great American Egg Drop

Set Up:

1. Create a large open space in your classroom.
2. Open the garbage bag and tape it to the floor on the far side of the open space. (Your students will be dropping their protected eggs from six feet high onto this spread-out bag.)
3. You can place a chair near or on the bag for students to stand on and drop their egg from, if this feels safe. If not, your students can simply drop their eggs from as high as they can reach when they are standing.

Framing:

"Middle school can be a challenging place. You are exposed to many new people, ideas and opportunities. Some of the new things you encounter can be very positive and help you to grow and mature. Other experiences can be very hurtful such as choosing to use drugs, being the recipient of put-downs, peer verbal or physical violence and being in unhealthy relationships. It is important that you learn how to protect yourselves with healthy friendships and support systems that will help you bounce back and make healthy choices."

Procedure:

1. Split the class into teams of four to six people.
2. Give each team an egg, 36 inches of tape, 20 straws, flip chart paper and markers.
3. Explain to the students that the challenge of this activity is to construct a container for their eggs that will prevent them from breaking when dropped from a height of six feet. The egg represents a middle school student like you. The straw and tape of the container represents a network of healthy relationships and support systems. The six foot drop represents a giant put-down.
4. Tell students that the egg must be inside the container/network somehow (the straws cannot be used as a nest on the floor that the egg drops into) and should be able to withstand a drop from six feet.
5. Also explain that the second part of the challenge is to create a name and a commercial for their support container that lets everyone know why theirs is the best, most protective, most efficient system known to human kind. They can make posters for their commercials and/or act them out for the whole group—however they'd like to present their commercial.
6. Tell the teams they have 20 to 30 minutes to develop their support container/network and commercial. Each team will present their commercial right before dropping their eggs.

7. After 20 to 30 minutes gather everyone back together in a large group. Have students sit on the floor of the room in a horseshoe shape so that there is sort of a stage in the middle for the egg drops.

8. Ask for volunteers to start the presentation process and have the first team present their commercial and drop their egg. Each team should have a representative drop the team's egg from a height of about six feet or just have him/her reach up as high as he/she can and drop it from there.

9. Save the posters from the commercials and post in classroom.

Reflection:

Questions for Discussion:

1. "What are some common themes you identified in effective peer support networks?"

2. "How do you get/ask for what you need in a healthy relationship?"

3. "What are some characteristics of a healthy relationship?"

4. "What were you surprised by during this activity and why?"

 Additional Thoughts

• *Occasionally an egg will break. Use this as an opportunity to discuss what happens when students lose their connections with friends, family and support and what students can do to help each other reconnect.*

Nutrition

LESSON 16

In this lesson students will review the components of a healthy diet.

ACTIVITY	LEARNING OBJECTIVE	TIME	PROPS	HEALTH SKILLS
Food Pyramid Tag	**At the conclusion of this activity, students will be able to:** • Identify the components of a nutritionally balanced diet. • Describe the importance of specific foods in the food pyramid guide. • Work together to integrate the components of a nutritionally-balanced diet.	15 minutes	• Post-its® or index cards and tape • Pens	• Core content • Accessing information
Food Pyramid Juggle	• Plan a healthy meal, using information from the dietary guidelines and the food guide pyramid. • Analyze some social pressures that affect nutrition behaviors. • Describe proper eating habits.	40 minutes	• About 25–30 fleece balls or tossable items that represent foods from different food groups • Markers	• Core content • Goal setting • Decision making • Self-management • Analyze influences • Interpersonal communication

TEACHER'S NOTES:

FRAMING	SET-UP PROCEDURE	REFLECTION

Food Pyramid Tag

Set Up:

1. Create a large open space in your classroom.

Framing:

"The food pyramid is a great resource for making sure you are eating a nutrition-ally balanced diet. We are going to review the different categories in the pyramid by identifying a variety of foods, what they contribute to our bodies and how the variety and combination of foods keeps us going!"

Procedure:

1. Ask the students to form a circle inside the large open space.

2. Pass out Post-it notes or an index card and pen to each student.

3. Ask each student to identify and describe the function of a unique compo-nent from a healthy, balanced diet and write it on the Post-it. For example, "Orange gives us fiber and Vitamin C" or "Chicken gives us protein which is good for our muscles."

4. Review their replies to eliminate repeated foods and ensure that there is a bal-anced representation of foods. As needed, get replacements for repeated foods or add to or create an under-represented food category. You should still end up with one Post-it per student.

5. Have students stick the Post-its onto their shirts and tell them that for the rest of the activity they will be known as the item on their Post-its.

6. Explain to the class that they are going to play a tag game in which one per-son will start as the tagger. When that person tags someone, they become attached by linking elbows and then two people are taggers, and so on until the entire class is connected.

7. Remind students that they represent different parts of a nutritious diet and that the object of the tag activity is to make sure that the tagger gets all of the things they need for a healthy day of eating.

8. So if, on the taggers' chain there are no dairy products, they will be looking for those and must shout out what they are trying to find. So, for example: "We need dairy!" Students who have not been tagged must also shout out what the food on their Post-its are. So, for example: "I am salmon!"

9. Ask for a volunteer to start as the tagger, review safety guidelines (remember to choose a safe speed like fast walking) and begin!

Reflection:

Questions for Discussion:

1. "Did your chain stay balanced or did it get overloaded with one food group or another?"
2. "Was someone on your chain keeping track of the different foods you had or was everyone keeping track? How did you know what foods you needed?"
3. "Does anyone want to name some or all of the major food categories?"
4. "What skills did you use to collect all of the components?"
5. "How can these skills be used in eating a balanced diet daily?"

 Additional Thoughts

• *Do not allow students to break through, jump over or under the chain of connected elbows.*

Food Pyramid Juggle

Set Up:

1. Clear a large open space in your classroom.
2. Have enough objects in front of you to make up the total number of recommended servings for one person from the Food Pyramid.
3. Have the masking tape and markers readily available.

Framing:

"Just about everyone here has seen the Food Pyramid guide. We know that the Food Pyramid guide is just that, a guide or reference for recommended amounts and types of foods we should be eating for a healthy, balanced diet. We also know that the amount of servings and food content change depending on our age, level of activity and culture. Even with this great resource in place, it is sometimes quite a challenge to follow the recommendations."

Procedure:

1. Have your students join you in a circle.
2. Ask them to identify the food groups that make up the Food Pyramid.

3. Ask the students to determine how many servings of each food group are recommended for the "average" person. Write the food groups on the masking tape and place each of these words on a separate ball for each serving.

4. Tell your students that they are going to establish a sequence for tossing the objects through the entire group.

5. Have one person throw (gently) one fleece ball/tossable to someone across the circle. That person in turn throws to someone opposite him/her and this continues until a person-to-person sequence is set that includes everyone. Do not throw to the person next to you.

6. Once the sequence has been established, the first person (initiator) starts the ball again, to reinforce it. For every item tossed, the challenge is to keep the pattern of people that you toss to and receive from the same.

7. Explain to your students that "We are going to share a day of meals—as represented by our tossables—by tossing various items to one another through the sequence we just established. We will start with breakfast, add lunch, a snack and finally dinner. What foods do you think would make up a healthy breakfast for the average person?" Separate the representing tossables from the different food groups as students identify them and "eat breakfast" by passing those foods through the group in the established pattern.

8. Acknowledge the successes and challenges that occurred in getting through breakfast and then go through the same process of separating out a healthy lunch. Repeat the tossing sequence starting with breakfast and adding lunch.

9. Repeat the entire process after adding a snack and then dinner. So, the students' final round will take them through a day of healthy eating, from breakfast to dinner.

Reflection:

Questions for Discussion:
1. "What was it like to try to 'eat' all of the foods on the Food Pyramid?"
2. "What factors influence decisions about food choices?"
3. "How does your environment affect your food choices?"
4. "How do boredom, stress and happiness affect your eating habits?"
5. "How does your culture and family influence your eating habits?"

 Additional Thoughts

• *For an extra challenge, pass a rubber chicken around the outside of the circle to represent distractions from eating well. Have students identify distractions and analyze social pressures from peers, adults and the media.*

LESSON 17

In this lesson students will find their nutrient match and learn how to select a nutritious meal at a fast food restaurant.

ACTIVITY	LEARNING OBJECTIVE	TIME	PROPS	HEALTH SKILLS
I Need Someone Who…	**At the conclusion of this activity, students will be able to:** • Describe the importance of specific nutrients in the food pyramid.	20 minutes	• Objects representing foods from a variety of sources (1 for each student in matched pairs, see Procedure)	• Core content • Interpersonal communication • Accessing information
Fast Food Frenzy	• Integrate a nutritionally balanced fast food meal into a proper eating pattern. • Make healthy nutrition decisions in pressurized situations.	20 minutes	• 5 Hula Hoops™ • 20–30 objects representing foods from a variety of fast food restaurants	• Core content • Goal setting • Decision making • Interpersonal communication • Advocacy

TEACHER'S NOTES:

FRAMING	SET-UP PROCEDURE	REFLECTION

I Need Someone Who

Set Up:

1. Clear a large open space in your classroom.

Framing:

"One of the reasons we reinforce eating a variety of foods from different sources is so that you will get the benefit of all the nutrients you need to be healthy. Sometimes it is not enough to know what you 'should' be eating but why you 'should' be eating certain foods."

Procedure:

1. Divide the class in half and have each group line up on either side of the open space.

2. Place a bag of objects near each group of students. Each bag should have the same objects. For example, two bottles of water, one in each bag. No sharp objects!

3. Explain to your students that the objective of the activity is to find the person who has the exact same item that they have, keeping their eyes closed until such meeting happens.

4. Tell them that the objects in the bags are different nutrient sources and that they must find their partner by stating what nutrients come from the object they chose. For example, bananas have potassium, carbohydrates and fiber. Say "I need someone who has potassium, carbohydrates and fiber and is yellow!" until they find their match. What they can't say is, "I need someone who has a banana."

5. Have students turn their backs to one another and select an item from the bag nearest their line. Give them a few minutes to identify the nutritional value of their chosen object.

6. Reinforce the safety guidelines of walking slowly, using one hand as a "bumper" and stopping to reorient themselves if they need to before moving.

7. On the count of three have students close their eyes, turn around and begin searching for their match from the opposite side by saying "I need someone who…".

8. Tell your students if they meet someone who they think is a match, they need to verify it. If it is not a match they should continue to seek their match with eyes closed.

9. Allow time for all matches to happen, and ask the matches to simply observe and not move until the final match takes place.

Reflection:

Questions for Discussion:

1. "What food do you have and what nutrients does it provide us with?"

2. "What do those nutrients help your body do?" (i.e., build muscle, give us energy, build strong bones, etc.)

 Additional Thoughts

• *It is a good idea to begin this activity by reinforcing the Full Value Contract. Be sure to offer the role of spotting to students who are not comfortable with moving with their eyes closed.*

• *Remind your students that you will be actively spotting.*

• *Be aware of students' stress responses to this activity and encourage them to stop, breathe and then keep going if tensions begin to rise!*

. . . .

Fast Food Frenzy

Set Up:

1. Clear a large, open square space in your classroom.

2. Place a Hula Hoop™ in each corner of your large open square and put the last hoop in the middle.

3. Place all of the food objects in the hoop in the middle.

Framing:

"Have you ever felt the "push to be quick" when trying to decide what to select in a fast food restaurant? The person at the register is offering all sorts of options. The people behind you are edging closer and closer. Being able to sort through the unhealthy foods and select a nutritious meal in those situations is a skill."

Procedure:

1. Ask your students to divide into four equal teams. Have each team stand near a Hula Hoop™ in each of the four corners.

2. Tell the class that their goal is to select a nutritionally-balanced dinner as quickly as possible from the "fast food restaurant" in the middle of the square and bring it back to their "table" or hoop.

3. Explain that the way to get food is to send one representative at a time to the middle and select only one item at a time to carry back with them. Items may also be retrieved from neighbor's "tables"…also only one at a time and carried by one representative.

4. Students may not physically protect their "tables."

5. Remind the class that food must be carried, not thrown.

6. The game is over when the first team lets everyone know they have a healthy dinner in their hoop by saying, "We're full!"

7. Play several rounds switching between selecting a healthy breakfast, lunch or dinner.

Reflection:

Questions for Discussion:

1. "What are some of the foods normally found in a fast food restaurant?"

2. "Can you find healthy foods there?"

3. "What did your team select for their healthy meal?"

4. "What do you need to think about when you're trying to be healthy and eat fast food?"

Reflection Activity:

5. Ask the students to get back into their teams and identify at least six ways they could help each other and themselves make healthy choices at fast food restaurants.

 Additional Thoughts

• *This activity is similar to Be the Best/Share the Health from the Grade 6 Fitness Unit.*

LESSON 18

In this lesson students will explore the issues around fad dieting and body image.

ACTIVITY	LEARNING OBJECTIVE	TIME	PROPS	HEALTH SKILLS
Have You Ever?	At the conclusion of this activity, students will be able to: • Recognize that people often have different nutrition/body image habits. • Recognize some of the influences media and peers have on weight management and body image. • Dispel some of the myths associated with unhealthy weight management practices.	15 minutes	• 1 poly spot per student	• Accessing information • Self-management • Analyze influences
Oh, The Shape I'm In!	• Explain how normal body size and shape is often misconceived. • Analyze social affect body image. • Better apply communication/conflict resolution skills.	20 minutes	• 1 60–foot long rope	• Goal setting • Decision making • Interpersonal communication • Analyze influences • Core content

TEACHER'S NOTES:

FRAMING	SET-UP PROCEDURE	REFLECTION

Nutrition Have You Ever?

Set Up:

1. Clear a large open space in your classroom.

Framing:

"Creating an environment in which young people can share thoughts, ideas, concerns and issues has been an important part of this class. Being able to share and discuss and feel valued in the process are things that we have done very well. We have created a healthy atmosphere! Let's keep up the good work as we answer the following questions about our eating patterns and body image beliefs."

Procedure:

1. Ask students to form a circle and pass out the poly spots so that each student has one in his or her hand.

2. Tell students that in a moment you are going to ask them to randomly scatter themselves throughout the open space, place their poly spot down on the floor and stand on it.

3. Say to students, "As you can see, I do not have a spot to stand on, but I will soon be looking for one! This is important because I am going to ask you a question that begins with 'Have You Ever?' If you answer 'Yes' to my question, you will need to find a new spot. I will also be looking for a spot which means that one of you will not have one. The person left without a poly spot will ask the next question. Since we are focusing on nutrition and body image, let's make the questions relevant to those topics in the context of our own experience." For example:

   Have you ever…

   Gotten a haircut that you didn't like?
   Skipped a meal?
   Been worried about how you look?
   More sample questions can be found in the appendix (page 350)

4. Have students find their spot and begin playing.

Reflection:

Reflection Activity:

1. Have students form one large circle and ask the group to respond to the following question with a Thumbs Up meaning "Yes," Thumbs Sideways meaning "So, So," or a Thumbs Down meaning "No."

2. "Were you surprised by the number of people who moved to a particular question?"

3. The instructor selects a few people whose thumbs are up and asks them to explain what question surprised them and why.

4. Follow this same procedure with the different thumb positions.

Questions for Discussion:

5. "Can you tell us some common myths about fad dieting?"

6. "What do people expect to happen when they fad diet? Is that healthy?"

7. "Let's name some of the people and things that give us our ideas about how our body should look. Are those good influences? If they aren't who and/or what do you think will give us healthy ideas about how our body should look?"

 Additional Thoughts

• *Begin the activity by asking a few questions to set the tone and model appropriate behaviors.*

. . . .

Oh The Shape I'm In!

Set Up:

1. Clear a large open space in your classroom.
2. Tie the ends of the rope together in a square knot—to form a large circle.

Framing:

"Throughout history each generation has had its own standard of the ideal male and female body shape and appearance. Sometimes people make poor choices in trying to achieve that ideal. Sometimes they even begin to be unable to see themselves or their physical shape as it truly is. In other words they become blind to what they look like as they try to become perfect—or what they think is perfect."

Procedure:

1. Ask your students to stand in a fairly open circle around the rope.
2. Lay the rope out on the ground at their feet.

3. Explain to them that the object of the activity will be to work as a group to form the rope into different shapes while everyone attached to the rope has their eyes closed.

4. Tell the students that they must be holding the rope and can talk with one another throughout the process, but the real challenge will be keeping their eyes closed.

5. After checking for questions, ask the class to close their eyes, reach down and grab the rope, stand up and form a square.

6. Tell your students to let you know when they feel as though they have made a square, at which time they can open their eyes and see what shape they are in!

7. Repeat the process having the students make a triangle and a circle.

Reflection:

Questions for Discussion:

1. "Sometimes we truly believe we are in much better "shape" health-wise, than we really are...how did this activity represent that thinking?"

2. "How do media and peer messages affect our ability to realistically gauge our body image and decisions about health behaviors?"

3. "What are some guidelines and quality resources that give us a healthy body image?"

 Additional Thoughts

• *This is a great opportunity to reinforce the dangers of perfectionism when related to body image as well as refute the "reality" of models in magazines who are air brushed to perfection.*

• *Be sure to offer the role of spotter to those who prefer to participate without eyes closed.*

• *You can divide the class into two smaller groups if you have more than 20 students.*

LESSON 19

In this lesson students will revisit having a healthy body image and identify influences contributing to nutrition and weight management patterns.

ACTIVITY	LEARNING OBJECTIVE	TIME	PROPS	HEALTH SKILLS
Pictures of Me	**At the conclusion of this activity, students will be able to:** • Analyze social pressures from peers, adults, and the media that affect body image. • Predict the effect of food choices made in childhood and adolescence on adult health.	30–90 minutes	• Paper (as large as possible—poster size is good, one sheet for each student) and materials for drawing, painting or collaging. If possible, frames for final products	• Core content • Analyze influences • Accessing information • Self-management • Advocacy

TEACHER'S NOTES:

FRAMING	SET-UP PROCEDURE	REFLECTION

Pictures of Me

Set Up:
NONE

Framing:

"This activity is a great way to develop an appreciation for your own and your friends' historic and cultural identity. In it you will think about yourself in the past, the present and the future. As you think about yourself as you have been, are and will be, identify the messages that influenced you to be yourself at that time. Where did those messages come from? Think about how we see ourselves change over time. How many of you can remember a time in your life when you felt differently about the way you look than you do today? In this activity, we are going to explore those changing perceptions through creative imagery. If you choose, you can draw an actual portrait of yourself, write a description of yourself or use images from magazines, nature, etc. The first picture of you will be..."

Procedure:

1. Give students one sheet of paper each and supplies to share.

2. Ask students to fold the paper into three sections with the longest edge on the top and then open the paper so that there are three panels to work on.

3. Explain to students that they are going to be creating separate representations in each panel. In the first panel have students create a reflection that represents how they remember themselves looking as children. The description can be written, drawn, a collage, etc. or a combination of these.

4. In the middle panel, have students describe themselves as they look now.

5. Between the first and second panels they will create a bridge or connection by citing three messages received from others that influenced how they look now (e.g., Uncle Dave told me I am strong), and three messages students gave themselves that shaped how they look now (e.g., I love my curly hair). The bridge will consist of six messages total.

6. Finally, in the third panel, ask students to illustrate how they would like to look, sound, and feel after this class/semester is over—their future image.

7. Have students create another bridge or connection between the second and third panels stating three nutritional or fitness changes students can make that will help them achieve this image (e.g., I can eat more fruit), and three messages students would like to give themselves as they progress toward their vision (e.g., My body is strong, I can ride my bike 20 miles). Again the bridge should consist of six messages total.

Reflection:

Questions for Discussion:

1. "Name one thing you learned about the relationship between messages you received while growing up and your body image."

2. "Can you name some best nutritional practices for building a healthy body throughout your whole life?"

3. "What can happen to people as they get older when they don't follow good nutritional practices?" (e.g., heart, disease, cancer, diabetes, not being able to play softball, etc.)

 Additional Thoughts

• *This activity may be debriefed in a variety of ways. Students can share their images with the class after each panel is finished, or after the first and second panels are completed, then after the third is completed.*

Physical Fitness

LESSON 20

In this lesson students will identify multiple opportunities for fitness and recognize the benefits of cardiovascular fitness.

ACTIVITY	LEARNING OBJECTIVE	TIME	PROPS	HEALTH SKILLS
Fitness Whomp 'Em	**At the conclusion of this activity, students will be able to:** • Identify some different types of recreational activities. • Increase awareness of opportunities for different fitness activities. • Create potential fitness goal partners.	20 minutes	• Boffer or swimming noodle	• Core content • Accessing information • Advocacy • Interpersonal communication
Fast Back	• Explain the principles of cardiorespiratory fitness. • Differentiate between elevated heart rates from stress and cardiorespiratory exercise.	20–30 minutes	• Boundary markers • Alphabet Soup kit	• Core content • Self-management • Interpersonal communication

TEACHER'S NOTES:

FRAMING	SET-UP PROCEDURE	REFLECTION

Fitness Whomp 'Em

Set Up:

1. Create a large open space in your classroom.

Framing:

"Have you ever said to your parents or your friends, 'I'm bored? There's nothing to do around here.' This activity will help us to discover many different ways to be active—and not bored—and maybe even give you some people you could team up with to be active."

Procedure:

1. Ask the class to form a circle and place yourself in the center so that the peripheral students are within a boffer's length of your reach.

2. Tell the class that this is a fast-moving activity in which they all need to be on their toes.

3. The first round of action starts when someone in the circle says the name of someone else in the circle. The person in the middle tries to tap the named person on the toes with the boffer before he/she names someone else in the circle, and so on.

4. If the person in the middle taps the person called on the toes before the outside person says another student's name, the person on the outside changes places with the person in the middle.

5. After the person leaving the middle hands the boffer to the incoming person, the new person in the middle has five seconds to say someone's name and begin the process again.

6. Stop the action after a few rounds and tell the group you are going to make a change. The activity will be the same except that the saying of names will be replaced with the saying of fitness activities.

7. Have each person select and act out a different fitness activity; e.g., rock climbing, skating swimming and so on. One student per activity. Two runners, for example, won't work. Once the students have picked and developed a quick action that signifies their activity, ask them to state their activity and demonstrate their action at least once more. Do this in an organized fashion; go around the circle, so everyone has a chance to begin to learn them.

8. Continue original activity, but replace the saying of names with the saying of fitness activities. For example, if the person on the outside of the circle said, "skiing," the student representing skiing would have to say another student's activity, i.e., "swimming" before the person in the middle tapped them on the toes.

Reflection:

Questions for Discussion:

1. "What are some of the different activities we heard?"

2. "Where could we access those activities in our community?"

3. "Did someone have an activity you like or would like to learn how to do?"

Reflection Activity:

4. Give your students a few minutes to make a date with someone in the class to do one of the activities mentioned together. (If this seems like it needs guidance to keep from being a "popularity contest," you should pair people up.) Ask them to write down the date, activity and its duration. Let them know that you'll be checking in on whether they accomplished that or not.

 Additional Thoughts

• *Be sure to follow up with students as to when they completed their partner activity.*

Fast Back

Set Up:

1. Clear a large, open rectangular space in your classroom.

2. Create two sets of three zones as shown in the diagram. (Zone A, Assembly Zone and Zone B for each side of the rectangular area.) These zones can be delineated by border markers of any sort, but rope works well.

3. Make the Assembly Zone midway between Zones A and B.

4. The distance from Zones A and B to the Construction Zone can range from 10–20 yards.

5. Divide your foam blocks in half. Use half for each side and set them up as follows.

6. Place all of the foam blocks (with the cutouts removed) in Zone A.

7. Place all of the cutouts of the letters and numbers in Zone B.

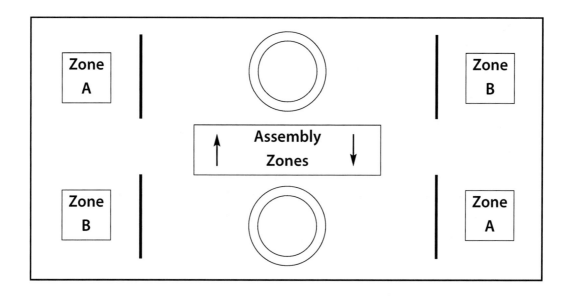

Framing:

"Elevating our heart rate by exercising our heart and lungs is one of the most important things we can do for life-long health and wellness. Sometimes, our heart rate changes in response to situations other than aerobic exercise."

Procedure:

1. Divide the class into two groups of about 12 students and have them each stand around one of the two Assembly Zones.

2. Explain to the class that they are about to partake in a competition involving speed and creativity.

3. You can say something like: "During this activity, there will be two roles—assemblers and gatherers. The assemblers need to stay inside and the gatherers need to stay outside the Assembly Zone for the entire activity. As you can see there are objects on either side of the outer boundary lines—each Assembly Zone has a Zone A and B. The gatherers' role is to bring the objects from Zones A and B to the Assembly Zone where the assemblers will put them all together."

4. The end product will be a foam sculpture. It needs to:
   • have all the objects from your team's Zones A & B connected to one another
   • integrate a fitness-related word
   • fit into the Assembly Zone with the assemblers.

5. Groups must have at least three but no more than five assemblers.

6. Tell students that gatherers can only carry one object at a time. The objects must be carried, not passed or thrown from Zones A & B to the assembly zone. Gatherers can put the objects into the Assembly Zone, but they may not step into the zone or help assemble.

7. Assemblers must stay inside the Assembly Zone and create the sculpture as quickly as possible.

8. Finally, tell students that they will be tracking their heart rate at several different points during the process of the activity. When they hear the word "Stop," everyone stops what they are doing immediately, finds their pulse and counts it for six seconds. You should count the seconds so they can focus on counting their pulse. Once the count is done, they should return to action.

9. Give students five minutes to establish roles and plan.

10. Begin the activity by having the students take a resting heart rate count.

11. Stop them for a second heart rate count when about half of the objects on at least one side are in the Assembly Zone.

12. Ask for a third heart rate count when all of the objects on at least one side are in the Assembly Zone.

13. Ask for a fourth heart rate count when the first team finishes their sculpture and stop the competition.

Reflection:

Take time to view and discuss both sculptures. (What do they look like? What word was chosen and why? What would you have done if you'd had time to finish? Etc.)

Questions for Discussion:

1. "How did your heart rate change during the course of the activity?"

2. "What was the difference between the changes in the gatherers' and the assemblers' heart rates?"

3. "Do these changes in heart rate show us that there are healthy and unhealthy ways to raise your heart rate?"

4 "What are some real life examples of healthy and unhealthy ways to elevate your heart rate?"

 Additional Thoughts

• *This activity may be best played in a large space, outdoors or a gymnasium.*

LESSON 21

In this lesson students will learn about the consequences of lack of physical fitness and begin to establish proper exercise, nutrition and sleep patterns.

ACTIVITY	LEARNING OBJECTIVE	TIME	PROPS	HEALTH SKILLS
Hospital Tag	**At the conclusion of this activity, students will be able to:** • Identifiy some specific outcomes of participation in physical activity. • Identify some limitations of being injured.	15 minutes	• 4 cones for boundary markers	• Self-management • Interpesonal communication
Healthy Lifestyle Relay	• Identify twenty components of healthy fitness, eating and sleep behaviors. • Identify and work toward individual and group goals.	30 minutes	• 20 spots from Key-punch kit • Boundary markers • Boundary rope • Masking Tape • Markers • Stopwatch	• Core content • Goal setting • Decision making • Interpersonal communication • Self-management

TEACHER'S NOTES:

FRAMING	SET-UP PROCEDURE	REFLECTION

Hospital Tag

Set Up:

1. Clear a large open space in your classroom.

Framing:

"We know that exercise is important—it keeps our bodies healthy and prevents disease. This activity will illustrate what happens to our bodies when we choose not to move."

Procedure:

1. Ask your students to form a circle inside the open space.
2. Explain to them that everyone will start the game with two invisible band-aids, one in each hand and that everyone will have the opportunity to tag one another.
3. Tell the students that when they are tagged the first time, they will need to use one of those bandaids to cover up the spot where they were tagged. They cannot remove that hand/band aid for the remainder of the game. Their free hand can still be used to tag others.
4. Upon being tagged a second time, players need to cover the spot where they were tagged this time with their remaining hand/bandaid.
5. At this point students are still in the game; however, they have no free hands to tag anyone so their only option is to simply run around trying to avoid being tagged again.
6. When tagged a third time, players are finished and freeze where they are tagged.
7. Continue the game until there are one or two people left.

Reflection:

Questions for Discussion:

1. "What are some problems that people have when they aren't physically fit?"
2. "What were some of the limitations you experienced while being 'injured' during this activity?"
3. "How does exercise contribute to life-long health and disease prevention?"

Healthy Lifestyle Relay

Set Up:

1. Prepare the Keypunch spot markers by placing a piece of masking tape above and beneath each number, the length of the spot marker.

2. Clear a large open space in your classroom.

Framing:

"We have identified the components of proper fitness, eating and sleep behaviors for achieving a healthy lifestyle. As a class, you need to come up with a plan that combines all of these behaviors into a sequenced routine. Practicing such routines helps individual behaviors become healthy habits."

Procedure:

1. Have students form a circle inside the space and pass out spot markers and magic markers to each person.

2. Ask students to brainstorm the components in proper fitness, eating, and sleep patterns for achieving a healthy lifestyle. (e.g., strength training three times a week, eating nine fruits and vegetables a day, getting eight hours of sleep, etc.) Have students write each component down in large letters on the masking tape on the spot markers, ensuring that there is only one component to a spot marker.

3. Place a rope in a large circle at one end of the open space. Ask students to randomly place all of the spot markers inside the circle.

4. Set up a short rope as a start line at the other end of the open space. Leave enough room for the class to gather behind the start line.

5. Tell the class that they will have three attempts to reach their best time for touching the twenty healthy lifestyle components.

6. The rules are:
   - Only one person is allowed inside the rope circle at a time.
   - They need to touch the spot markers with the components written on them in sequence.
   - They need to call out that component as they do so.
   - They must come up with a pattern that everyone contributes to as well as one that is quick and efficient.

7. Explain that each attempt will be timed and that the time will start when the first person crosses the start line and the last person crosses over as they finish.

8. Also highlight that this is a team effort though only one person at a time is

allowed within the circular rope boundary. Everyone may stand around the outside to support one another.

9. Finally, planning will take place behind the start line and can happen between each round.

Reflection:

Questions for Discussion:

1. "When you look at the healthy lifestyle components we came up with, is there anything there that shouldn't be or anything missing?" Follow up with, "If so, why?"

2. "Can you identify the strategies your group used to implement an effective pattern for touching on proper fitness, nutrition and sleep components?"

3. "Can you identify the strategies you used as an individual to do your part in implementing the pattern?"

4. "Can you identify ways in which you could use the group and individual strategies to help you achieve a healthy lifestyle?"

LESSON 22

Students work together to support one another in staying active and review principles of physical fitness.

ACTIVITY	LEARNING OBJECTIVE	TIME	PROPS	HEALTH SKILLS
Team Tag	**At the conclusion of this activity, students will be able to:** • Begin to comprehend the role that cooperation has in keeping physically active. • Identify strategies for maintaining exercise programs.	20 minutes	• 1 different colored fleece ball per 4–5 students	• Analyze influences • Goal setting • Decision making
Let's Get Together For Fitness	• Define and give examples of the five components of fitness. • Define and apply F.I.T.T. principles. • Differentiate between lifestyle and sport activities.	15–20 minutes	• Deck of Fitness Convening Cards (see appendix page 352) • Stopwatch	• Analyze influences • Interpersonal communication

TEACHER'S NOTES:

FRAMING	SET-UP PROCEDURE	REFLECTION

Team Tag

Set Up:

1. Clear a large open space in your classroom

Framing:

"Most of us have had the experience of starting and then stopping an exercise program. We stopped because we became bored, lost our motivation or things outside of our control changed. One week turns into two, two into three and before you know it, you are back in front of the TV or computer instead of up and moving around. That is when you need a friend to help you get back into the fitness game!"

Procedure:

1. Ask students to form small groups of four to five players.
2. Give each small group a different colored fleece ball.
3. Explain to the class that this game is like Everybody's It except instead of individuals playing against one another, there are teams and you can tag anyone but your own teammates.
4. In this version, if someone gets tagged, they stop wherever they are but can get back into the game if the "re-play" object is tossed to them. The "re-play" object is the differently colored fleece ball each team has.
5. If a player with the "re-play" object is tagged, they need to toss it to another player on their team and then have it tossed back to them to get back into the game.
6. Players are not allowed to interfere with other teams' "re-play" objects.
7. When the game is over, after a minute or two, the team(s) with the most players standing gains a point.

Reflection:

Questions for Discussion:

1. "What did it feel like when someone helped you get back in the game?"
2. "What did it feel like to help someone get back in the game?"
3. "Do you think it would help you stay fit if you had a friend to exercise with?"
4. "What are some ways that you can encourage each other to keep exercising inside and outside of school?"

 Additional Thoughts

• *Beanie Babies® or any soft tossable may be substituted for fleece balls.*
• *This activity may be best played in a large space, outdoors or in a gymnasium.*

Let's Get Together For Fitness

Set Up:

1. Clear a large open space in your classroom.

Framing:

"Who remembers the different components of fitness and the F.I.T.T. principles or the difference between lifestyle activities and sport activities? Don't worry if you can't remember everything. You will have some help. We are going to play a card game but the cards we are going to use are a bit different because they are all related to physical fitness."

Procedure:

1. Ask students to form a circle inside the space.
2. Have the Fitness Convening Cards handy.
3. Tell your students that they are going to be using the Fitness Convening Cards for the next activity. Show the students an example of a card and explain the different categories. (These cards can be made by copying those in the appendix page.)

   The Fitness Convening Cards deck is a set of 20 cards. (Make 5 copies of page 351 and cut cards to size). Each card has two words and two pictures. The words represent the Principles of Fitness and the different types of physical activity.

   - Principles of Fitness =
     - Flexibility
     - Strength and Endurance
     - Aerobic
     - Body Composition

   - Types of Physical Activity =
     - Lifestyle
     - Sport

   The pictures represent visual examples of the principles of fitness and F.I.T.T.

   - Principles of Fitness
     - Lifting (muscular strength and endurance)
     - Runner (aerobic)
     - Stretching (flexibility)
     - Balance Scale (body composition)

- F.I.T.T. =
    - Frequency (arrows in circle)
    - Intensity (arrow in target)
    - Time and Type (stop watch)

4. Tell the students that you will be passing the cards out so that everyone has one card and your first challenge will be not to look at your card!

5. Explain to the students that the next challenge will be to organize into different groups based on the information on your cards and according to your directions. The groups will change in size and each time there is a change the new group will have a task to solve.

6. For the first challenge have the class find everyone in the group with the same principle of fitness word (flexibility, strength and endurance, cardio, body composition). There will be four groups total. Once the groups are formed, their task is to define and give examples of the principles of fitness.

7. For the second challenge have the class find everyone with the same picture that represents each of the four principles of fitness (lifting, running, stretching and balance scales). There will be four groups for this challenge. Once the new groups have formed, their task is to identify an example of a principle of fitness other than the one represented on the card. For example, the group with the step class cards might give continuous running as another example of cardio.

8. For the third challenge have the students find someone with the same principle of fitness (word) AND the corresponding picture (flexibility and picture of person stretching). The class will end up in 10 groups for this challenge. There is no task for this challenge.

9. For the fourth challenge, have the students form groups that have all three of the F.I.T.T. model (frequency=arrows turning, intensity=arrow on target, time and type=stop watch) symbols on their cards. The groups should aim for three members, but there may be more or fewer in a group depending on how many students you have. Once the groups are formed, the task is to define and give examples of the F.I.T.T. model.

10. Finally, for the last challenge have the students find the people who have the same types of activity (lifestyle or sport) word written on their card. There will be two groups at the end of this challenge. Once the groups have formed, the task is to come up with five examples of lifestyle activities and sport activities.

Reflection:

None needed as reflection takes place during the activity.

Additional Thoughts

• *Any of these group sorting activities can be timed for an additional challenge. If you do this, you should repeat the grouping challenges to allow students to decrease their time. To ensure that the second time doing the same grouping isn't too easy, shuffle the cards between attempts or have each student randomly trade cards with several other students.*

• *If the group is small, the challenge begins with each student receiving multiple cards. The entire class must then sort the cards into the subgroups as quickly as possible.*

LESSON 23

In this lesson students will learn how to manage consequences of making unhealthy choices and implement a plan to promote health and fitness.

ACTIVITY	LEARNING OBJECTIVE	TIME	PROPS	HEALTH SKILLS
Pathway to Health and Fitness	**At the conclusion of this activity, students will be able to:** • Develop a plan of personal health practices that promote health and fitness. • Identify some life skills for health.	40 minutes	• 30 spot markers (you can use the back of Keypunch spots) • Markers • Masking tape	• Analyze influences • Interpersonal communication

TEACHER'S NOTES:

FRAMING	SET-UP PROCEDURE	REFLECTION

Pathway to Health and Fitness

Set Up:

1. Clear a large open space in your classroom.

2. Prepare the spot markers by putting an X on the numbered side of each spot marker that is not on the pathway. Either leave the appropriate numbers on your spot markers or use masking tape to number them—as in the diagram below.

3. You will need to create the "pathway to lifelong health and fitness" that the class will follow. To help you create this pathway, map it out on a piece of paper (graph paper works well) and devise a route that will use 30 spots and begin at the entrance side of the area and end at the exit side. Don't share this with your students!

4. Lay your spots out, numbered or Xed side down, in a five by six grid.

5. Solutions can involve forward, side or backward movements. Diagonal moves or moves that skip rows are not allowed.

6. The more moves you create in your solution, the more difficult the activity will be. If you want a challenging Pathway you could use only 5 X spots and 25 number spots.

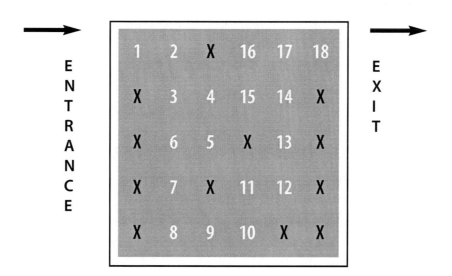

Framing:

"Developing a personal health and fitness plan involves accessing quality information. Implementing a personal health and fitness plan involves making healthy choices. This activity will help us understand the consequences of making unhealthy choices and identify skills needed to stay on the pathway to health and fitness."

Procedure:

1. Tell the class that the challenge for this activity is to find the Pathway to Health and Fitness. This is accomplished by discovering the correct sequence of steps to get one person from the entrance to the exit.

2. To do this they will select a spot, turn it over and read the writing to determine if it is a healthy choice. If it is a healthy choice (as represented only by the next number—if 4 was the last overturned and correct number, only 5 would be a healthy choice) step on the spot and repeat the process with another spot within range. If you have made an unhealthy choice you must exit the Pathway exactly the way you entered.

3. Only a healthy choice spot would remain turned over, students must turn their unhealthy choices back with number/X side down before exiting the Pathway.

4. One person at a time is allowed to enter the Pathway. If they make healthy choices they may continue.

5. People on the Pathway may only move forward, backward or sideways. Diagonal moves or moves that skip a row are not allowed.

6. After the briefing, group members may position themselves anywhere around the Pathway to assist the person on the Pathway and to observe. No verbal or written communication is allowed with the person on the Pathway. Nonverbal communication is allowed.

7. The person on the Pathway should not be touched.

8. The group will rotate turns so that no person enters the grid for a second time until everyone has entered once.

9. Remind the class that they need to be careful not to duplicate unhealthy choices.

Reflection:

Questions for Discussion:

1. "What were the steps you took to find the pathway to health and fitness?"

2. "How did you feel about trying to find the path to health and fitness even though you were set back by unhealthy choices?"

3. "What skills did you access to stay on the path to health and fitness?"

4. "How can you use these skills to maintain your own health and fitness plan?"

 Additional Thoughts

• *If you have more than 20 students, you may need two grids. You can also split the class and have them share the same grid. The groups would enter from opposite sides and solve separate pathways. This adds chaos and difficulty to the problem.*

Substance Abuse Prevention

LESSON 24

In this lesson students will revisit the concept of positive peer pressure and think about how to help each other stay safe and substance free.

ACTIVITY	LEARNING OBJECTIVE	TIME	PROPS	HEALTH SKILLS
Leader/ Follower	**At the conclusion of this activity, students will be able to:** • Describe leadership qualities as related to substance abuse prevention. • Summarize qualities in positive peer role modeling as related to substance abuse prevention.	10 minutes	• None	• Analyze influences • Interpersonal communication
Spaghetti Junction	• Begin to demonstrate refusal and negotiation skills. • Evaluate the consequences of making a decision. • Discuss coping strategies for dealing with situations where other people's thinking can affect them. • Discuss applying resistance skills in situations involving drugs.	30 minutes	• 5 pieces of accessory cord, each one a different color, per group	• Advocacy • Decision making • Self-management

TEACHER'S NOTES:

FRAMING	SET-UP PROCEDURE	REFLECTION

Leader/Follower

Set Up:

1. Clear a large open space in your classroom.

Framing:

"Many changes take place during adolescence and there are lots of opportunities to make healthy and not so healthy decisions. Peer pressure is something that can be healthy or unhealthy. We can choose to be leaders and followers who set standards for healthy behaviors, such as not using substances, reaching our goals and encouraging success with our peers."

Procedure:

1. Have the group stand in a circle while you give them directions.
2. Ask the students to silently and without physical acknowledgement, choose someone in the class to represent their leader and another person to represent their follower. Each student will have their own personal leader and follower, but the leader and the follower won't know that (in the beginning at least).
3. Tell the class that when you say, "Go," the group will begin to move at a fast walk with the objective of keeping their leader in front of them and their follower behind them.
4. Allow the action to continue for two to three minutes and then stop. Have students go to their leader and follower and tell them their roles, shake their hand and thank them. In this way, everyone knows what their roles were.

Reflection:

Questions for Discussion:

1. "What leadership qualities do you look for in others when considering positive role models?"
2. "Specifically, what qualities do you look for when deciding how to make healthy choices around substance abuse prevention?"
3. "What leadership qualities do you exhibit when considering being a positive role model?"
4. "Specifically, what leadership qualities do you exhibit when deciding how to model healthy choices around substance abuse prevention?"
5. "What are some examples of positive peer pressure in relation to choosing not to use or abuse substances?"

Spaghetti Junction

Set Up:

1. Tie four of the ropes into loops. Thread the fifth rope through the center of the other four loops so that it links them all together, like a key ring holds a set of keys. You'll need to make enough so that each group (consisting of four to five people) gets one.

2. Place the ropes on the floor or on top of a desk in front of each group so that the loops are tangled and bunched together. (Try not to create a tangled mess that can't be sorted through while at the same time not spreading them out so much that it is obvious which one is linking the other four. Think in terms of layers.)

Framing:

"There is a big party on Friday night and you and your friends need to make a plan so you can go and not get "into trouble." You know that there may be some alcohol and/or pot there and that people may be "hooking up," but you and your friends have decided you don't want to partake in those behaviors. However, you and your friends do want to go because other people will be there too. Agree on a pact with your friends, all of them, that will keep you safe and let you have fun!"

Procedure:

1. Divide your class into groups of four to five people.

2. Explain to the class that the objective is to choose the rope that links all the others by examining the ropes visually and making a consensus decision that the group supports.

3. No one may touch or move the ropes during the activity but students are free to move around the ropes, to point and share their opinions.

4. The challenge for each small group is to agree on which rope they think supports all the others before touching the ropes.

5. After a rope has been selected by the group, ask these questions before checking the accuracy of the selection:

> "Is everyone committed to this solution?"
> "Would you bet something of value on your answer?"
> "If not, why?"
> "What prevents you from committing to this solution?"

6. Allow one person to lift the selected rope. It may take some jiggling to get the ropes to untangle to reveal if the group chose the right one.

Reflection:

Questions for Discussion:

1. "Can you identify the challenges, successes and influences in achieving consensus?"

2. "Can you share the consequences of your group's decision?"

3. "How did you use your refusal and negotiation skills during this activity?"

4. "How will these skills be helpful in maintaining a pact with your friends that will keep you all safe and also let you have fun in situations involving drugs?"

5. "What are some of the components of a strong pact?"

 Additional Thoughts

• *If students choose the "wrong" loop, have them examine their decision-making process to figure out where they could have made a better choice.*

LESSON 25

In this lesson students will practice the buddy check-in system for social situations as well as begin to understand how to access community resources and take personal responsibility for staying substance free.

ACTIVITY	LEARNING OBJECTIVE	TIME	PROPS	HEALTH SKILLS
I'm OK, You OK? Tag	At the conclusion of this activity, students will be able to: • Begin to employ the skill of accessing peer support in chaotic situations. • Discuss strategies for accessing support in potentially dangerous situations.	15 minutes	• 4 cones for boundary markers	• Accessing information • Self-management
It Takes A Village	• Apply effective communication skills. • Identify some helping agencies. • Connect personal responsibility with staying substance free.	30–40 minutes	• Game Frame • 40-feet of rope or webbing • Masking tape • Pens	• Self-management • Interpersonal communication • Advocacy • Goal setting • Decision making

TEACHER'S NOTES:

FRAMING	SET-UP PROCEDURE	REFLECTION

I'm OK, You OK? Tag

Set Up:

1. Clear a large open space in your classroom.

Framing:

"One strategy for managing challenging social situations is to have a "buddy" and a plan. Your friends, or buddies, can be sources of support that you touch base with during the event. However, finding your buddy amid the confusion of the party, dance, athletic event may be a challenge. This activity will help you practice finding one another amid the chaos."

Procedure:

1. Ask students to find a partner and form a circle inside the open space, standing next to their partners.
2. Tell the students they are going to play a fun tag game with their partner.
3. Say that "in other words, just you and your partner will be chasing one another, but everyone will do that at the same time."
4. Ask the class to imagine that they are at a big dance or party with their friend and you have both agreed to check in every so often to make sure you are both OK.
5. Explain that this tag game represents the party and that when you tag your partner, you say, "Are you OK?" Your partner says "I'm OK," and counts to ten, while you get away.
6. Tell students that once they are tagged, their partner becomes the tagger and will chase them after they count to ten. When they find their partner, they tag that person and say, "Are you OK?" that person says "I'm OK," counts to ten and repeats the process.
7. Remind students that once they have answered the questions, the person who is now being chased should move away from his/her partner while that person is counting to ten.
8. Have each partnership decide who will start as the tagger and begin.

Reflection:

Questions for Discussion:

1. "What is it like to find your support 'buddies' in different settings?"
2. "How did the chaos of the setting affect your ability to make good decisions?"

3. "Do you think this pretend party was like a real party in finding your support 'buddy' among lots of chaos?"
4. "If so, how? If not, why?"
5. "What did you do to stay connected with your partner?"
6. "How can you use those skills in different social settings?"

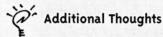 **Additional Thoughts**

• *Demonstrating a gentle tag is highly recommended.*

. . . .

It Takes A Village...

Set Up:

1. Clear a large open space in your classroom and set up the Game Frame in the middle of that space.
2. Place the rope or webbing on one side of the Game Frame.

Framing:

"Have you ever heard the saying, 'It takes a village to…?' In this activity the rope represents a young person like you, and you represent the village or support network. Your job is to help this person travel safely through the web of adolescent challenges toward a healthy future."

Procedure:

1. Divide the class so that half of the students are on each side of the web.
2. Pass out pens and masking tape.
3. Ask students to think about different social settings, people and materials related to substance abuse. For example, steroids or diet pills to help gain or lose weight are an example of materials. The bleachers at the local park are an example of setting.
4. Have each student write one of these examples on a piece of masking tape and attach it to the bungee cord in the web. Be sure that there is at least one example surrounding each hole.
5. Ask students to think of different local support groups or helping agencies available to keep young people substance free. Again have them write a different one on a piece of masking tape and this time tape it to themselves.

6. Explain to the class that their objective is to get this young person (the rope) safely through the web of substance challenges using all the support and help they identified.

7. Tell the class that the rope must pass through every web opening to complete the task and that the rope needs to be entirely off the floor before they begin.

8. Also, when the rope is passed through the first opening, no more than three to four feet can be passed through at one time.

9. Once the three to four feet of rope has been received through the first opening, the rope must be passed back through a new opening to the other side. In other words, no more than four feet of rope can accumulate on one side of the web before it must be passed back to the other side.

10. The rope may not touch the web frame or web itself. If a touch occurs, the leading end of the rope must move backwards through three openings, and then it can start moving forward again.

11. If at any time the rope touches the floor, the rope must be started over again from the beginning.

12. If a person touches the web, the rope must move backwards through three openings.

13. Once the back end of the rope is successfully passed through the last hole, the activity is complete.

14. Members of both groups must remain on the side of the web that they start on.

Reflection:

Questions for Discussion:

1. "How did you provide the necessary support to one another to get this young person safely through and substance free?"

2. "What was happening with the group's communication right before and right after there was a touch?"

3. "What examples did you see of individual contributions that made a difference?"

4. "What are the multiple roles and responsibilities people play in a coordinated community effort (village) to prevent substance abuse?"

 Additional Thoughts

• *Be aware that too much or too little rope may lessen the effectiveness of the activity. Try to stick with the recommended forty feet.*

• *You may want to use question two during the activity as a way to check in with the group's process.*

LESSON 26

In this lesson students will enhance decision making and problem solving skills.

ACTIVITY	LEARNING OBJECTIVE	TIME	PROPS	HEALTH SKILLS
Needle and Thread Tag	**At the conclusion of this activity, students will be able to:** • Better apply the skill of making decisions in a healthy and timely manner.	10 minutes	• None	• Analyze influences • Interpersonal communication
ATOD 12 Bits	• Discuss the progression of alcoholism. • Describe the impact that substance abuse has on future health. • Begin to recognize the consequences of drug abuse.	30–40 minutes	• 12 Bits clues (in appendix)	• Accessing information • Analyze influences • Decision making • Interpersonal communication

TEACHER'S NOTES:

FRAMING	SET-UP PROCEDURE	REFLECTION

Needle and Thread Tag

Set Up:

1. Clear a large open space in your classroom.

Framing:

"Sometimes we are in situations where we need to make decisions that impact our health very quickly. Being able to leave dangerous situations, change the momentum in a potentially violent conflict and know when you are not safe and need to get help are all important skills that require clear thought and fast action. This activity will help you practice those skills."

Procedure:

1. Ask the group to form a circle with one arm length between each person and about two or three feet of space behind them. Students need space to move behind the circle. They can't be up against the wall or desks.
2. Have one student step outside the circle and another step into the center.
3. Explain to the class that the person on the inside of the circle is the runner and the person on the outside is the tagger. The objective is to have the runner sew up the circle before being tagged by the tagger.
4. Tell the class that sewing is achieved by running between two people. As soon as the person runs through the two people in the circle, they link hands to close that opening.
5. The runner can go in and out of the circle but must decide all movements in a quick and decisive manner. The runner can't spend a lot of time in the middle trying to avoid the tagger. The tagger must remain on the outside of the circle and try to tag the runner before the circle is completely "sewn up."
6. Repeat this with different runners and taggers.

Reflection:

Invite students to pause for a moment and reflect silently on what they need to do to improve their ability to make good decisions in a healthy and timely manner.

Alcohol, Tobacco and Other Drugs 12 Bits

Set Up:

1. Have enough Twelve Bits clues so everyone in your class can get at least one. Twelve Bits information sheets that you can copy and cut into single clues and the solution can be found in the appendix (page 354).

2. Reading the clues and solution will help you have a better understanding of this activity.

Framing:

"Many times we do not realize the impact that drugs have on us or the people around us. During this activity the group will become detectives and use isolated information about a sequence of activities that happened at a middle school to determine to whom and in what order they occurred. This must sound pretty vague to everyone, but that is why this mystery needs detectives."

Procedure:

1. Divide students into groups of eight to twelve. Ask groups to sit in a circle, where they won't be bothered by the discussion in other groups, and hand each student a Twelve Bits clue.

2. Keep distributing Twelve Bits clues until they are all gone. It's OK if a student has more than one.

3. Tell the students that they need to put together the sequence of activities using the clues you just passed out. Each group needs to use the clues to discover the order in which things happened and to whom.

4. Explain that all the information they need to solve the problem, as well as the directions, are on the clues, but the most important point is that they may not show their clues to anyone else. They can discuss their clues.

5. One of the clues looks like this:

> Although you may tell your group what is on this slip, you may not show it to anyone else.
>
> Sandy learned that marijuana is also called pot, grass, weed, reefer, dope, Mary Jane, Acapulco Gold and Thai Sticks. It looks like dried parsley, mixed with stems that may include seeds and is typically eaten or smoked.

6. Give students 15 minutes to try to figure out what happened when.

7. Have students read their group's solution.

8. Provide the solution to the class if they are unable to solve it and if they request the answer. The solution is also in the appendix (page 354).

Reflection:

Reflection Activity:

1. Ask students to form a circle. Pass out paper and pens to each person. Have students write something on the sheet that they learned or felt about the progression of substance abuse/alcoholism and its effects on future health.

2. Ask students to scrunch up the pieces of paper and place them into a mid-floor receptacle. Shake them up, remove a rumpled sheet and read aloud. Allow discussion to occur.

3. This type of activity may allow someone who is shy or unsure of speaking up to share their thoughts in a non-threatening way.

 Additional Thoughts

• *If the class is larger than 12, make two sets of slips and have two groups work on the same problem simultaneously.*

• *While reading students' comments during the debrief you may find that a message is inappropriate or offensive. Simply put it aside without reading it aloud and reach for another. This is why it is important that you read the comments.*

LESSON 27

In this lesson students will explore negotiating risk factors and finding support needed to move safely through social situations.

ACTIVITY	LEARNING OBJECTIVE	TIME	PROPS	HEALTH SKILLS
Pipeline	**At the conclusion of this activity, students will be able to:** • Examine attitudes toward risk taking behaviors. • Discuss how substance use interferes with relationships. • Explain how substance use affects decision-making and judgment. • Recognize that there are alternatives to drug abuse.	30–40 minutes	• Pipeline Kit • Several lengths of rope • Masking tape • Markers	• Core content • Goal setting • Decision making • Self-management • Advocacy • Interpersonal communication

TEACHER'S NOTES:

FRAMING	SET-UP PROCEDURE	REFLECTION

Pipeline

Set Up:

1. Create a long, curvy pathway with the ropes. See the following diagram for guidance.
2. Place mesh bag from Pipeline kit at the far end of the pathway.
3. Prep the Pipeline pieces by lining the bottom of each piece with a length of masking tape.
4. Have the golf ball, the rubber egg, and the tiny marble handy.

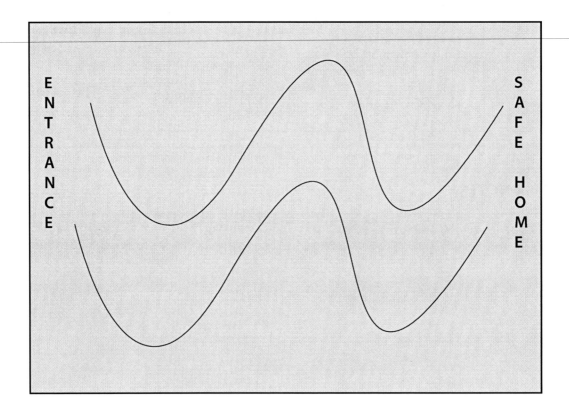

Framing:

"Risk factors are behaviors that represent a potential health threat. There are many precautions you can take each day to prevent injuries and reduce the chance of getting hurt. Risk factors can also be offset by positive behaviors, including making smart choices and practicing habits that promote good health."

Procedure:

1. Ask students to gather in a circle at the opposite end.
2. Pass a piece of prepped Pipeline to each student.

3. Pass the markers to each student.

4. Tell the class that they are going to have the opportunity to visit a number of different social situations. The students in the various settings will be represented by the objects. Hold up the marble, golf ball, and the rubber egg.

5. Ask students to identify three social gatherings from most challenging to least challenging in terms of level of risk and the ability to make healthy choices. Explain again that for this activity, the balls will represent themselves in those situations, starting with the golf ball as the least risky and the smallest marble as the highest risk. So they could decide, for example: a church picnic is represented by the golf ball; a football game is represented by the rubber egg and a party where the parents aren't home is represented by the marble.

6. Have students identify the possible sources of support available to them in those social situations by writing a different one on the masking tape in each piece of Pipeline.

7. The class's goal is to successfully travel through the pathway, from entrance to safe home, keeping the students in each setting (as represented by the balls) safe while carrying them only with Pipeline pieces.

8. Pipeline pieces cannot touch each other. The balls can only travel forward or stop.

9. Only one ball can travel at a time.

10. If a ball falls to the floor or rolls backward, have the group stop, state a key learning that will help them stay safe (on the Pipeline moving forward) and then continue on with their process.

11. Once past the starting line, students cannot touch the balls unless resetting after a drop or backward roll.

12. If any of these rules are broken, the ball has to return to the start.

Reflection:

Questions for Discussion:

1. "How did the level of risk affect your interaction with the support system?" (i.e., "The marble flew so fast over the Pipeline pieces that it was hard to offer it support" or "We were really able to slow the egg down and keep it safe.")

2. "Can you share some examples of times when you or someone you know tried to support someone who was taking unhealthy risks and how did those situations affect your relationship?"

3. "How does substance use or abuse affect decision-making and judgment?"

4. "The marble was very risky, but kind of fun…what are some other ways to experience the thrill of the marble without the danger and unhealthy consequences?"

Middle School

Appendices

Grade 6 Lesson 8 - Language Cards for Bridge It

Ball = Taco	**Ball = Big Mac**
Cup = Dog	**Cup = Truck**
Paper = Milk	**Paper = Orange Juice**
Straw = Basketball	**Straw = Book**
Balloon = Dress	**Balloon = Jacket**
Tape = Sister	**Tape = Brother**
Ball = Pizza	**Ball = Burrito**
Cup = Horse	**Cup = Bicycle**
Paper = Sneaker	**Paper = CD**
Straw = Spoon	**Straw = Yarn**
Balloon = DVD	**Balloon = Water**
Tape = Mother	**Tape = Father**

Grade 6 Lesson 18 - Food Pyramid

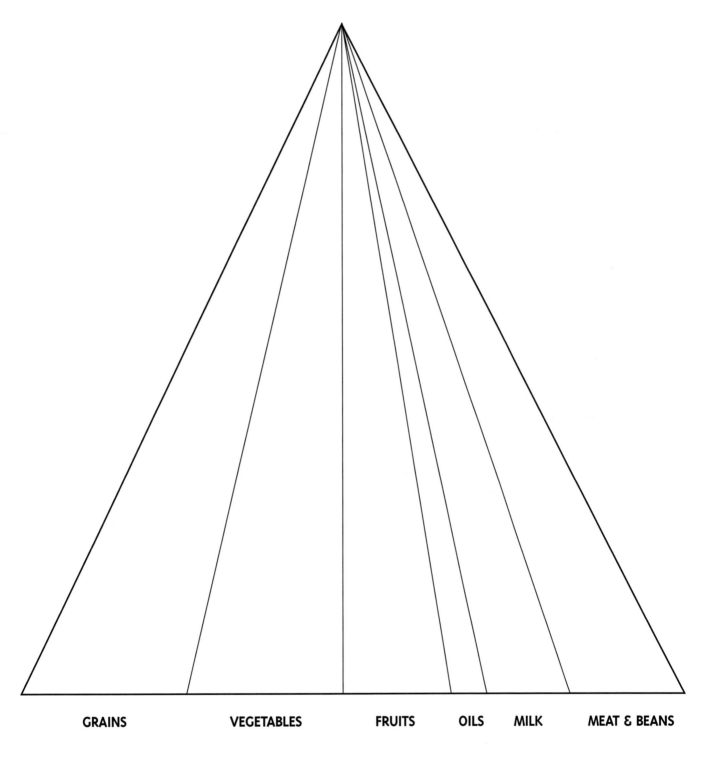

GRAINS   VEGETABLES   FRUITS   OILS   MILK   MEAT & BEANS

Activity, Moderation, Personalization, Proportionality, Variety

2005 USDA's MyPyramid

Grade 6 Lesson 19 - Fast Food, Emotions, Advertisements & Choices for Health Examples

FAST FOOD

Big Mac
French Fries
Milkshake
Big Gulp
Pizza
Popcorn

EMOTIONS

Happy
Serious
Friendly
Talkative
Strong
Curious

HEALTHY CHOICES

Swimming
Skating
Bicycling
Skate Boarding
Basketball
Soccer

ADVERTISEMENTS

Ronald McDonald

Grade 6 Lesson 19 - Multicultural Food Find Lists for Cards

AFRICAN-AMERICAN FOODS

Carbohydrates:

Cornbread	Biscuits
Grits	Rice

Vegetables:

Beets	Okra
Hominy	Greens

Fruit:

Berries	Fruit Juice
Peach	Watermelon

Dairy:

Buttermilk	Pudding

Protein:

Black-Eyed Peas	Catfish
Pork	Crayfish

Sparingly:

Candy	Lard
Meat Drippings	

ASIAN-INDIAN FOODS

Carbohydrates:

Naan	Roti
Steamed Rice	Rice Noodles

Vegetables:

Cabbage	Green Papaya
Pumpkin	Plantain

Fruit:

Fruit Chutney	Lychee
Papaya	Tamarind

Dairy:

Sweet Curds	Buffalo Milk

Protein:

Cashew Nuts	Dal
Sprouted Beans	Mutton

Sparingly:

Coconut Milk	Sesame Oil

Grade 6 Lesson 19 - Multicultural Food Find Lists for Cards
Continued

CHINESE-AMERICAN
Carbohydrates:

Dumpling	Wonton Wrappers
Rice Sticks	Fried Rice

Vegetables:

Bamboo Shoots	Black Mushroom
Bok Choy	Water chestnut

Fruit:

Guava	Mango
Persimmon	Litchi

Dairy:

Fish Bones	Soybean Milk

Protein:

Bean Paste	Mung Beans
Duck	Pork

Sparingly:

Duck Sauce	Peanut Oil

JEWISH FOODS
Carbohydrates:

Bagel	Kasha
Pita Bread	Challah

Vegetables:

Beets/Borscht	Latke
Olives	Pickles

Fruit:

Fig	Dried Apricot
Sabra	Dates

Dairy:

Gouda Cheese	Yogurt

Protein:

Brisket	Lentils
Lox	Gefilte Fish

Sparingly:

Cream Cheese	Honey

Grade 6 Lesson 19 - Multicultural Food Find Lists for Cards
Continued

MEXICAN-AMERICAN FOODS
Carbohydrates:

Corn Tortilla	Sweet Bread
Masa	Sopa

Vegetables:

Agave	Jicama
Green Tomatoes	Prickly Pear Cactus

Fruit:

Avocado	Zapote
Apple	Platano

Dairy:

Evaporated Milk	Queso Blanco

Protein:

Garbanzo Beans	Black Beans
Lamb	Sausage

Sparingly:

Lard	Sour Cream

VIETNAMESE-AMERICAN FOOD
Carbohydrates:

French Bread	Cha Gio
Cellophane Noodles	Mung Bean Vermicelli

Vegetables:

Eggplant	Leek
Tofu	Ca Tim

Fruit:

Pineapple	Lemon
Carambola	Longan

Dairy:

Fish bones	No Milk

Protein:

Crab	Squid

Sparingly:

Sesame Paste	Sesame Oil

Grade 6 Lesson 22

BE SMART...DON'T START or BE FIT...IT'S TIME TO QUIT				
The most common situation for taking a first smoke is with a _____.	3 of the major diseases caused by smoking are emphysema, heart disease and _____.	Nicotine narrows _____ in the body.	_____ makes breathing very difficult, especially breathing out (exhaling).	Most patients diagnosed with _____ die within a few years.
_____ use is the number one cause of preventable deaths in America.	Nicotine raises the heart rate _____ beats per minute immediately.	Smokeless tobacco causes cancer of the _____.	_____ % of youth smokers report being addicted.	12–17 year olds who smoke cigarettes are ___ times more likely to smoke marijuana.
_____ use is the most likely addictive behavior to be established in adolescence.	One cigar smoked in less than an hour has as much nicotine as _____ pack(s) of cigarettes.	FREE SPACE	A pocket sized packet of chew contains as much nicotine as _____ packs of cigarettes.	True or False Cigarette smoke contains Arsenic (a poison).
True or False Cigarette smoke contains formaldehyde (embalms dead bodies).	One harmful effect of smokeless tobacco use is loss of _____.	_____ smoke produces the same poisons found in the air around toxic waste dumps.	True or False Low tar, low nicotine cigarettes are more addictive than regular cigarettes.	Lack of _____ is an individual risk factor for tobacco use.
_____ % of teenagers who smoke daily have tried to quit and failed.	True or False Tobacco affects the smoker and anyone in the smoker's environment.	Each day 6000 young people try a cigarette and _____ of them become daily smokers.	Smokers have a ___ % greater death rate from heart disease than non-smokers.	_____ smoke causes wheezing, coughing, colds, and asthma attacks.

Grade 6 Lesson 22

BE SMART...DON'T START or BE FIT...IT'S TIME TO QUIT				
The most common situation for taking a first smoke is with a _friend_.	3 of the major diseases caused by smoking are emphysema, heart disease and _lung cancer_.	Nicotine narrows _blood vessels_ in the body.	_Emphysema_ makes breathing very difficult, especially breathing out (exhaling).	Most patients diagnosed with _lung cancer_ die within a few years.
Tobacco use is the number one cause of preventable deaths in America.	Nicotine raises the heart rate _10–15_ beats per minute immediately.	Smokeless tobacco causes cancer of the _mouth_.	_70_ % of youth smokers report being addicted.	12–17 year olds who smoke cigarettes are _100_ times more likely to smoke marijuana.
Nicotine use is the most likely addictive behavior to be established in adolescence.	One cigar smoked in less than an hour has as much nicotine as _one_ pack(s) of cigarettes.	**FREE SPACE**	A pocket sized packet of chew contains as much nicotine as _three_ packs of cigarettes.	_True_ or False Cigarette smoke contains Arsenic (a poison).
True or False Cigarette smoke contains formaldehyde (embalms dead bodies).	One harmful effect of smokeless tobacco use is loss of _teeth_.	_Secondhand_ smoke produces the same poisons found in the air around toxic waste dumps.	True or _False_ Low tar, low nicotine cigarettes are more addictive than regular cigarettes.	Lack of _refusal skills_ is an individual risk factor for tobacco use.
_40_ % of teenagers who smoke daily have tried to quit and failed.	_True_ or False Tobacco affects the smoker and anyone in the smoker's environment.	Each day 6000 young people try a cigarette and _half_ of them become daily smokers.	Smokers have a _70_ % greater death rate from heart disease than non-smokers.	_Secondhand_ smoke causes wheezing, coughing, colds, and asthma attacks.

Grade 7 Lesson 9 - Stress Reduction Stations

PROGRESSIVE RELAXATION

Have students either lie down or sit comfortably in their chairs with their eyes closed. Tell them to take several deep breaths to begin to relax. The purpose of taking the breaths is to quiet the mind and body as much as possible before beginning the progressive relaxation process.

Progressive relaxation involves the tensing and relaxing of all muscle groups as well as the mental release of tension. Start at the feet, move to lower leg, then to upper leg, hands, arms, torso, shoulders, face and finally the entire body. Tense the muscles in each area for a count of five, then release the tension with a long exhale, followed by three deep breaths. Repeat this process two times for each muscle group separately as well as the entire body collectively.

Have students continue to breathe slowly and deeply for about 10-20 breaths. Students then count slowly to 10, moving each body part with each number. For example, 1, start to wiggle your toes, 2, move your lower leg, 3, gently shake your entire body and so on.

GUIDED IMAGERY SCRIPT

Be sure to read this script with a steady and soothing tone of voice. Students will most likely giggle a bit as they settle into relaxing. Keep going, encouraging them to keep breathing slowly and calmly focusing on relaxing.

Script:

Make yourself as comfortable as possible. Close your eyes. Now take a few deep breaths, taking the air in through your nose if you can, and then slowly exhaling through your nose. With each exhale, you will find yourself relaxing more and more, feeling more and more at peace.

Breathing in calm…exhaling away any tension. Breathing slowly, deeply, take the air in and let the air out. Allow yourself to relax.

In a few moments, I am going to describe a very vivid scene in which you will picture yourself walking along a beach. I want you to imagine this scene as clearly as possible using all of your senses. I will count down from five to one. When I say one, you will be walking along a beach. Keep breathing slowly, and deeply.

5…4…3…2…1

It is a summer day. The sun is warm and its light is dancing on the waves making them sparkle and shine. The sky is crystal clear, bright blue without a cloud in sight. You can hear the peaceful sound of the waves coming slowly into the shore and then moving back out to sea.

You notice the feel of the sand under your feet as you walk and a soft breeze on your skin. It is warm and very comfortable. You decide to sit down.

You are looking at the sea. Watching the waves roll slowly in and out…hearing the rush of the water moving back and forth. With each wave you find yourself feeling more and more relaxed. It is peaceful. You are calm.

Enjoy this feeling of calmness…the warmth of the sun…the sound of the waves.

In the distance you hear the sound of seagulls playing in the surf. You look out into the distance and feel the breeze energizing you.

Pause

In a few moments, I will count from one to three. When I reach the count of three you will find yourself back in this room. You will feel completely refreshed and totally relaxed. Open your eyes and sit up when you are ready.

1. . . 2. . . 3.

Be sure to allow everyone to reorient themselves to the room and sit up slowly before the noise escalates!

Grade 7 Lesson 15

NUTRITION QUESTIONS

Name five leafy green vegetables.

What foods are the best natural sources of potassium?

What do carbohydrates do for our bodies?

Name three different types of protein that are not animal based.

What does a vegetarian eat?

Name five sources of Vitamin C.

How much water per day do you need to be healthy?

Why is it important to have enough calcium each day?

Name five types of whole grains.

Name five foods that are high in saturated fat.

How many servings of fruit should you have each day? Does drinking juice count for all of them?

What does protein do for our bodies and how much should we eat each day?

What are sources of sugar in our daily diet and how much should we have each day?

Name three healthy breakfast choices that include dairy products.

POPULAR NUTRITION MYTHS

Eating no carbohydrates is a healthy way to lose weight.

Never drink fluids before or during competition.

Honey is more nutritious than sugar.

Dieting is the most effective way to lose fat.

When you stop working out, your muscles turn to fat.

You need protein supplements if you are going to weight train.

Milk and dairy products are fattening.

Lifting weights will make you bulk up and gain weight.

If I run for three miles I can eat the whole bag of potato chips and it won't matter.

Foods that are labeled "organic" are free of pesticides.

Non-caloric sweeteners are safe and help me lose weight.

Imported fruits and vegetables are not safe.

Consuming a candy bar or non-diet cola before exercise gives me extra energy.

Ground beef that is lean is a good food choice.

Grade 7 Lesson 16

MEDIA MESSAGES QUESTIONS

1. Look at the pictures in your magazine and answer the following questions:
    - What body types are shown?
    - What body types are missing?
    - Do most of the people featured in your magazine look like people you know?
    - Are there any photos that are shocking to you? If so, why?
    - What do you think is the magazine's message to its readers about the normal or acceptable body type for males and females? Teenagers?

2. Look at the articles/headlines in your magazine and answer the following questions:
    - What are most of the articles and headlines about?
    - How many articles or headlines are about weight loss or diet issues?
    - What is the specific emphasis placed on these topics?
    - What messages are these articles and headlines sending to their readers?
    - How do these articles and headlines make you feel?

3. Look at the advertisements in your magazine and answer the following questions:
    - What types of products are most of the ads trying to sell?
    - How many ads were for products to help you lose weight?
    - How many ads were for products to help you gain weight?
    - What kinds of food were advertised?
    - How are the pictures of people in the ads used to sell the products?
    - Are the ads marketing healthy choices?
    - What thoughts or feelings about your body and image do the ads bring up?

Grade 8 Lesson 18

QUESTIONS FOR NUTRITION HAVE YOU EVER?

Have you ever...

Broken a bone in your body?
Gotten a haircut that you didn't like?
Smoked cigarettes?
Skipped a meal?
Made yourself throw up after eating?
Gotten an "A" on a test?
Tried a drug of any kind?
Had a friend in trouble?
Been worried about how you look?
Gone on a diet?
Been worried about your parents' behavior?
Done something you regretted later?
Had a friend who had trouble with eating?
Had a friend who made your life miserable?
Had a friend who made your life wonderful?
Been told you need to lose weight?
Wished you could do something to change _____? (your height, your nose, etc.)

Grade 8 Lesson 22 - Fitness Convening Cards

Grade 8 Lesson 22 - Fitness Convening Cards

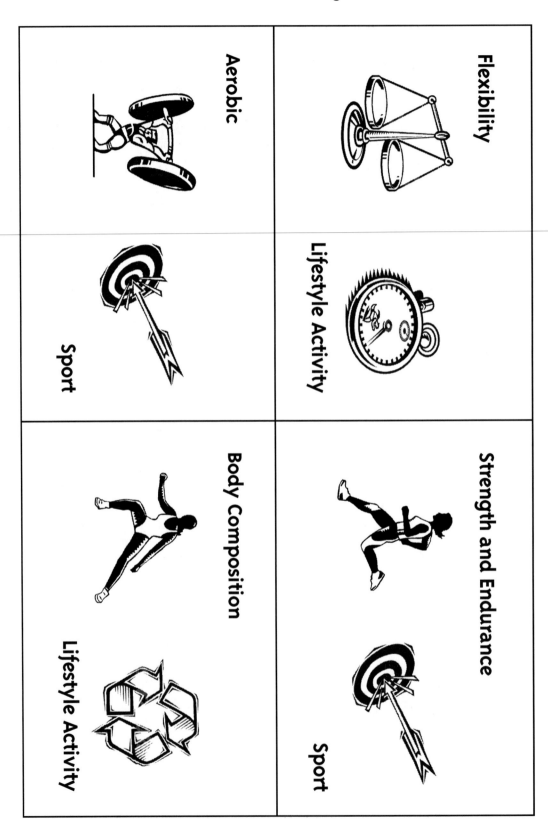

Grade 8 Lesson 26 - ATOD 12 BITS and Solution

Although you may tell your group what is on this slip, you may not show it to anyone else.

Of all the "controllable" health risks studied, Kelly was most concerned about cocaine, since she almost lost a close friend to an overdose when he overestimated the capabilities of his mental and physical powers while under the influence of the drug.

All four friends spent their fifth period discussing the specific drugs and comparing their notes on the effects.

Although you may tell your group what is on this slip, you may not show it to anyone else.

The focus of ATOD Monday was to learn about the health consequences of alcohol and other drugs. Four primary "controllable" health risks were studied by four friends, who then shared the information in peer groups later that day.

The hard facts were tough to believe...such as all alcoholic beverages contain ethyl alcohol. The only difference is the amount of alcohol. Twelve ounces of beer equals one ounce of whiskey.

Although you may tell your group what is on this slip, you may not show it to anyone else.

The friends learned about health risks during the first four periods. Each friend learned about a different health risk during the same period, before switching to the next period and health risk. By the end of the fourth period, each had studied the four primary health risks highlighted on ATOD Monday.

Due to the increase of smoking by women, lung cancer overtook breast cancer in 1987 as the leading cancer killer of women. Young women tend to be the largest percentage of smokers; and women are slower to give up the habit than men.

Grade 8 Lesson 26 - ATOD 12 BITS and Solution Continued

Although you may tell your group what is on this slip, you may not show it to anyone else.

Each friend studied four highlighted "controllable" health risks in their own sequence of periods. Aaron learned about the dangers of nicotine before he studied the hazards of cocaine. He learned that smokers are responsible for twice as many accidents and fires as non-smokers – fires caused by unattended cigarettes or smoldering ashes in garbage cans and upholstery kill between 2,000 - 4,000 people annually.

Although you may tell your group what is on this slip, you may not show it to anyone else.

Sandy learned that marijuana is also called pot, grass, weed, reefer, dope, Mary Jane, Acapulco Gold and Thai Sticks. It looks like dried parsley, mixed with stems that may include seeds and is typically eaten or smoked.

Although you may tell your group what is on this slip, you may not show it to anyone else.

Each friend was more concerned about one particular risk over another for different reasons, and arranged their sequence so they would learn about the risk they were most concerned about last.

While specific depressants weren't taught on ATOD Monday, the students did learn that the effects of depressants such as barbiturates, and tranquilizers, are in many ways similar to the effects of alcohol. Small amounts can produce calmness and relaxed muscles but somewhat larger doses can cause slurred speech, staggering gait and altered perception.

Grade 8 Lesson 26 - ATOD 12 BITS and Solution Continued

Although you may tell your group what is on this slip, you may not show it to anyone else.

You have all the information you need to find the answer to the following question: (Only one answer is correct.) In what sequence did Pat study the primary health risks highlighted on ATOD Monday.

Although you may tell your group what is on this slip, you may not show it to anyone else.

Pat learned the facts about alcohol after attending the first period lecture. Alcohol circulates very quickly to all parts of the body, including the brain. It is carried there directly by the blood and quickly interferes with the control center.

Although you may tell your group what is on this slip, you may not show it to anyone else.

During the first period, Sandy studied cocaine.

Snorting cocaine causes excess nasal discharge, which coats and irritates the vocal cords.

Although you may tell your group what is on this slip, you may not show it to anyone else.

The friend who arrived at school early that day began his or her first period learning about nicotine.

Grade 8 Lesson 26 – ATOD 12 BITS and Solution Continued

Although you may tell your group what is on this slip, you may not show it to anyone else.

All of the information you have is important, yet only some of it will help you solve this problem.

Kelly arrived at school early on ATOD Monday.

Marijuana impairs the function of reproductive glands and hormones, damages the respiratory system and retards social and emotional growth.

Although you may tell your group what is on this slip, you may not show it to anyone else.

Nicotine is an alkaloid in tobacco, commonly believed to be responsible for dependence. It first stimulates then depresses the nervous system. It stimulates the cardiovascular system, causing increases in heart rate and blood pressure. It increases oxygen requirements of the heart muscle, but not the supply.

SOLUTION			
Aaron	**Sandy**	**Kelly**	**Pat**
Alcohol	Cocaine	Nicotine	Marijuana
Nicotine	Alcohol	Marijuana	Cocaine
Cocaine	Marijuana	Alcohol	Nicotine
Marijuana	Nicotine	Cocaine	Alcohol

Rubric for Comprehensive Health - Wachusett, MA Regional School District

The Advanced Learner	The Proficient Learner	The Capable Learner	The Novice Learner
Demonstrates an understanding of the significance of basic health facts and concepts.	Demonstrates an understanding of the significance of basic health facts and concepts.	Relates basic health facts to concepts and themes.	Relates basic facts about health and identifies themes.
Relates health concepts and understanding about healthful behavior to personal experience and prior knowledge	Relates health concepts and understanding to personal experience and prior knowledge	Demonstrates an understanding of healthful behavior and correlates knowledge from other disciplines.	Describes the relationship of health concepts to knowledge from science and social studies.
Communicates knowledge and understanding using sophisticated vocabulary and a variety of media: oral presentation, written essay, charts, diagrams, graphs.	Communicates knowledge and understanding through a variety of media: oral presentation, written essay, charts, diagrams, graphs.	Uses a variety of media: oral and written presentations, charts, diagrams, graphs to convey understanding.	Presents information that advocates for healthful behavior.
Uses reference materials, models, graphs, and charts to identify relevant information.	Relates health concepts and understanding to personal experience and prior knowledge.	Uses reference materials, models, diagrams, and charts to identify relevant information.	Uses models, diagrams, and charts to identify relevant information.
Applies principles and concepts of safety to risk assessment.	Communicates knowledge and understanding through a variety of media: oral presentation, written essay, charts, diagrams, graphs.	Demonstrates an understanding of basic concepts related to safety and risk assessment.	Describes safety information relevant to risk assessment.
Applies understanding of healthful living to personal goals for growth and behavior.	Uses reference materials, models, graphs, diagrams, and charts to identify relevant information.	Relates health concepts to personal experience, service providers, and current events.	Identifies health concepts as they relate to personal experience and current events.
	Describes the relationship of basic safety concepts and principles to risk assessment.		
	Demonstrates an understanding of health concepts as they relate to service providers, institutions, and current events.		

Activity Reference List

References

Bandura, A. (1986). *Social foundations of thought and action. A social cognitive theory.* Englewood Cliffs, NJ: Prentice Hall.

Caine, Renate and Geoffrey (1991). *Making Connections: Teaching and the Human Brain,* Alexandria, VA, ASTD.

Epstein, L.H. (1998). Integrating theoretical approaches to promote physical activity. *American Journal of Preventive Medicine,* 15, 257–265.

Frank, Laurie (2001). *The Caring Classroom.* Beverly, MA: Project Adventure, Inc.

James, W. (1977). Psychological foundations: Habit. In J.J. McDermott (Ed.). *The Writings of William James.* Chicago: University of Chicago Press.

Janis, I.L. & Mann, L. (1977). Decision making: *A psychological analysis of conflict, choice, and commitment.* New York: Collier Macmillan.

Kennerson, C., et.al. (2000). "Productive conversation" in Senge P., *Schools that Learn,* New York, NY, Doubleday..

Kohn, A. (1996). *Beyond Discipline: From Compliance to Community.* Alexandria, VA: Association for Supervision and Curriculum Development.

Kolb, D.A. (1984). *Experiential learning: Experience as the source of learning and development.* Englewood Cliffs, NJ: Prentice-Hall, Inc.

Luckner, J. and Nadler, R, (1997). Processing the Experience 2nd edition, Dubuque, Iowa, Kendall/Hunt.

Marcus, B. & Forsyth, L. (2003). *Motivating People to Be Physically Active,* Champaign, IL: Human Kinetics.

Weil, Andrew (1997). *8 Weeks to Optimum Health.* New York: Fawcett Columbine, The Ballantine Publishing Group.